A History of
European Mass
Spectrometry

A History of
European Mass
Spectrometry

Edited by Keith R. Jennings

Published by
IM Publications LLP, 6 Charlton Mill, Charlton, Chichester,
West Sussex PO18 0HY, UK
Tel: +44-1243-811334, Fax: +44-1243-811711
E-mail: info@impublications.co.uk
Web: www.impublications.com

ISBN: 978-1-906715-04-5

British Library Cataloguing-in-Publication Data
A catalogue record for this book is available from the British Library

Designed by Edge Creative (www.edgecreative.com)
Printed in the UK by Latimer Trend & Company Ltd, Plymouth

Contents

vi

PREFACE

The construction of Thompson's mass spectrograph in Cambridge almost exactly a century ago followed by Aston's improved instruments and his pioneering work on non-radioactive isotopes is widely known. This was followed by rapid developments in instrumentation in European and North American laboratories including the double-focussing instrument described by Mattauch and Herzog in the mid-1930s. It was only when commercial instruments became available in the late-1940s that mass spectrometry emerged from physicists' research laboratories and began to be widely used first by chemists and later by biochemists.

In the sixty years or so since then, European scientists and engineers have made many major contributions to the development of new instruments and techniques. They have also advanced our understanding of the fundamentals of ionisation and fragmentation processes and developed new methods for the determination of molecular structure and mixture analysis. Detailed accounts of these contributions are to be found in the scientific literature but they necessarily give little idea of the contributors themselves or of the difficulties that had to be overcome before success was achieved.

Most newcomers to mass spectrometry in the last ten years will have little concept of the difficulties faced in obtaining the mass spectra of four solid samples during a working day before the invention of the vacuum lock probe. This was followed by several hours of counting spectra and trying to interpret them. Many will never have seen a magnetic deflection instrument and will be familiar only with mass spectrometers having both the operation of the instrument and the interpretation of the data under computer control. During the past sixty years, instruments designed and built in Manchester and Bremen have appeared in laboratories throughout the world and many of the major advances have had their origin in European laboratories.

This small volume aims to give an insight into how some of the more important developments came about, from the advent of the first commercial instruments to the present day. It cannot, of course, be comprehensive but it is hoped that the various accounts, several of which contain personal reminiscences, both provide a human background to these developments and convey the excitement of being part of the European mass spectrometry community during this period. Each author has been encouraged to treat his or her subject as they see fit and this has produced a variety of styles which it is hoped will add interest to the book. As editor, I must take responsibility for the overall balance of the book and for the inevitable omission of subjects because of constraints on its length. I gratefully acknowledge the advice and encouragement of colleagues too numerous to mention and thank the various bodies who have allowed material to be reproduced from elsewhere.

K.R. Jennings
February, 2012

viii

ACKNOWLEDGEMENTS

We are most grateful to the many people who have contributed to this book, with their memories, photographs and help.

We are particularly grateful to the following organisations whose financial support of the book has made its publication possible.

British Mass Spectrometry Society
Bruker Daltonics
Deutsche Gesellschaft für Massenspektrometrie
Waters Corporation

The foundations of mass spectrometry in Europe—the first fifty years

Keith R. Jennings

University of Warwick, Coventry, UK

During the latter half of the nineteenth century, aided by the development of increasingly reliable vacuum pumps, chemists and physicists in various European countries endeavoured to understand the nature of electrical discharges through rarefied gases. In 1858, building on the work of Michael Faraday, Julius Plücker, a mathematician turned physicist working at the University of Bonn in collaboration with Heinrich Geissler, described a series of experiments on discharges in gases at low pressures. As the pressure was reduced, they observed changes in a variety of discharges in tubes containing different gases. Their most important observation was that the discharge produced a fluorescent glow on the walls of the discharge tube. When a magnetic field was applied to the tube, the glow moved in such a manner as to suggest that whatever was responsible for producing it was negatively charged. In a later study with his student, Johann Wilhelm Hittorf, in 1869, it was shown that a solid object placed between the cathode and the fluorescence on the wall of the tube cast a shadow on the wall, suggesting that whatever caused the fluorescence travelled in straight lines. Unaware of Hittorf's work, Sir William Crookes carried out similar studies in his London laboratory in the 1870s. Meanwhile, in Berlin, Eugene Goldstein had extended Hittorf's studies and in 1876 was probably the first to use the term "cathode rays".

There was still no clear picture of the nature of cathode rays. C.F. Varley, an English electrical engineer, was probably the first to suggest that they were corpuscular, i.e. electrically charged particles. Both Arthur Schuster, professor of physics in Manchester, and Crookes considered that they were either atoms or molecules that had picked up a charge. Goldstein, however, by working at very low pressures, was able to show that they could travel in a rectilinear manner over distances much greater than the mean free paths of atomic and molecular species. Consequently he, together with other German scientists, such as Georg Wiedermann and Heinrich Hertz, considered that the rays were electromagnetic in nature since attempts to deflect them by applying an electric field were inconclusive. Neither theory appeared to be capable of explaining all observations but in the early 1890s, both Hertz and Philipp Lenard demonstrated that cathode rays could penetrate thin metallic foil. This suggested that they consisted of particles that were very much smaller than atoms and, in 1895, Jean Perrin collected cathode rays in a Faraday cylinder and demonstrated that they carried a negative charge. The problem was finally resolved in 1897 when J.J. Thomson, who succeeded Lord Rayleigh as professor of physics in the Cavendish Laboratory in Cambridge, showed that cathode rays were indeed composed of particles and by measuring their charge to mass ratio, e/m, was able to show that their mass was around 1/1800 of that of a hydrogen atom, the lightest atom known. The particles were named electrons, as first suggested by the Irish physicist, G.J. Stoney, and Thomson was subsequently awarded the Nobel Prize for physics in 1906 for the discovery of the electron and his work on discharges in gases.

Some 20 years earlier in 1886 while he was still working in Berlin with Hermann von Helmholtz, Goldstein suggested that there were probably positive rays moving in the opposite direction to cathode rays. He was able to demonstrate their existence by working with perforated cathodes. Because of their appearance, he termed these rays *kanalstrahlen* or canal rays; their colour varied with the gas in the tube—air gave a yellowish glow, hydrogen a rose-purple glow and neon a bright red glow. They affected a photographic plate and

Opposite: Francis William Aston, *c.* 1920s at work in his laboratory.
Photo: © Science Museum/ Science & Society Picture Library.

caused fluorescence on the walls of the tube. Goldstein was unable to demonstrate that they were positively-charged particles, however, since they appeared not to be deflected by a magnetic field. There was then little interest in canal rays for a number of years but in 1898, another former student of Helmholtz, Wilhelm Wien, who had succeeded Lenard at the Technische-Hochschule in Aachen, began an extended study of their properties. He constructed an apparatus in which the cathode of the discharge tube was pierced and connected to a single tube which led to a velocity filter. This consisted of crossed homogeneous electric and magnetic fields such that for ions of a given velocity travelling along the axis of the filter, the deflection caused by the electric field was exactly balanced by that caused by the magnetic field. The electric field was applied between two parallel plates and the ions passing through the filter had a velocity $v = E/B$ where E and B are the strengths of the electric and magnetic fields, respectively. The ions then struck a flat surface coated with a Willemite screen. By using stronger magnetic and electrical fields than had been available to Goldstein, he was able to deflect the canal rays and to demonstrate that they were composed of heavy, positively-charged particles. He was the first to measure the ratio of charge to mass, e/m, for the H^+ ion, subsequently known as the proton, and also made measurements on some heavier ions and thereby laid the foundations of the mass spectrograph. His results working with heavier ions, however, were difficult to interpret because of the relatively high pressure within his apparatus. The velocity filter was developed by others in subsequent years and was used in the first double-focussing mass spectrometers built in the 1930s.

From about 1907 onwards, Thomson began work on positive ion beams in Cambridge in addition to working as Professor of Natural Philosophy at The Royal Institution in London to which he had been appointed in 1906 whilst continuing to hold his chair in Cambridge.

Sir J.J. Thomson *ca* 1900.
Photo: © Science Museum /
Science & Society Picture
Library.

Francis Aston in his
laboratory.
Photo: © Science Museum /
Science & Society Picture
Library.

Initially, he could obtain evidence only of the H^+ ion reported by Wien. Much of his early work on positive ions was fraught with difficulties arising from having to work at pressures which were not sufficiently low to avoid frequent charge exchange processes occurring. At the end of 1909, however, Thomson invited Francis W. Aston, who had previously been working on the Crookes Dark Space in discharge tubes at Birmingham University, to join him as a research assistant. They constructed an improved apparatus in which the discharge was struck in a large bulb of up to 2 L capacity at a lower pressure than had been possible in earlier work. Attached to this was a metal cathode in the form of a tube 6 cm in length and of internal diameter 0.1 mm to 0.5 mm. On exiting the cathode, the beam of ions passed through a vessel to strike a flat fluorescent screen normal to the beam. An important feature of this region was that the pressure was kept much lower than in the discharge tube by means of a tube of charcoal immersed in liquid air, the highly efficient absorptive power of which had been discovered in 1905 by James Dewar. Immediately on leaving the cathode tube, the fine pencil of rays travelling in the x direction was subjected to parallel electric and magnetic fields in the y direction which deflected the beam in the y and z directions, respectively. If A and B are constants depending on the strengths of the electric and magnetic fields, respectively, ions of a given e/m having a range of velocities v strike the screen at positions y and z where

$$y = A(e/mv^2) \quad z = B(e/mv) = (B/A)yv \text{ so that } z^2 = (B^2/A)y(e/m)$$

and so form one arm of a parabolic trace on the screen. These traces had not previously been observed because the pressure in the chamber had not been sufficiently low. For a constant value of y, z^2 is proportional to e/m so that by measuring z for a given value of y, relative values of e/m could be determined and since the trace for the H^+ ion was always observed and was readily recognised, values relative to this ion could be found.

Using this apparatus, Thomson was able to observe a variety of singly- and multiply-charged atomic ions including argon with up to three charges, krypton with up to five charges and mercury with up to eight charges. Interestingly, samples of neon obtained from various sources always gave a strong signal for an atom of mass of 20 accompanied by a much weaker signal corresponding to an atom of mass 22. Thomson initially ascribed the weaker signal to an impurity in the neon but later recognised that this was the first observation of a non-radioactive isotope. His apparatus may therefore be looked upon as the first example of a working mass spectrograph and in a subsequent experiment, in which he detected ions using a Wilson tilted electroscope and a Faraday cylinder, he can be said to have constructed the first mass spectrometer which was much superior to the mass spectrograph for measuring relative abundances of ions. Much of his work was summarised in his book published in 1913 in which he reports the observation of ions given by a number of common gases. He was puzzled, however, by the unpredictable behaviour of the ion of mass to charge ratio three times that of the proton which he tentatively ascribed to H_3^+. It was only many years later that it was realised that some of his observations had been of the HD^+ ion.

Thomson quickly realised that the analysis of positive rays was in many respects superior to other methods of chemical analysis based on optical spectroscopy. Whereas in the latter, trace impurities were often masked by the main components, positive ray analysis not only provided atomic and molecular weights of components but its use did not depend on the purity of the sample. His views are summarised in his prophetic statement:

"I feel sure that there are many problems in chemistry which could be solved with far greater ease by this than any other method. The method is surprisingly sensitive—more so even than that of Spectrum Analysis, requires an infinitesimal amount of material and does not require this to be specially purified."

Thomson and Aston had worked together on the discovery of the isotopes of neon and in 1919, Aston returned to Cambridge after working at the Royal Aircraft Establishment, Farnborough, from 1914 to 1918. Using the parabola mass spectrograph, he quickly confirmed the existence of neon isotopes and reported the existence of the isotopes of chlorine and mercury. Later that year he constructed an improved instrument, the first double-focussing mass spectrograph, in which ions passed first through two collimating slits and then entered a uniform electric field produced by two parallel plates where they were deflected through an angle θ. They then entered a uniform magnetic field which was perpendicular to the electric field and the direction of motion of the ions and they were then deflected in the opposite direction through an angle slightly greater than 2θ. This arrangement allowed ions of the same m/e but with slightly different velocities to be brought to focus at a point at which a detector could be placed and was the first example of the use of velocity focussing in a mass spectrograph. Ions of different m/e were brought to focus at different points along a plane where they fell on a photographic plate. From the positions of the images, Aston was able to determine the relative masses of the ions. The resolution of this instrument was about 130 and the accuracy of mass measurement was about 1 part in 1000. With this instrument, he was able to carry out a systematic study of the isotopes of about 50 of the lighter elements for which he was awarded the Nobel Prize for chemistry in 1922. He used his measurements to introduce the "whole number rule" in 1920, a revival of William Prout's hypothesis of 1814, but it soon became evident that this rule was only an approximation.

Josef Mattauch with "Doppelfokus", his double-focussing mass spectrometer, around 1956. Photo: Archiv der Max-Planck-Gesellschaft, Berlin-Dahlem.

In 1925, both J.L. Costa in Paris and Aston in Cambridge described mass spectrographs of improved design with resolving powers of 600 which allowed them to measure masses with a precision of 0.01%. Aston went on to construct his third instrument in 1937, attaining a resolving power of about 2000. These instruments allowed him to investigate over 200 naturally-occurring isotopes and led him to introduce the packing fraction curve in 1927 which was of considerable interest in the field of nuclear chemistry. The use of a photographic plate as a detector and the lack of direction focussing limited the accuracy with which relative abundances of isotopes could be determined but these problems were largely overcome by the development of double-focussing instruments and the use of electrical detection such as the electrometer in the following decade.

There was now considerable emphasis placed on the development of the theory of ion optics. In 1933, N.F. Barber, working in Leeds, was the first to show that first-order focussing of an ion beam could be obtained in a sector instrument if the source, magnet apex and collector lie along a straight line and the ion beam enters and leaves the magnetic field at right angles. In the following year, Richard Herzog and Josef Mattauch reported more generalised calculations for various angles of deflection and W. Henneberg carried out calculations on the directional focussing properties of electric and magnetic fields. There was growing interest in using both velocity focussing and direction focussing to produce what became known as double-focussing instruments, thereby giving increased resolving power and accuracy of mass measurement. Kenneth Bainbridge in the USA was the first to use a Wien filter with a homogeneous magnetic field of equal strength in an early double-focussing instrument in 1932. In 1934, Herzog and Mattauch produced the design of a mass spectrometer that was double-focussing for all masses. In this instrument, an electric field deflected the ion beam through an angle of 31.8° and the resultant parallel ion beam traversed a field-free region before entering a 90° magnetic sector so that ions of different m/e were brought to focus along a plane of 25 cm length where a photographic plate was placed. The first instrument built to this design, known as Mattauch–Herzog geometry, was constructed at the University of Vienna the following year and produced a much improved mass resolution of about 6000. This allowed measurements of increased accuracy to be made of many isotopic masses. Almost simultaneously, double-focussing instruments of different designs were built by Arthur Dempster in Chicago in 1935, and by Bainbridge and Edward Jordan at Harvard in 1936.

As the 1930s drew to a close, mass spectrometry in Europe was still seen primarily as a method of determining accurate isotopic masses and, despite Thomson's prophetic prediction in 1913, it was still not regarded as a technique to be used for chemical analysis. Production of ions by the use of electrical discharges, thermal ionisation, electron ionisation and the spark source had all been described but no commercial instruments were being manufactured. Two developments in the USA in 1940, however, had far-reaching consequences which changed the whole emphasis. The first was the development of the magnetic sector analyser by Alfred Nier coupled with the introduction of an improved electron ionisation source based on earlier designs of Dempster and Walker Bleakney. The second was the decision by the American oil industry to use mass spectrometry as a method of analysing light hydrocarbon mixtures used as aviation fuel. This led to the production of the first commercial mass spectrometers by the Consolidated Electrodynamics Corporation in the USA and towards the end of the 1940s, the first commercial European instruments were produced by Metropolitan-Vickers in Manchester in the United Kingdom and by MAT in Bremen in Germany. This made the technique available to physicists, chemists and biologists throughout Europe and the following chapters describe some of the contributions made by them to mass spectrometry over the next 60 years.

LITERATURE FOR FURTHER READING

J.J. Thomson, *Rays of Positive Electricity and Their Application to Chemical Analysis, 1st and 2nd Edns.* Longmans, Green & Co., London (1913, 1921).

J.J. Thomson, *Recollections and Reflections.* G. Bell and Sons, London (1936).

F.W. Aston, *Mass Spectra and Isotopes, 1st and 2nd Edns.* Longmans, London (1933, 1941).

W. Wien, *Kanalstrahlen.* Akademische verlagsgesellschaft mbh, Leipzig (1923).

R. Herzog, "Ionic and electro-optical cyclindrical lenses", *Z. Physik* **89,** 447 (1934).

J. Mattauch and R. Herzog, "Uber eine neuen massenspektrographen", *Z. Physik* **89,** 786 (1934); "A double-focusing mass spectrograph and the masses of N^{15} and O^{18}", *Phys. Rev.* **50,** 617 (1936).

Fundamentals

Nico M.M. Nibbering

Vrije Universiteit, Amsterdam, The Netherlands

INTRODUCTION

Since the late 1940s, tremendous developments in the field of mass spectrometry have taken place. Of course, the roots of mass spectrometry go back to the work of the British physicists J.J. Thomson, who discovered the electron, and F.W. Aston, who developed the mass spectrograph and discovered and measured a large number of isotopes. Earlier, the German physicists E. Goldstein discovered so-called canal rays in a discharge tube and W. Wien made major contributions through his studies of electron beams and positively charged atomic beams. In the 1930s, the Austrian physicist J.H.E. Mattauch and his student, R. Herzog, designed one of the first double-focussing mass spectrometers. Thomson was very far-sighted in his statement in 1921: "I believe there is no branch of science where promise of great discoveries is more hopeful than those which will result by researches which involve the application of physical principles and physical measurements to chemical phenomena".

In the 1940s mass spectrometry was applied very successfully by the petroleum industry for the quantitative analysis of hydrocarbon mixtures. The peaks of the fragment ions in their mass spectra, however, were often difficult to correlate with the original molecular structures, so much so that there was even a "sudden death theory" proposed. That is, upon electron ionisation, a charged "soup of atoms" from the original molecule was generated which eventually formed the fragment ions. Then, in the 1950s, the American chemist S. Meyerson showed by his research that the $C_7H_7^+$ ions from aromatic hydrocarbons had the tropylium ion structure and F.W. McLafferty demonstrated that in the molecular ions of aliphatic aldehydes, a γ-hydrogen migration took place to form an enolic radical cation together with the expulsion of an olefin. It became clear that the fragment ions were generated from the electron ionisation-induced decomposing molecular ions by well-defined mechanistic pathways. Since then, an enormous amount of research has been carried out by the worldwide community of mass spectrometrists to elucidate the underlying chemistry that is responsible for the fragment ions that appear in mass spectra. This chapter is an attempt to highlight the contributions that have been made by European mass spectrometrists to understand, in depth, the chemistry of ions that takes place inside the mass spectrometer, both unimolecularly and bimolecularly. These contributions have become increasingly advanced by the development of very sophisticated physical and experimental methods and computational chemistry. They will be described in other chapters and be mentioned in this chapter only where appropriate. Furthermore, the text will be organised around themes that have obviously been important for the progress of knowledge in gas-phase ion chemistry.

HYDROGEN AND CARBON ATOM RANDOMISATION

One of the most powerful methods of obtaining insight into the chemical behaviour of ions inside the mass spectrometer is stable isotopic labelling of molecules. Numerous publications have shown, on the basis of site-specific deuterium labelling, that in many organic ions generated by electron ionisation, either a partial, or even a complete, hydrogen atom randomisation occurs both in the ion source and during their flight to the detector of the mass

Nico Nibbering

Opposite: Methyl radical loss from the molecular ion of methyl crotonate; see Scheme 1.

Peter Derrick

Karsten Levsen

Dudley Williams

spectrometer. Metastable ion studies, particularly time-resolved studies of ions decomposing in the time range of ps to µs following ionisation by use of the field ionisation kinetics method in combination with isotopic labelling, have revealed the underlying chemistry for hydrogen atom randomisation. In the latter field, the groups of P.J. Derrick when at University College London, UK, T. Gäumann of the Ecole Polytechnique at Lausanne, Switzerland, H.-F. Grützmacher of the University of Bielefeld, Germany, K. Levsen of the University of Bonn, Germany and of the author of the University of Amsterdam, The Netherlands, have been very active.

Some illustrative examples are the retro–Diels–Alder reaction of ionised cyclohexene, the randomisation of the hydroxyl and *ortho*-hydrogen atoms in ionised benzoic acid and of the hydrogen atoms in the molecular ion of 1,3-butadiene. For the retro-Diels–Alder reaction, it was shown by P.J. Derrick's group that the ethylene loss was accompanied by a competitive 1,3-allylic hydrogen shift. The latter led to successive migrations of the double bond along the ring and, consequently, to an increasing hydrogen atom randomisation at longer molecular ion lifetimes, being complete at $\sim 10^{-9}$ s prior to the ethylene loss. For ionised benzoic acid, it was found by K. Levsen's group that, at ion lifetimes $<6 \times 10^{-11}$ s, the original OH group was lost and that 88% of the molecular ions at 10^{-5} s had suffered from a complete exchange between the hydroxyl and the two *ortho*-hydrogen atoms prior to OH elimination. The randomisation of the hydrogen atoms in the molecular ion of 1,3-butadiene turned out to be complete at an ion lifetime of $\sim 10^{-11}$ s as probed from the loss of a methyl radical from its molecular ion and shown by the author's group. This might give the impression that the carbon atoms of ionised 1,3-butadiene would also randomise very rapidly. ^{13}C-labelling showed, however, that the eliminated methyl radical contained more than 85% of the terminal carbon atoms at molecular ion lifetimes of $\sim 10^{-11}$ s and that, at longer ion lifetimes, the inner carbon atoms participated increasingly, although slowly, in this methyl loss, which became random at 10^{-5} s. These observations were interpreted as being due to the formation of a methylcyclopropene ion at short ion lifetimes that, at longer ion lifetimes, equilibrated with the 1,3-butadiene structure by ring opening and ring closure reactions. In any case, the results obtained showed that hydrogen and carbon atom randomisation are independently occurring processes that proceed by different routes. A similar conclusion was drawn earlier by the group of D.H. Williams of the University of Cambridge, UK, from the behaviour of metastably decomposing radical cations of benzene. In an elegant study, it was shown that the acetylene loss from benzene labelled with ^{13}C in positions 1,3 and 5 and benzene labelled simultaneously with ^{13}C and deuterium in position 1 occurred after a complete hydrogen atom **and** carbon atom scrambling. The scrambling of the carbon atoms was rationalised in terms of intermediate isomers, such as prismane and benzvalene, while for the hydrogen atom scrambling, rupture and re-formation of the C–H bonds, independently of carbon atom scrambling, must take place. In many cases, it is better to call the hydrogen atom randomisation process a hydrogen atom exchange reaction when it concerns specific positions of the ions. Benzoic acid, mentioned above, is such an example. Other very illustrative examples are the complete exchange between all hydrogen atoms of the four phenyl rings of protonated tetrabenzylmethane at 10^{-5} s and the exclusive exchange between all hydrogen atoms of the phenyl rings of protonated α,ω-diphenylalkanes, having a methylene chain of $(CH_2)_{20}$, via proton transfer from ring to ring and proton walk along the rings, as shown by the group of D. Kuck at the University of Bielefeld, Germany. The underlying chemistry of fragmentation of electron ionised aliphatic hydrocarbons is extremely complex, with questions still unanswered. This has been shown by the heroic synthetic work and mass spectrometric research performed over many years by the group of T. Gäumann on extensively ^{13}C-labelled molecules that were frequently simultaneously extensively deuterium labelled.

METASTABLE IONS AND POTENTIAL ENERGY SURFACES

In the 1960s, two publications appeared in which the results described have proved to be of paramount and fundamental importance for studies of gas-phase ions. The first is from the group of J.H. Beynon, then at ICI in Manchester, England and later at the University of Swansea, Wales. It concerns so-called metastable ions decomposing in the field-free region between the electric and magnetic sector of a normal geometry double-focussing mass spectrometer. Such decompositions can give rise to "metastable peaks" with different shapes such as Gaussian, dish-topped and flat-topped peaks. Beynon showed that these shapes reflect the amount of kinetic energy that is released upon dissociation. Metastable ions have lifetimes of ~1–10 μs and thus 10^7–10^8 vibrations have occurred before dissociation, so that, in general, it can be assumed that these ions have little, or even no, energy in excess of the transition state. The kinetic energy release, therefore, can provide insight into the transition state structure of ions and the energy barrier at the potential energy surface that the ions pass. The second publication is from K.R. Jennings, then at the University of Sheffield, England and later at the University of Warwick, Coventry, England, who developed the method of collision-induced dissociation. This has become the most widely applied technique to determine the structures of long-lived, i.e. non-decomposing ions, within the timescale of the mass spectrometer.

These publications together have enabled the construction, in the mid 1970s, of potential energy surfaces for unimolecular reactions of ions, in particular by the group of D.H. Williams of the University of Cambridge, England in cooperation with G. Hvistendahl of the University of Oslo, Norway. They first explained, on the basis of orbital symmetry considerations, that, for example, the one-step 1,2-elimination of molecular hydrogen from protonated formaldehyde is a symmetry-forbidden reaction and, therefore, has a high energy barrier which consequently gives rise to the dish-topped metastable peak observed. In a similar way, they reasoned that the one-step 1,1-elimination of molecular hydrogen from protonated benzene is a symmetry-allowed reaction, having a low energy barrier which should, therefore, lead to a narrow Gaussian metastable peak, as was indeed observed. Then, they considered two-step reactions of isomeric ions A$^+$ and B$^+$ for which three distinct types of potential energy surface were taken into account. The first is that the two ions each exist in potential wells, but that the barrier for their interconversion is less than that required for their unimolecular dissociation. An example is any pair of the isomeric butyl cations, in which interconversion occurs by rapid 1,2-hydrogen atom and methyl shifts—explaining the hydrogen and carbon atom randomisation discussed in the "Hydrogen and carbon atom randomisation" section—prior to predominantly allyl cation formation by expulsion of a methane molecule. The second is the case where the barrier for interconversion of A$^+$ and

John Beynon

Keith Jennings

Georg Hvistendahl

B⁺ is higher than their unimolecular dissociation thresholds. The ions will then be distinct species and will behave completely independently. The third case is a situation where no direct dissociation channel of A⁺ is available, but an isomerisation of A⁺ to B⁺ occurs in a rate-determining step over a high energy barrier. The B⁺ ion generated in this way will then have more internal energy than when B⁺ is generated directly from a suitable precursor molecule. This higher internal energy may manifest itself in a higher kinetic energy release upon dissociation. This was shown to be the case for protonated acetone which, following isomerisation to protonated propanal, exhibited a larger kinetic energy release for elimination of ethylene than for the loss of ethylene from protonated propanal itself. Thanks to the original research of the groups mentioned, the use of potential energy surfaces coupled with results from computational chemistry has now become common practice in gas-phase ion chemistry studies.

HIDDEN HYDROGEN ATOM REARRANGEMENTS

The concept of charge localisation has been a very useful tool since its introduction in the 1960s for the interpretation of mass spectra in terms of chemical structures, notwithstanding the serious criticism it has received in a number of publications. Moreover, sometimes the fragmentations of the ions were thought to be comparable with the thermal decompositions of their neutral counterparts. This was shown not to be correct, at least for methionine, the electron ionisation-induced fragmentation of which has been studied extensively by the author's group. It was found to be completely different from its Curie-point pyrolytically-induced fragmentation, notwithstanding the great similarity of the corresponding spectra as evidenced by a cooperative study with M.A. Posthumus from the Institute for Atomic and Molecular Physics (Amolf) in Amsterdam, The Netherlands. For example, the neutral product with the mass of 101 Da was generated by the successive loss of water, carbon monoxide and molecular hydrogen from neutral methionine, while the ion *m/z* 101 was formed in a one-step elimination of methanethiol from the molecular ion.

Then, in the mid 1970s, D.H. Williams and J.H. Beynon argued in favour of the concept of charge localisation, on the basis of energetic data that radical sites in molecular radical cations weaken local bonding and that, preferentially, the term "charge radical localisation" should be used as a model for which there is experimental support. The charge site can induce the direct heterolytic bond cleavage and the radical site can lead to a homolytic rupture of the adjacent bond. By applying these types of primary bond cleavages together with the well-known McLafferty rearrangement, one can rationalise the origin of many peaks in the electron ionisation mass spectra. Such spectra of many organic molecules, however, also frequently show peaks corresponding to radical eliminations from their molecular radical cations that are unexpected in view of the primary fragmentation channels mentioned above and are, therefore, called pseudo-direct bond cleavage reactions. Notable examples are the radical cations of saturated carboxylic acids, esters and amides that have been studied by the group of H. Schwarz of the Technical University of Berlin, Germany by use of very extensive deuterium and ¹³C-labelling in combination with collision-induced dissociation (CID) and computational chemistry. It was shown that the radical eliminations from these ions took place via multistep pathways including hydrogen atom rearrangements

Helmut Schwarz

which are energetically more favourable than a direct bond cleavage. These hydrogen atom rearrangements, however, occur in the charge radical carrying part of the ion and the migrated hydrogen atoms remain there upon radical elimination. That is, the rearrangements cannot be inferred from the shifts of peaks in the mass spectra of the isotopically-labelled molecules, for which, in 1980, H. Schwarz introduced the concept of "hidden" hydrogen atom rearrangement. A very simple example to demonstrate such a hidden hydrogen atom rearrangement is given below in Scheme 1.

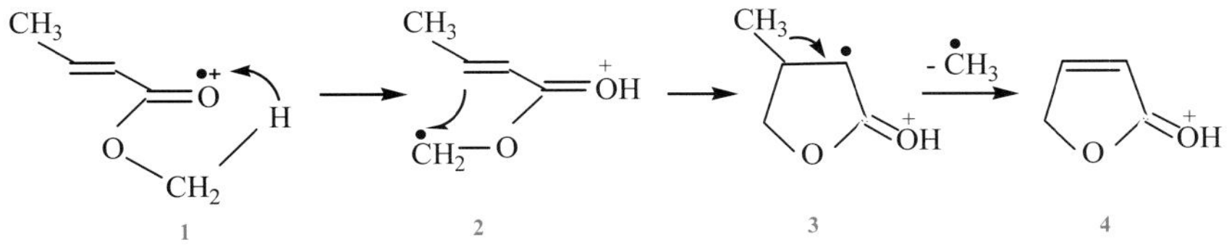

Scheme 1

It concerns the methyl radical loss from the molecular ion of methyl crotonate, which by D-labelling was shown to be the methyl group at the double bond. Following a 1,4-hydrogen shift in the molecular ion **1**, the generated distonic ion **2** (for distonic ions see later) can undergo ring closure to give the five-membered ring ion **3** which, by homolytic cleavage, eventually eliminates a methyl radical to give the protonated α,β-unsaturated γ-butyrolactone species **4**.

ION–NEUTRAL COMPLEXES IN UNIMOLECULAR ION DECOMPOSITIONS

At the end of the 1970s, the group of D.H. Williams observed that the kinetic energy released during the loss of carbon monoxide from metastably decomposing isobutyryl cations was only $0.4\,kJ\,mol^{-1}$, while that from the isomeric n-butyryl cations was $3.3\,kJ\,mol^{-1}$. This large difference was explained by assuming that during elongation of the C–C bond of the n-butyryl cation the incipient n-propyl cation isomerises to the isopropyl cation prior to final departure of carbon monoxide, see Scheme 2

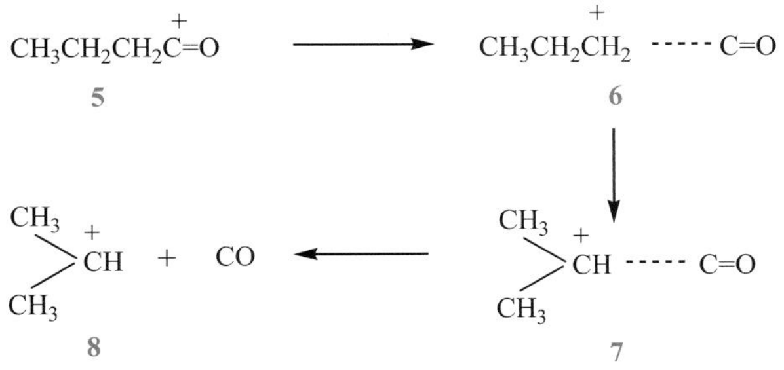

Scheme 2

Some of the energy released during the exothermic isomerisation (about $67\,kJ\,mol^{-1}$) can then appear as kinetic energy. The intermediate ions in Scheme 2 resemble ion–molecule complexes that owe their stability to an ion–dipole interaction. Such "weakly coordinated cations" were also proposed for the interconversion of the similarly behaving metastably

Pierre Longevialle

René Botter

decomposing oxonium ions $CH_2=O(+)-CH_2CH_2CH_3$ and $CH_2=O(+)-CH(CH_3)_2$ via stretching of the C—O bond and isomerisation of the incipient propyl cations prior to decomposition. In 1980, P. Longevialle of the CNRS in Gif-sur Yvette, France and R. Botter of the Centre d'Etudes Nucléaires de Saclay, Gif-sur-Yvette, France, reported on the electron ionisation-induced fragmentation of the 3,20-diaminopregnane steroid. Its molecular ions lead in the ion source to the formation of protonated ethyleneimine with m/z 44, but its metastable ions eliminate neutral ethyleneimine with the mass of 43 daltons. The resulting (M−ethyleneimine)•+ ions subsequently expel an ammonia molecule which contains the original amino group of position 3 **and** a hydrogen atom of the amino group of position 20 as shown by D-labelling. This observation implies the very important phenomenon that a direct transfer of a hydrogen atom from the amino group at position 20 to the amino group at position 3 takes place. Due to the rigid steroid skeleton structure, this transfer must proceed via an ion—molecule complex in which the ion and neutral species can move around each other in such a way that the original amino groups can come close together to enable the direct hydrogen atom transfer. This process has been pictured in Scheme 3.

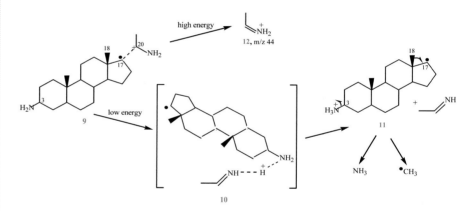

Scheme 3

That is, following homolytic cleavage of the C(17)—C(20) bond of ion **9,** the protonated ethyleneimine generated moves in the low energy metastable ion to the amino group at position 3 where it then can transfer its proton via complex **10** to give the ion **11** eventually, but is expelled from the high energy ion to form the free ion **12**. Subsequently ion **11** either eliminates an ammonia molecule by heterolytic cleavage or the C(18) methyl group by homolytic cleavage. The observations described were also made for a number of N-substituted 3,20-diaminopregnanes, so that solid evidence was provided for the occurrence of ion—neutral complexes in unimolecular dissociations. Subsequently, an overwhelming number of publications have appeared from many different groups that have shown that the intermediacy of such ion—neutral complexes is a very common phenomenon for an extremely broad range of types of low energy ions. The work of Longevialle and Botter, therefore, was a very important breakthrough in the field of gas-phase ion chemistry and as G. Bouchoux of the Ecole Polytechnique in Palaiseau, France, has stated in one of his publications: "Attractive forces extend largely beyond the covalent interatomic distances giving rise to long range chemistry and to a new dimension in the description of chemical events".

Guy Bouchoux

DISTONIC IONS

The term distonic ion was suggested by L. Radom of the Australian National University in Canberra, Australia, in 1984 and it concerns species in which the charge and radical are positioned at different atoms. If they are at adjacent atoms, then the corresponding ion is called an α-distonic ion and, if they are separated by one heavy atom, then it is a β-distonic ion etc. Such ions can be found in many publications before 1984, but were not then termed distonic ions. They are very common intermediates in gas-phase ion dissociations and are frequently more stable than their isomers, having the conventional structure.

Three groups have performed extensive research in the area of distonic ions. They are the groups of H.E. Audier of the Ecole Polytechnique in Palaiseau, France, S. Hammerum of the University of Copenhagen, Denmark, and H. Schwarz, who have studied many aliphatic amines, alcohols, ethers, carboxylic acids and derivatives etc. by use of a variety of methods in combination with stable isotopic labelling. These studies have shown that especially the metastable ions extensively rearrange via distonic ion intermediates and, in many cases. so much so that the metastable ion beam is a mixture of ion structures containing a reduced amount, or even none, of the original molecular ion structure. The latter has been shown by H. Schwarz's group to be the case for ionised valeramide, among others, indicating that care must be exercised in using metastable ion data for the purpose of obtaining structural information on the original neutral molecule. Several methods are available to generate and characterise distonic ions, such as isomerisation, fragmentation and ion/molecule reaction and by CID, neutralisation–reionisation and again ion/molecule reaction, respectively. A very nice example is the formation of the archetypal methyleneoxonium radical cation $^{\bullet}CH_2^+OH_2$, as reported in 1994 by the group of H.E. Audier in cooperation with S. Hammerum. This ion is not only more stable than the conventional radical cation $CH_3OH^{\bullet+}$ but is also separated by a large barrier from it. The CID spectrum of $CH_3OH^{\bullet+}$ at a low ion source pressure is typical for that structure, but in the presence of water in the ion source it changes completely into that being characteristic for the $^{\bullet}CH_2^+OH_2$ structure. In other words, water catalyses the transformation of $CH_3OH^{\bullet+}$ into $^{\bullet}CH_2^+OH_2$. Details of the associated mechanism have been uncovered by D-labelling experiments in combination with theoretical calculations, which have shown that the water molecule drags one of the C–H hydrogen atoms of the methanol radical cation across the C–O bond to give the distonic methyleneoxonium radical cation. In simplified form this interesting reaction has been summarised in Scheme 4.

Henri Audier

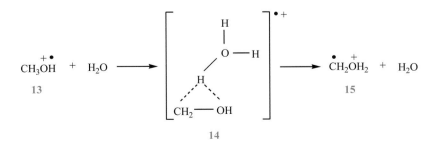

Scheme 4

A similar transformation was found by the author's group to occur in the dimer radical cation of methyl chloride, where the neutral methyl chloride drags one of the methyl hydrogen atoms of the ionised methyl chloride over the C–Cl bond to give the methyl chloride solvated distonic radical cation $^{\bullet}CH_2ClH^+$.

Two other examples are from the group of H. Schwarz in cooperation with the group of the author. The first, in 1984, is the distinction of the distonic ions, $^{\bullet}CH_2{}^+XCH_3$ (X=Cl, Br), from their conventional isomers, $CH_3CH_2X^{\bullet+}$, by allowing them to react with nitric oxide, NO, and acetonitrile, CH_3CN. The distonic ions reacted with NO by $CH_2{}^{\bullet+}$ transfer and with CH_3CN by methyl cation transfer, whereas the conventional isomeric ions reacted with NO by electron transfer and with CH_3CN by proton transfer as summarised in Scheme 5.

$$\underset{\mathbf{17}}{\overset{+}{C}H_2NO} \xleftarrow{+NO} \underset{\mathbf{16}}{\overset{\bullet}{C}H_2\overset{+}{X}CH_3} \xrightarrow{+\,CH_3CN} \underset{\mathbf{18}}{CH_3C\overset{+}{N}CH_3}$$

$$\underset{\mathbf{20}}{NO^+} \xleftarrow{+NO} \underset{\mathbf{19}}{CH_3CH_2X^{+\bullet}} \xrightarrow{+\,CH_3CN} \underset{\mathbf{21}}{CH_3C\overset{+}{N}H}$$

Scheme 5

The second, in 1987, is the generation of the distonic methyleneammonium ion, $^{\bullet}CH_2{}^+NH_3$, by the ion/molecule reaction of ionised ketene with ammonia as given in Equation (1):

$$NH_3 + \underset{\mathbf{22}}{CH_2{=}C{=}O^{+\bullet}} \longrightarrow \underset{\mathbf{23}}{H_3\overset{+}{N}{-}\overset{\bullet}{C}H_2} + CO \qquad (1)$$

This substitution reaction was relatively facile notwithstanding that a direct nucleophilic attack on a radical cation would be a "forbidden" process.

NEUTRALISATION–REIONISATION MASS SPECTROMETRY

In the years 1966–1968 R. Lavertu's group at the Centre de Cinétique physicochimique du CNRS et Ecole des Industries Chimiques, Université de Nancy, France, and F.M. Devienne of the Laboratoire de Physique Moléculaire des Hautes Energies in Peymeinade, France, reduced beams of small cations in collision experiments to generate neutral molecules in the gas phase in this way. Their work was not widely recognised until ten years later, however, when several research groups rediscovered the technique which has become known as neutralisation–reionisation mass spectrometry. In brief, a mass selected ion beam of a few keV is collided with a gas such as Xe in a first collision cell to neutralise the ions by electron capture. Subsequently, remaining ions are removed from the beam by a charged deflector electrode and the neutral molecules remaining in the beam are then reionised by collision with gases such as He or O_2 in a second collision cell. The transit time from the first to the second collision cell is in the order of a few μs, so that neutrals corresponding to the mass of the selected ion beam can be detected as survivor signals if they are stable species

for a few μs. In addition, fragment ions can also be generated in the reionisation step which can serve to characterise the structure of the survivor ion.

Two groups have been very active in this field which are those of J.K. Terlouw of the University of Utrecht and, since 1988, at McMaster University in Hamilton, Ontario, Canada, and of H. Schwarz. In cooperation, they have shown that the neutral molecules of acetylene derivatives $XC \equiv CY$ ($X = H$, OH, NH_2; $Y = OH$, NH_2), prepared by neutralisation of the decarbonylated ions from propiolic acid, its amide, square acid and its amine derivatives, are stable species in the gas phase, in contrast to their non-existence in solution. In a similar way, they have provided evidence for the existence of free neutral carbonic acid, H_2CO_3, and carbamic acid, H_2NCO_2H, in the gas phase in agreement with earlier theoretical predictions, that the energy barrier for their unimolecular dissociation into CO_2 and H_2O and CO_2 and NH_3 is higher than $167\,kJ\,mol^{-1}$. The instability of these molecules in solution is due to the fact that a rapid decomposition and deprotonation is promoted by acid/base or solvent catalysis, although recently, experimental evidence has been provided that carbonic acid can persist for nanoseconds in aqueous solution and that it has an acidity comparable to that of formic acid. An interesting variant of the technique is that of collision-induced dissociation ionisation (CIDI). In that case no collision gas is admitted in the first collision cell which allows the transmission of neutral molecules, generated therein by a metastable ion decomposition, to the second collision cell for ionisation and fragmentation and hence characterisation. The group of Terlouw has shown in this way that the neutral species eliminated from the molecular ion of aniline is HNC and that from ionised pyridine is HCN. A very surprising result from his group was the elimination of a hydroxymethyl radical and **not** a methoxy radical from the molecular ion of methyl acetate. The mechanistic proposal for this reaction is presented in Scheme 6 where, following a 1,4-hydrogen atom shift from the ester methyl group to the carbonyl oxygen, the generated ion **25** rearranges to the hydrogen-bridged radical cation **26**, that eventually dissociates into the acetyl cation **27** and hydroxymethyl radical. It is now generally recognised from the work of J.K. Terlouw that hydrogen-bridged radical cations occur frequently and are therefore common intermediates in gas-phase ion dissociations.

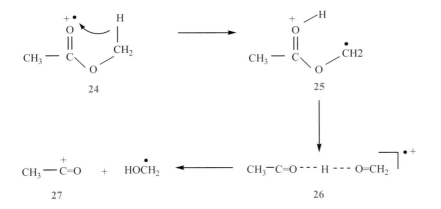

Scheme 6

Hans Terlouw

Neutralisation–reionisation mass spectrometry has furthermore been shown to be a very powerful method of identifying reactive intermediates, as will be discussed in the "Reactive intermediates" section below.

AROMATIC RADICAL CATION AND ARENIUM ION CHEMISTRY

Hans-Friedrich
Grützmacher (left)

Three groups have worked for many years in the area of the gas-phase chemistry of ionised aromatic compounds as the main theme of their research, those of H.-F. Grützmacher of the University of Bielefeld in Germany and F. Cacace and M. Speranza of the University of Rome in Italy. The first mentioned group has applied isotopic labelling and a variety of mass spectrometric methods to study both radical cations of alkylbenzenes and related compounds and protonated alkylbenzenes. Some illustrative examples from this group will now be presented. It was shown by D-labelling that hydrogen atom loss by the radical cation of N,N-dimethyl-N′-phenylformamidine is ~85% an *ortho*-hydrogen atom, the remaining ~15% stemming from the N,N-dimethylformamidine group. The former is due to a rate-determining intramolecular aromatic substitution reaction leading to ion **29** (see Scheme 7) from which the *ortho*-hydrogen atom can be lost easily by a homolytic cleavage. A similar rate-determining aromatic substitution takes place in the radical cation of benzalacetone leading to ion **31** (see Scheme 7). In that case, however, not only an *ortho*-hydrogen atom, but also a hydrogen atom from the other positions of the phenyl ring is lost due to a complete randomisation of the aromatic ring hydrogen atoms. This different behaviour can be explained by considering the possible positions of the charge and radical in the ions **29** and **31**. In the former, the charge is fixed at the N,N-dimethyl nitrogen while the radical can be delocalised over the aromatic ring and the adjacent N=C bond, whereas in the latter, both the charge and radical can be delocalised over the aromatic and pyrilium ring. It is known that the barrier for 1,2-hydrogen atom shifts in radicals is high which prevents such a shift in ion **29**. The barrier for 1,2-hydrogen shifts in protonated phenyl rings is known, however, to be low and leads to a so-called proton walk along the aromatic ring of ion **31** and consequently to the hydrogen atom randomisation mentioned above.

Scheme 7

X = H, Halogen

28

29

30

31

This proton walk also leads to *ipso*-substituted and sp³-hybridised carbon atoms at the *meta*- and *para*-positions if they carry substituents. These substituents can then be eliminated easily as radicals by homolytic cleavage. The experimentally observed abundances of the (M−substituent)•⁺ ions from ring-substituted benzalacetones are indeed much higher than those from ring-substituted *N,N*-dimethylformamidines. The group also studied the aromatic substitution reaction intermolecularly, that is via ion/molecule reactions by use of Fourier transform ion cyclotron resonance (FT-ICR). It is then possible to investigate either the reaction between the radical cation of the aromatic compound and a neutral molecule or that between the neutral aromatic molecule and the radical cation as the reactant ion. In that way, it was found that, with reference to Scheme 8, the radical cation of a mono- or di-substituted halobenzene **32** reacted with low efficiency with neutral ammonia to form, in a rate-determining step, the *ipso*-substituted addition product **33,** this being directly comparable with the intramolecular aromatic substitution reaction discussed above. Subsequently the *ipso*-halogen atom is eliminated to generate the corresponding anilinium ion **34**.

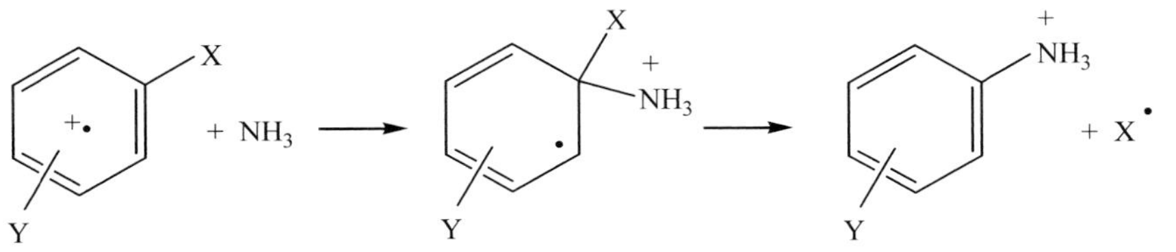

32   **33**   **34**

X = Halogen; Y = H, Halogen

Scheme 8

The radical cation of ammonia, however, reacted with the halobenzenes only by an efficient charge transfer reaction. The question then remained why the *ipso* substitution occurred with low efficiency, i.e. why is there kinetically a significant activation energy barrier. This was explained by a charge migration during the addition from the arene radical cation to ammonia in the collision complex prior to bond formation between the two species.

This is necessary because the charge is at the radical cation at the beginning of the reaction, but localised at the quaternary ammonium substituent in the addition product (*cf.* ion **29** in Scheme 7). It also implies that the neutral arene generated becomes electronically excited because of the endothermic charge migration, this being possible by the energy gained in the ion–molecule complex formation. This description of the reaction is in line with the theoretically known configuration mixing model, which predicts that the activation energy barrier for the reaction between a radical cation and a neutral nucleophile arises from an avoided crossing of the electronic configurations of the initial and final states of the reaction. The group has also shown the occurrence of rapid intramolecular ring-to-ring proton transfer in (ω-phenylalkyl)benzenium ions, usually leading to a complete exchange of the aromatic ring hydrogen atoms on the μs timescale. An interesting case is protonated 1-(4-*t*-butylphenyl)-3-phenylpropane. This ion eliminates isobutane, following protolysis of the bond between the phenyl ring and the *t*-butyl group, which then subsequently, as a

Dietmar Kuck

Maurizio Speranza

Fulvio Cacace

cation, abstracts a hydride from either the α- or γ-benzylic position in a 1:1 ratio as shown by D-labelling.

This result implies that the *t*-butyl cation can hop from ring-to-ring, most probably via an intermediate ternary [arene.(CH$_3$)$_3$C$^+$.arene] complex, as a truly "disolvated cation", as suggested by D. Kuck. In any case, protonated alkylbenzenes are important species as they are the prototype intermediates in electrophilic aromatic substitution reactions. These reactions have been studied for many years by the groups of F. Cacace and M. Speranza who used the method of stationary radiolysis, although the former group has also applied the technique of β-decay of covalently-bonded tritium atoms for the production of gaseous cations. The method of radiolysis involves γ-irradiation of a bulk gas containing about 0.1 mol% or less of the neutral substrate of interest at pressures that can range from 0.1 kPa to 133 kPa. This results in a random distribution of ions, electrons, radicals and excited molecules throughout the bulk gas, the nature of which determines their fate. Radicals can be trapped by appropriate scavengers, excited molecules will be de-excited by the many collisions with the bulk gas molecules, electrons can collide with walls of the reaction vessel or give rise to negative ions that can be neutralised by reactions with positive ions, undesired positive ions can be removed by reactions with appropriate bases etc. This leaves the fully thermalised cations before they react with the neutral substrate molecules of interest to give charged intermediates that are rapidly trapped by suitable nucleophiles and converted into neutral end products, amenable to analysis by gas chromatography, gas chromatography/mass spectrometry and nuclear magnetic resonance for structural and stereochemical characterisation. The radiolysis method is thus largely complementary to mass spectrometric methods in the study of ionic reactions in the gas phase and is especially powerful because it is capable of trapping ions with a lifetime of 10^{-7} s or less and the analysis of its neutral products.

For example, the group of F. Cacace has shown that, at atmospheric pressure, the neutral products from the gas-phase reaction of radiolytically-formed cyclohexyl cations with water are predominantly cyclohexanol and cyclohexanone with a minor amount of 1-methylcyclopentanol. This result provided evidence that the cyclohexyl cation is a stable species in the gas phase, contrary to mass spectrometric measurements which had led to the conclusion that the incipient cyclohexyl cation had completely rearranged to the 1-methylcyclopentyl cation. This group has studied the alkylation of aromatic compounds, such as toluene, by the different *t*-butyl, *i*-propyl and ethyl carbenium ions. At high pressure, the reaction of the *t*-butyl cations with toluene yields exclusively *para*- and *meta-t*-butyltoluenes in the ratio of 95:5. As the pressure is reduced, this ratio gradually shifts towards a limiting value of 37:63. This has been explained—with reference to Scheme 9—as follows: at high pressure, the reaction is kinetically controlled to generate the arenium ion intermediate **36** which is excited because of the reaction exothermicity; this is collisionally stabilised to give thermalised ions **37** which are subsequently deprotonated by a gaseous base to form the *para-t*-butyltoluene end product. A small proportion of the ions may isomerise to ring protonated *meta-t*-butyltoluene **38** which, following deprotonation, will result in the formation of the corresponding neutral end product. At lower pressure, however, the intermediate ions **36** are no longer efficiently collisionally stabilised, which enables them to isomerise increasingly

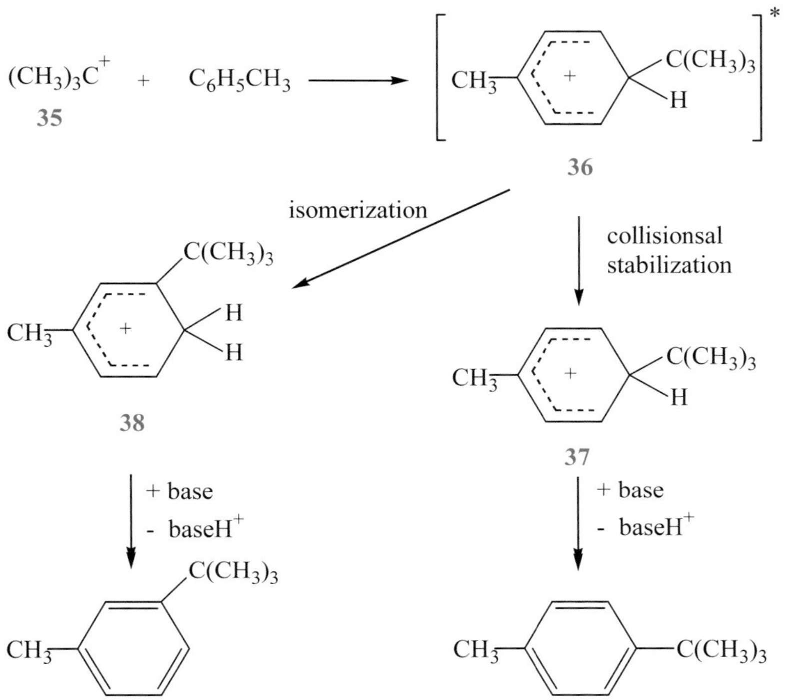

Scheme 9

to the more stable ions **38** with the result that deprotonation then leads to neutral products characterised by an increasing thermodynamic control of isomeric composition. The high *para:meta* ratio at high pressures, however, shows that the *t*-butyl cation is a very selective electrophile. Less selective are the *i*-propyl cations which react at high pressure kinetically controlled to give *ortho*-, *meta*- and *para-i*-propyltoluene in the ratio of 43:32:25, that becomes 44:40:15 at lower pressure. Still more unselective are the ethyl cations, giving at high pressure *ortho*-, *meta*- and *para*-ethyltoluene in the ratio of 43:34:22.

Another very interesting research topic from the F. Cacace group has been the silylation of aromatic rings by the trimethylsilyl cation, $(CH_3)_3Si^+$. This silicon analogue of the *t*-butyl cation had been found by high pressure mass spectrometry to form an adduct with aromatic substrates that did not transfer a proton to strong bases. The conclusion, therefore, was that the adduct consisted of a trimethylsilyl cation which was π-bonded to the aromatic ring. A radiolytic study was then undertaken, in which mixtures of methane, trimethylsilane and an arene were irradiated at nearly atmospheric pressure, but a silylated aromatic product was not detected. Addition of the sufficiently basic triethylamine to these mixtures turned out to be successful in promoting the formation of a silylated aromatic compound, thereby providing evidence for the existence of a stable σ-bonded intermediate silylated arenium ion, such as **39**.

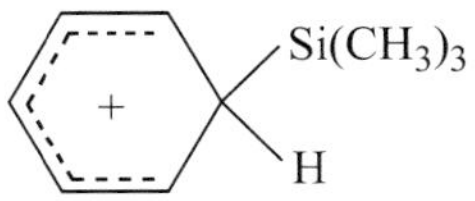

Reactions of $(CH_3)_3Si^+$ with methylbenzenes, including toluene and the xylenes, showed that this ion is a moderately selective electrophile, although less selective than $(CH_3)_3C^+$ with lower steric requirements because of its longer C–Si bond.

Most relevant is that electrophilic aromatic silylation is unprecedented in both the gas and the liquid phase and, for the first time, was firmly demonstrated by use of the radiolytic method. Speranza's group extended the research of electrophilic aromatic substitution to the class of hetero-aromatic compounds, including pyrrole, N-methylpyrrole, furan and thiophene. These molecules were allowed to react with the large variety of ionic electrophiles CH_3^+, $C_2H_5^+$, $i\text{-}C_3H_7^+$, $t\text{-}C_4H_9^+$, $(CH_3)_3Si^+$, $(CH_3)_2F^+$, $C_6H_5^+$, CH_3CO^+, $C_6H_5CO^+$ and CF_3^+. All these electrophiles showed a significant positional selectivity with little or no substrate discrimination. For pyrrole the majority of the electrophiles were found to attack its β carbon atoms, while in furan, preferentially substituted σ-bonded intermediate ions were formed by proximity effects because of interaction of the electrophiles with the lone-pair electrons of oxygen. For pyrrole, theory predicts that the reactivity of ionic electrophiles with a high lowest unoccupied molecular orbital (LUMO) energy will be charge-controlled, while that of those with a low-lying LUMO will be orbital-controlled. The former will, therefore, preferentially attack the β carbon atoms of pyrrole, at which the total net negative charge is located, while the latter will preferentially attack the α carbon atoms, which have the highest occupied orbital (HOMO) with a high π-electron density. With the exception of the $(CH_3)_2F^+$, CH_3CO^+ and $C_6H_5CO^+$ electrophiles, a qualitatively good linear correlation between the site selectivity of the ionic electrophiles toward the β and α positions of pyrrole, expressed as the log (β/α) values, and the LUMO energies of the electrophiles has indeed been found. Application of the configuration mixing model (vide supra this section), known theoretically, has provided an even better quantitative correlation between the log (β/α) values and so-called G values. These are expressed by the difference between the vertical electron affinity of the electrophile and the vertical ionisation energy of the formally localised π $C_\alpha=C_\beta$ bond of pyrrole and the extent of interaction between the reactant and product configurations in the corresponding transition state.

PHOTODISSOCIATION

The method of photodissociation has not only been valuable, but also more effective than CID in a number of gas-phase ion structure determinations. Two groups should be mentioned: that of W.J. van der Hart at the University in Leiden, The Netherlands, and that of T. Gäumann. Each group applied visible laser light but the latter additionally used infrared multiphoton absorption to excite and dissociate the ions, known as infrared multiphoton dissociation (IRMPD). The ions studied in the visible region were radical cations that were trapped in ICR traps, enabling one to follow the photon-induced ion decay as a function of the irradiation time because of the large residence times. In addition, measurement of the photodissociation rate as a function of the wavelength provides a photodissociation spectrum, which closely resembles the absorption spectrum of the ion if its internal energy, after excitation, is above the dissociation limit. The photodissociation spectrum can then be used as a fingerprint for ion structure determination. The reason that radical cations were selected for study was that their lowest electronically-excited state is obtained by an

Wim van der Hart

25

excitation from the HOMO to the singly-occupied molecular orbital (SOMO). These are often close in energy and, consequently, the cations will absorb visible light if the transition is allowed. For even-electron ions, the transition from the doubly-occupied HOMO to the empty LUMO is usually in the ultraviolet (UV) region. A few examples from W.J. van der Hart's group will now be considered.

Ionised ethylene oxide photodissociates at wavelengths around 480 nm, which agrees with its ring-opened ion structure $(CH_2-O-CH_2)^{\bullet+}$. Propylene oxide ions do not photodissociate, however, in contrast to the $(M-CH_2O)^{\bullet+}$ fragment ions from 4-methyl- and 2-methyl-1,3-dioxolane which photodissociate at wavelengths around 475 nm. The latter ions thus have the ring-opened propylene oxide structure $(CH_3CHOCH_2)^{\bullet+}$, the fractions being 60% and 20%, respectively, as determined from their photon-induced decay curves at a wavelength of 475 nm. The remaining percentages of ions appeared to be methyl vinyl ether formed by rearrangement of part of the ring-opened propylene oxide ions. This rearrangement also occurs in the molecular ions of propylene oxide following ring opening, which explains why no photodissociation is observed at a 475 nm wavelength. Another example concerns the structure of $C_6H_6O^{\bullet+}$ ions, generated from the molecular ions of 2-phenoxyethyl chloride by elimination of chloroethene. From ion/molecule reaction studies in the author's group, the conclusion had been drawn that these ions were a mixture of phenol and 2,4-cyclohexadienone, the latter being formed via a 1,5-H-shift to the *ortho* position of the phenyl ring and loss of chloroethene. The 2,4-cyclohexadienone structure was seriously questioned afterwards but eventually, by a photodissociation study carried out in cooperation with W.J. van der Hart, it was convincingly shown that this ion was indeed formed. The photodissociation spectra of the $C_6H_6O^{\bullet+}$ ions from 2-phenoxyethyl chloride and bicyclo[2.2.2.]oct-2-ene-5,7-dione, its $(M-CH_2O)^{\bullet+}$ fragment ion serving as the 2,4-cyclohexadienone reference structure, were similar and showed intense peaks at 360 nm and 550 nm. These photodissociation spectra were very different from those of ionised phenol and the $(M-C_2H_4)^{\bullet+}$ ion from phenyl ethyl ether showing a UV peak near or below 250 nm. This observation allows one to draw the important conclusion that the $C_6H_6O^{\bullet+}$ ions from 2-phenoxyethyl chloride are not generated by the intermediacy of ion–molecule complexes alone being responsible for the phenol ion formation. They are also formed from the original covalently-bonded structure accounting for the 2,4-cyclohexadienone ion generation.

The group of T. Gäumann observed from photon-induced decay curves at 488 nm that the $C_7H_8^{\bullet+}$ ions prepared from toluene at low ionising energies, i.e. via charge exchange, retain the original structure. The ions prepared at 14 eV and higher, however, turned out to be a mixture of about equal amounts of toluene and cycloheptatriene ions, these being known as the archetype of an aromatic six-membered ring expansion to a seven-membered ring. This group also studied the isomeric molecular ions of allyl bromide, cyclopropyl bromide, 1-bromopropene and 2-bromopropene by use of IRMPD at wavelengths from 9.28 μm to 10.67 μm. The corresponding spectra were quite different except for the 1- and 2-bromopropene ions. These ions could be distinguished, however, by the induction time in their photodissociation decay curves, their underlying photodissociations kinetics being described by an induction time followed by an exponential decay of the ion abundance. The induction time for the 1-bromopropene ions was 50–100 ms, whereas for the 2-bromopropene ions

Tino Gäumann

and also for the allyl bromide and cyclopropyl bromide ions it was less than 15 ms. These examples show clearly that photodissociation is a powerful and effective method to distinguish isomeric ion structures.

STEREOCHEMISTRY AND CHIRALITY

Stereochemistry and chirality are extremely important issues, not only in chemistry, but also in biology, where the shape and chirality of the molecules are essential for their recognition and communication through non-covalent interactions. These themes have received increasing attention in mass spectrometry because of the development of advanced instrumental methods over the last four decades. Research on these themes, however, in particular chirality, is not trivial. Three groups should be mentioned who have been, or still are, active in these areas of mass spectrometry. The first is the group of J.C. Tabet of the Pierre et Marie Curie University in Paris, France. This group studied the reaction between NH_4^+ and the isomeric *cis*- and *trans*-indanediol-1,2 in a chemical ionisation source, where the $(M+NH_4)^+$ ions were shown to eliminate a molecule of water that contained the benzylic hydroxyl group. From NH_3 pressure dependence measurements, a second order kinetic behaviour was observed for the H_2O loss in the case of the *cis*-isomer whereas, for the *trans*-isomer, a first order kinetic dependence was found. These results were interpreted as follows. In the case of the *cis*-isomer, the ammonium ion is chelated by the two hydroxyl groups (see ion **40** in Scheme 10) which inhibits the formation of a planar transition state around the benzylic carbon atom to enable nucleophilic substitution of the nascent water molecule by ammonia. Another ammonia molecule can react by a backside S_N2 attack upon the benzylic carbon atom of ion **40**, however, to give the amino protonated *trans*-1-amino-2-hydroxyindane **41**, as pictured in Scheme 10, and accounting for the observed second order kinetics.

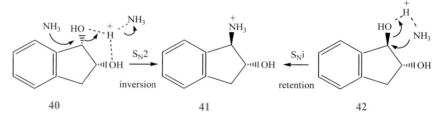

Jean-Claude Tabet

Scheme 10

In the case of the *trans*-isomer, a planar transition state can be developed in the $(M+NH_4)^+$ ion that enables the ammonia molecule to displace the water molecule in an S_Ni reaction, that is with stereochemical retention (see Scheme 10, reaction **42 → 41**). In a similar way, his group has shown that the $(M+NH_4)^+$ ions of *endo* and *exo* bicyclo-(1.2.2)-heptanyl acetates and benzoates eliminate acetic and benzoic acid by ammonia nucleophilic substitution in an S_N2 reaction with inversion and in an S_Ni reaction with retention of configuration, respectively, giving, in both cases, the protonated *exo* bicyclo-(1.2.2)-heptanylamine. The information obtained about the stereospecific S_N2 reaction was then used by the group to differentiate enantiomeric menthols by reacting these with the protonated chiral reagent

(S)-2-amino-1-butanol. It was established that the amino group of this reagent ion, in a stereospecific S_N2 process, i.e. without appreciable racemisation, displaced the R and S hydroxyl group of the enantiomeric R,S,R and S,R,S menthols, respectively, accompanied by the expulsion of water. The diastereomeric product ions generated in this way exhibited CID spectra that are sufficiently different for them to allow one to distinguish the original enantiomers from each other.

The second group is that of M. Speranza, which has published a number of very interesting results obtained by use of the radiolytic method. A few selected examples will be presented here. In the reaction of the benzenium ion, $C_6H_7^+$, with 2-chlorobutane, C_4H_9Cl, a $C_{10}H_{15}^+$ product ion and HCl are formed. In the ion–molecule complex $[C_6H_7^+ . C_4H_9Cl]$ initially generated, two routes are available for further reaction, namely proton transfer to give the complex $[C_6H_6 . C_4H_9ClH^+]$ or a dissociative proton transfer to give the three-body complex $[C_6H_6 . C_4H_9^+ . HCl]$ prior to formation of $C_{10}H_{15}^+$ and HCl. Differentiation between these two possibilities has become possible by using chiral R-2-chlorobutane as the neutral reagent. The 2-phenylbutane, recovered from the radiolytic experiment, showed a complete race-misation, so that the three-body complex $[C_6H_6 . C_4H_9^+ . HCl]$ with a free butyl cation must have been the exclusive intermediate in the reaction discussed. Another example is the study of the intramolecular racemisation and isomerisation of the chiral oxygen proto-nated (S)-*trans*-4-hexen-3-ol species. These processes can occur if the covalently-bonded structure is transformed into a non-covalently-bonded 1-methyl-3-ethylallyl cation–water molecule complex. The latter may happen for a small fraction of the ions generated upon protonation of (S)-*trans*-4-hexen-3-ol in the radiolytic experiment. From analysis of the recovered neutral products it was found that both the R enantiomer of the starting sub-strate and the racemate of the rearranged *trans*-3-hexen-2-ol were formed in proportions depending upon the experimental conditions. No racemate of rearranged *cis*-3-hexen-2-ol was observed. Experiments in the presence of $H_2^{18}O$ showed a relatively low incorporation of ^{18}O into the recovered neutral products mentioned. The extent of incorporation was used to correct the abundances of the neutral products for contributions of free 1-methyl-3-ethylallyl cations generated upon protonation of (S)-*trans*-4-hexen-3-ol and reacting with the background water molecules in the irradiated mixtures. This made it possible to obtain the rate constants of the intramolecular racemisation and isomerisation of the oxygen protonated (S)-*trans*-4-hexen-3-ol species, as being $(1.4–21.3) \times 10^6 s^{-1}$ and $(1.0–9.9) \times 10^6 s^{-1}$, respectively, over the entire temperature range of 40–120°C studied. These results, in combination with *ab initio* theoretical calculations, point to and are consistent with the intermediacy of the structured ion–molecule complexes **43** and **44** for the racemisation and isomerisation, respectively, in which the water molecule is coplanarly coordinated to the hydrogen atoms of the 1-methyl-3-ethylallyl cation.

Similar experiments were carried out on the oxygen methylated chiral (S)-*trans*-4-hexen-3-ol ion. In addition, in this case, no racemate of rearranged oxygen methylated *cis*-3-hexen-2-ol was observed and in the presence of $H_2^{18}O$ a negligible amount of ^{18}O incorporation into the recovered neutral products was detected. The rate constants of the intramolecular racemisation and isomerisation, however, were now found to be opposite to those of oxygen protonated (S)-*trans*-4-hexen-3-ol, that is $(1.9–9.8) \times 10^6 s^{-1}$ and $(2.9–15) \times 10^6 s^{-1}$,

43

44

respectively, over the entire temperature range of 40–120°C studied. Again, these results are consistent with the intermediacy of ion–molecule complexes such as **43** and **44**, the water molecule then being substituted for methanol. The observation that, for the oxygen protonated (S)-*trans*-4-hexen-3-ol species, intramolecular racemisation is faster than isomerisation, whereas for the oxygen methylated analogous ion the reverse is observed, has led to the conclusion that the transition states of these processes are located early and later on the reaction coordinate, respectively. The information obtained about the chiral ions discussed has subsequently permitted the unravelling of the regio- and stereochemistry of the gas-phase nucleophilic attack of the chiral allylic alcohol (S)-*trans*-4-hexen-3-ol, denoted by NuH, on the corresponding oxygen protonated and oxygen methylated derivatives. Firm evidence has been presented that not only the common S_N2 reaction takes place by attack of NuH on the carbon atom in position 3, but attack on the carbon atom in position 5 is even more favoured. This so-called S_N2' reaction leads in a concerted way to bond formation of NuH with the carbon atom in position 5 and bond cleavage between the carbon atom in position 3 and its substituent of water, *c.q.* methanol. In addition, it has been established that when the NuH approaches the oxonium ions from the direction *syn* to the leaving substituent, a preferred frontside S_N2 displacement occurs being favoured by preliminary proton bonding between the reaction partners. In the S_N2' reaction, however, the preliminary interaction of NuH with the π-LUMO of the oxonium ions takes place preferentially in an *anti*-position of NuH with respect to the leaving substituent, which determines the outcome of the reaction.

Eugene Nikolaev

The third group is that of E.N. Nikolaev of the Russian Academy of Sciences, Moscow, Russian Federation, who subsequently cooperated with the group of F.J. Winkler of the Technical University in München, Germany. They reported very large chiral effects for the gas-phase association of enantiomer-labelled racemates of dimethyl-(S)- and d_6-dimethyl-(R)-tartrates and di-isopropyl-(S)- and d_{14}-di-isopropyl-(R)-tartrates with methylammonium and ammonium ions, AH^+, in a FT-ICR cell. The abundant diastereomeric trimer adduct clusters SSS. AH^+, SSR. AH^+, SRR. AH^+ and RRR. AH^+ (S and R are the enantiomers of each tartrate) did not show the statistical abundances 1:3:3:1, but a pattern near 15:1:1:15 for the dimethyl tartrate and near 10:1:1:10 for the di-isopropyl tartrate system. In other words, the homochiral and propeller type structure clusters SSS. AH^+ and RRR. AH^+ are significantly more stable than the heterochiral clusters SSR. AH^+ and SRR. AH^+. Similar chiral effects have been observed in an elaborate chemical ionisation study of the association of dialkyltartrate trimers with hydronium, ammonium and primary aminium ions. In concluding this section, it can be stated that the groups involved have made major contributions by their pioneering studies, not only to the non-trivial determination of the stereochemistry and chirality of molecules by mass spectrometry, but also to a much deeper and more detailed insight into the interactions and mechanisms of reactions between chiral ions and molecules in the gas phase and beyond.

REACTIVE INTERMEDIATES

In many chemical reactions, intermediates occur which are highly reactive and hence elusive. Their characterisation, being important for reaction mechanistic studies, is often, but not always, successfully achieved by chemical trapping or matrix isolation combined with spectroscopic methods, such as infrared (IR) spectroscopy. Another approach is to generate them as gas-phase neutrals or ions and to characterise them by use of CID and neutralisation–reionisation mass spectrometry (NRMS) discussed above in the "Neutralisation-reionisation mass spectrometry" section. A great variety of reactive intermediates were generated by the groups of R. Flammang of the University of Mons-Hainaut, Mons, Belgium, in close cooperation with C. Wentrup of the University of Queensland, Brisbane, Australia, and of H. Schwarz.

The first group applied flash vacuum thermolysis (FVT) of suitable, mostly heterocyclic, precursor molecules to generate neutral reactive intermediates that, on-line, were monitored by mass spectrometry and identified by use of CID and NRMS. Examples are the formonitrile imine, $H-C\equiv N^+-N^--H$, and substituted nitrile imines, $R-C\equiv N^+-N^--R'$, the formonitrile ylide, $H-C\equiv N^+-CH_2^-$, and substituted nitrile ylides, $R-C\equiv N^+-CR_2'^-$, nitrile oxides $R-C\equiv N^+-O^-$ and cyanogen oxide, $N\equiv C-C\equiv N^+-O^-$, nitrile sulphides, $R-C\equiv N^+-S^-$, including the unsubstituted $H-C\equiv N^+-S^-$ species, nitrile selenides, $R-C\equiv N^+-Se^-$, and the highly unstable linear dinitrogen sulphide molecule, NNS.

Robert Flammang

Moreover, this group generated several novel heterocumulenes, such as iminoethenethiones, $RN=C=C=S$ ($R = CH_3$ and H), iminopropadienones, $RN=C=C=C=O$, bis-iminopropadienes, $RN=C=C=CNR'$ and linear ketenimines $R_2C=C=NR'$. The latter can also be described in terms of their resonance structure as being isonitrile ylides, $R_2C^--C\equiv N^+-R'$. Using the alternative technique of FVT, this group also generated the nitrile sulphides $R-C\equiv N^+-S^-$ ($R = CH_3$ and H) by use of successive ion/molecule reaction and NRMS experiments, as summarised in Scheme 11.

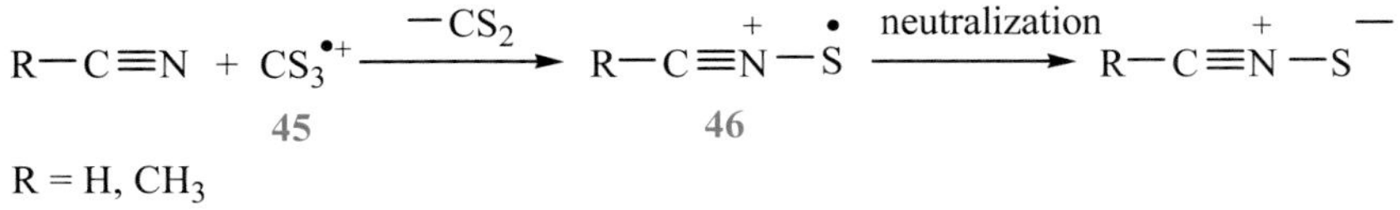

$$R-C\equiv N \ + \ CS_3^{\bullet+} \xrightarrow{\ -CS_2\ } R-C\overset{+}{\equiv}N-\overset{\bullet}{S} \xrightarrow{\text{neutralization}} R-C\overset{+}{\equiv}N-\overset{-}{S}$$
$$\qquad\qquad\qquad \mathbf{45} \qquad\qquad\qquad \mathbf{46}$$
$$R = H, CH_3$$

Scheme 11

This strategy was also applied successfully by the group of H. Schwarz. By use of the known chemistry of the radical anion $O^{\bullet-}$ with ethene (see the "Negative ions" section below) his group generated the radical anions of cyanovinylidene **48** and cumulenic butatrienylidene **49** from cyanoethene and butatriene by abstraction of $H_2^{\bullet+}$ by $O^{\bullet-}$, respectively, which subsequently were neutralised by oxidation in a NRMS experiment, see Scheme 12.

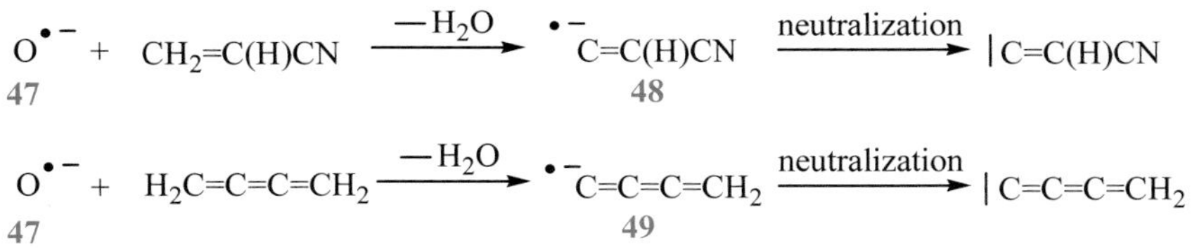

$$O^{\bullet-} \ + \ CH_2=C(H)CN \xrightarrow{\ -H_2O\ } \overset{\bullet\,-}{C}=C(H)CN \xrightarrow{\text{neutralization}} |C=C(H)CN$$
$$\mathbf{47} \qquad\qquad\qquad\qquad\qquad\quad \mathbf{48}$$

$$O^{\bullet-} \ + \ H_2C=C=C=CH_2 \xrightarrow{\ -H_2O\ } \overset{\bullet\,-}{C}=C=C=CH_2 \xrightarrow{\text{neutralization}} |C=C=C=CH_2$$
$$\mathbf{47} \qquad\qquad\qquad\qquad\qquad\qquad \mathbf{49}$$

Scheme 12

Cumulenes, such as the one obtained by oxidative neutralisation of **49** in Scheme 12 or those having the general structure $X(C_n)Y$ (X,Y = lone electron pair, H_2, O, S; $n \geq 2$) are interesting because of their possible role in the chemistry taking place in interstellar space. In addition, these molecules possess unique spectroscopic and chemical properties and have electronic ground states that follow an "odd/even" pattern, that is a "singlet/triplet" pattern for $X(C_n)Y$ when n = odd/even, respectively. The even numbered cumulenes, however, could not be detected by matrix isolation because of their exceptional reactivity. Yet, dissociations of their triplet ground states are quite endothermic according to theoretical predictions. This was confirmed by H. Schwarz and his co-workers who first generated $C_nS_2^{\bullet+}$ ions (n = 2–6) by electron ionisation-induced fragmentation of the fused four-ring system given in Scheme 13.

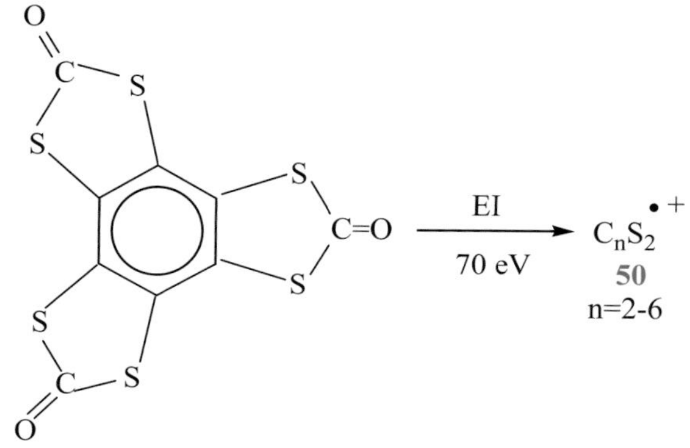

Scheme 13

Subsequently, the atom connectivity of the $C_nS_2^{\bullet+}$ ions **50** was established to be SC_nS by use of CID and NRMS experiments which provided the evidence that the neutral SC_nS (n = 2–6) cumulenes are indeed stable molecules.

In a similar way the OC_4O and OC_nS (n = 3–5) cumulenes were shown to be stable species as well as their corresponding radical anions and cations from which they were generated by oxidative and reductive NRMS experiments, respectively. In addition, the smallest member OCCS of the OC_nS series was generated by reductive neutralisation of its corresponding radical cation and indicated by *ab initio* MO studies to be in the triplet state.

In closing this section, it can be stated quite firmly that the application of NRMS, frequently in combination with theoretical calculations, by the groups mentioned above, has been invaluable for the study and characterisation of reactive intermediates that are otherwise experimentally inaccessible.

LOCATION OF C,C-DOUBLE AND TRIPLE BONDS IN ALKENES, ALKYNES AND DERIVATIVES

Alkenes and alkynes obtained as some of the products from the oil cracking process in the petroleum industry are important basic chemicals. They can be functionalised by reaction with a large variety of organic and inorganic molecules and so are important in the synthesis of new chemical compounds in the chemical and pharmaceutical industry and materials, such as polymers with specific physical and mechanical properties. Following gas chromatography (GC) of the complex mixtures containing alkene/alkyne compounds, analysis with the aim of identifying them by use of electron ionisation mass spectrometry is not successful because of the rapid isomerisations of the molecular ions (see the "Hydrogen and carbon atom randomisation" section) and consequently shifts of double bonds in particular. Chemical derivatisation by attaching functional groups at the double bond that direct the fragmentation prior to introduction into the mass spectrometer is then an option. Frequently only very minor amounts of material are available, however, such as in research of pheromones or metabolic pathways. Derivatisation should then preferably be performed in the ion source. Two groups have applied this approach, those of K.R. Jennings and of H. Budzikiewicz of the University at Köln, Germany. The first allowed ionised methyl vinyl ether (MVE) **51** to react with an olefin via [2+2]-cycloaddition to give the two isomeric cyclobutane species **52** and **53** that, in turn, decomposed via cycloreversion into the different methyl alkenyl ether radical cations **54** and **55**, as visualised in Scheme 14. The position of the double bond can then be deduced from the latter ions.

Herbert Budzikiewicz

Scheme 14

This approach is also applicable to locate the double bond in olefins that contain an additional functional group, such as an ester group, but not bound directly to the double bond. Ionised MVE also reacts with its neutral by ion/molecule reactions, however, which, in principle, could be suppressed or minimised by dilution with CO_2 or Ar. However, the latter will then become ionised by charge exchange, their ions in turn reacting further with the olefins by charge exchange and, consequently, giving EI-type spectra of the olefins that are not suited for double bond location. In addition to the tendency of MVE to polymerise in the ion source, its application in the GC/MS analysis of complex mixtures therefore has not become common practice.

The second group reasoned that the reactant gas should have the following properties: (i) readily available in high purity; (ii) not aggressive to the ion source or vacuum system; (iii) yielding ions with low mass and, consequently, not interfering with ions derived from the olefinic analyte; (iv) the recombination energy of the reactant ions should not exceed ~9.5 eV to avoid charge exchange with the olefinic analyte molecules; (v) ionisation should not be effected by proton transfer, as the possible hydrogen atom randomisation in the resulting carbenium ion would obscure the original location of the double bond; (vi) electrophilic attack of the reactant ion upon the double bond should lead to a relatively fast formation of characteristic fragment ions so that isomerisation reactions cannot compete effectively.

Based upon these considerations, the group of H. Budzikiewicz selected and examined methylamine and dimethylamine and the chemical ionisation (CI) gas isobutane as reactant gases. The radical cations of the two amines can be added to the double bond to give a mixture of two isomeric alkylamines, which by α-cleavage can fragment to yield four characteristic ions. The latter enable a straightforward localisation of the double bond. Unfortunately, these reactant gases turned out to be insufficiently sensitive for application to GC/MS analyses with capillary columns. When isobutane is used, its main t-butyl cation adds to the double bond, abstracts a hydride and transfers a proton to the double bond in a slightly exothermic reaction. The latter leads to an enhanced formation of alkyl ions by α-cleavage and concomitant proton addition to the incipient double bond as summarised in Scheme 15, sequences **56 → 57** and **58 → 59**.

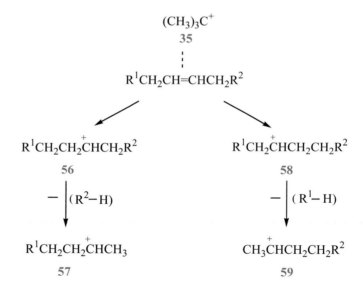

Scheme 15

It is interesting to note that the ratio $[M+t\text{-}C_4H_9]^+/[M-H]^+$ is ~1.5 to 2.1 for the Z-isomers and ~0.6 to 0.9 for the E-isomers by which they can be distinguished from each other.

A third reactant gas used was nitric oxide. Its NO^+ ion is a mild hydride abstractor and a strong electrophile. After its addition to the terminal carbon atom of 1-alkenes, a series of steps leads to the formation of the cyclic ion **60**, which subsequently eliminates an olefin by a 1,5-hydride migration to give ion **61**, see Scheme 16.

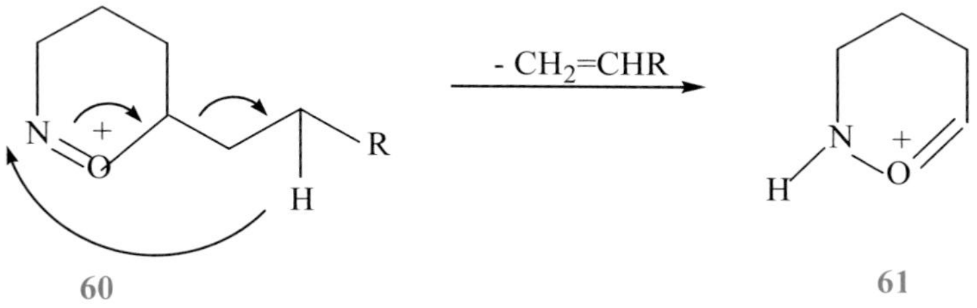

60   61

Scheme 16

Such cyclic ions are also formed after attack of NO^+ upon either end of a more central double bond in alkenes. That attack additionally leads to the formation of protonated oxime ions as exemplified for *n*-octadecene-6 in Scheme 17, where addition of NO^+ to the C(6) carbon atom eventually results in the observed preferential loss of the larger $C_{12}H_{22}$ neutral fragment.

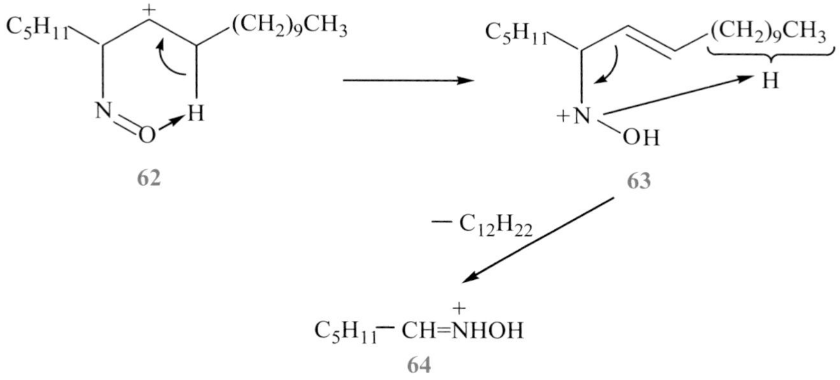

62   63

$$- C_{12}H_{22}$$

$$C_5H_{11}\!\!-\overset{+}{CH}\!\!=\!\!NHOH$$
64

Scheme 17

In general, ions with the elemental composition of $C_nH_{2n+2}NO$ in the CI NO spectra of olefins are thus indicating the location of the double bond. Furthermore, the ratio $[M+NO]^+/[M-H]^+$ is ~1.4 to 2.5 for the *Z*-isomers and ~0.6 to 0.9 for the *E*-isomers which allows one to distinguish them from each other. Comparison of the applicability of the different reactant gases discussed showed that nitric oxide, in general, would be a judicious choice for the localisation of double bonds. This is even more true for the localisation of triple bonds, where the NO^+ attack leads to specific bond cleavages as exemplified in Scheme 18 for *n*-octadecyne-6 upon addition of NO^+ to the triple bond carbon C(7).

The research described in this section has shown that knowledge of gas-phase ion chemistry can be applied successfully in the determination of double and triple bonds in olefinic and acetylenic compounds.

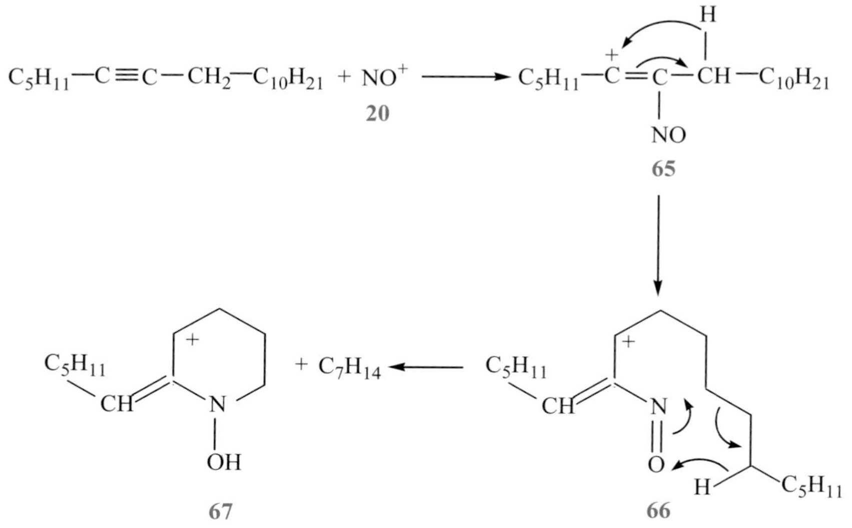

Scheme 18

BOND ACTIVATION AND CATALYSIS

Bond activation and catalysis constitute an extremely important area in chemistry where reactions of bare or ligated metal ions and corresponding neutral species with organic molecules can effect chemical transformations which otherwise cannot be achieved. Mass spectrometry is very suitable to use in the study of the elementary steps in bond activation and catalytic reactions.

It can provide detailed information about the energetics and kinetics of a bond-making and bond-breaking process at a strictly molecular level and it is capable of characterising reactive intermediates that are not within reach of condensed-phase methods. The group in Europe which has been very active in this field and which has reported its results in numerous publications is that of H. Schwarz.

Because of the limited text space, only a selected part of his research will be given here, the reader being referred for a more complete coverage to the literature listed for further reading at the end of the chapter.

One of his first research topics concerned the remote functionalisation of C–H and C–C bonds of aliphatic substrates, including nitriles, isonitriles, amines, alcohols, ketones, alkynes and allenes by transition metal ions. An illustrative example is the reaction of Fe^+ with unbranched aliphatic C_4–C_7 nitriles. It coordinates preferentially in an "end-on" fashion to the nitrile group, like Co^+, Ni^+, Cr^+ and Mn^+, leading to a linear or near-linear $-CH_2-C\equiv N-M^+$ entity. This "end-on" complex subsequently eliminates without any hydrogen atom randomisation in rate-determining steps H_2 and C_2H_4 from the remote ω and $(\omega-1)$ positions of the alkyl chain following activation of the ω and $(\omega-1)$ C–H bonds and ω C–C bonds by oxidative addition to the "anchored" M^+, respectively, while keeping the strain of the complex minimal, see Scheme 19.

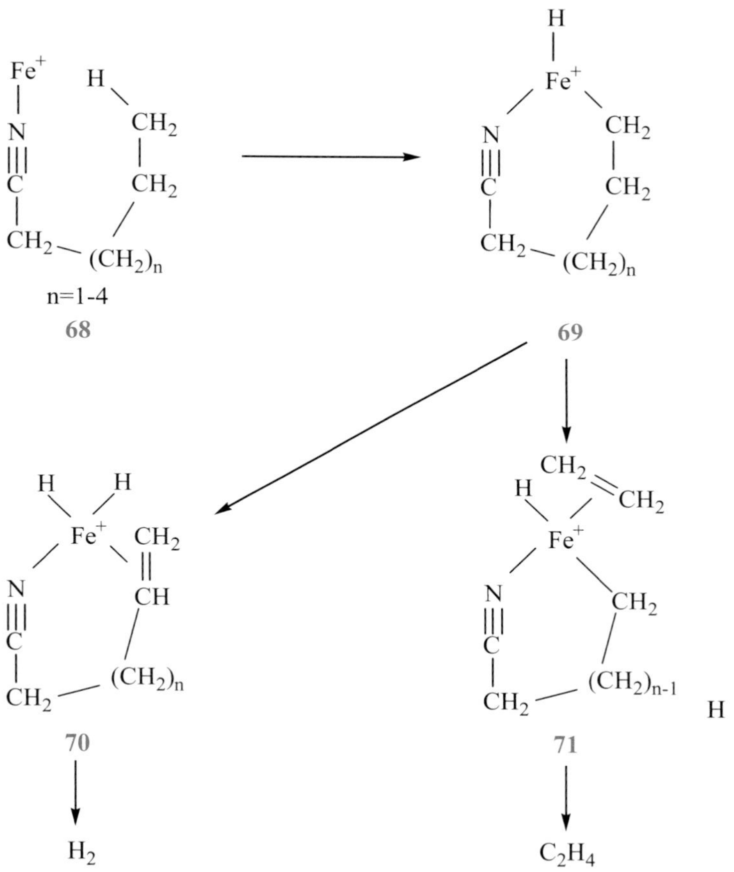

Scheme 19

If the carbon chain is lengthened, then activation of the internal C–H bonds starts to dominate. Another interesting result was that an aliphatic nitrile, such as 8,8-dimethylnonanenitrile containing a terminal t-butyl group, showed methane loss by a successive direct oxidative addition of the remotely terminal H_3C–C bond to Fe^+ and β-hydrogen atom transfer from either an "exocyclic" (~90%) or an "endocyclic" (~10%) C–H bond of the generated metallacycle. In addition, α-branched aliphatic nitriles R^1R^2CHCN with R^1 and R^2 = alkyl unexpectedly showed loss of methane in addition to H_2 and C_2H_4. In this case, the unprecedented mechanism for the methane loss involves the following steps: (i) oxidative addition of the C–CN bond to Fe^+; (ii) β-hydrogen atom transfer to the metal centre; (iii) oxidative addition of a remote H_3C–C bond to the metal centre and (iv) reductive elimination of methane, see Scheme 20.

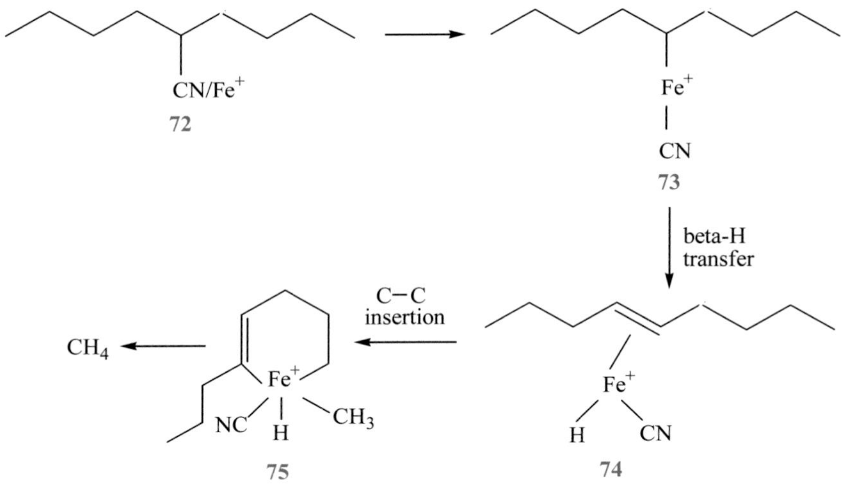

Scheme 20

Cu^+ differs from the above-mentioned metal ions in the sense that it preferentially coordinates in a "side-on" fashion to the nitrile group which therefore leads to activation of bonds in the vicinity of the functional group.

Subsequently, the group focussed much research on the activation of the C–H bond of the inert molecule of methane in order to functionalise, and thus transform, this natural gas molecule into "more valuable" products in view of the very great economic interest. In the literature it had already been reported that thermalised ground-state mono-atomic 3d- and 4-d-transition metal cations do not react with methane because of their occupied 4s orbital and unfavourable thermodynamics. The bare third-row transition metal cations $M=Ta$, W, Os, Ir and Pt, however, were known to be able to dehydrogenate methane in a stoichiometric manner to give $M(CH_2)^+$ due to their particularly strong metal–carbene bond of more than $465\,kJ\,mol^{-1}$ which is a result of relativistic stabilisation. The group discovered that bare Pt^+ catalysed partial oxidation of methane by molecular oxygen to form methanol, formaldehyde and higher oxidation products, as summarised in the catalytic cycle, Scheme 21.

The first step in this cycle is the dehydrogenation of methane with an efficiency of 0.8 to give the key intermediate $PtCH_2^+$ ion **77**. This ion then reacts with O_2 to either regenerate the Pt^+ ion **76** by forming HCO_2H or to give the PtO^+ ion **78** by liberating formaldehyde in the percentage ratio of 70:30, respectively. The PtO^+ ion **78** in turn reacts with methane to regenerate either the Pt^+ ion **76** by forming methanol or the $PtCH_2^+$ ion **77** by liberating water in the percentage ratio of 25:75, respectively. Unfortunately, the $PtCH_2^+$ ion also reacts slowly with methane and molecular oxygen to lead to the irreversible formation of unreactive products. Nevertheless, from modelling of the kinetic data, obtained from FT-ICR experiments, a turnover number of about six was calculated for the catalytic cycle in Scheme 21 and a conversion of methane into 10% methanol, 25% formaldehyde and 65% HCO_2H. The $PtCH_2^+$ ion **77** also reacts with ammonia with an efficiency of 0.3 to give the product ions $CH_2NH_2^+$ (70%), $PtC(H)NH_2^+$ (25%) and NH_4^+ (5%). In this way, Pt^+ plays

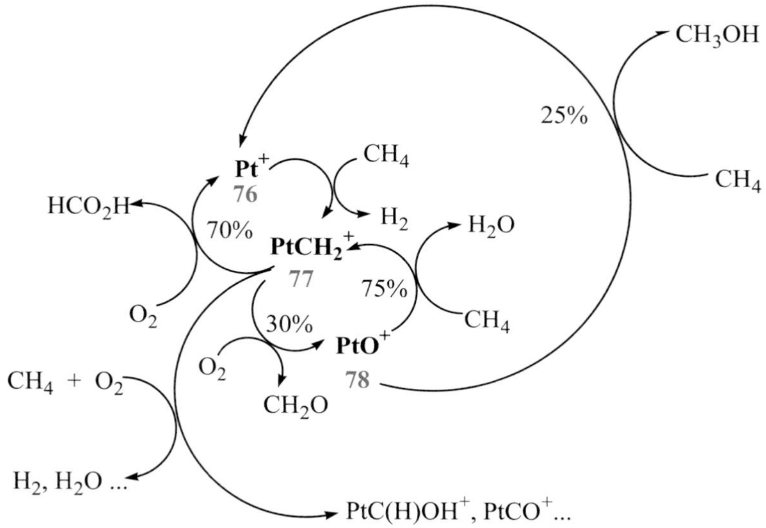

Scheme 21

a unique role in both activating methane and mediating efficient C–N bond coupling with ammonia. Even more interesting and challenging would be a direct amination of methane by reaction with $M(NH)^{+/-}$. Based upon several considerations, $Fe(NH)^+$ would be a suitable candidate, but this ion cannot be made directly since reaction of Fe^+ with ammonia is too endothermic. The gas-phase synthesis of $Fe(NH)^+$ can be achieved, however, by reaction of Fe^+ with HN_3 or NH_2OH. Indeed, the $Fe(NH)^+$ ion showed a high reactivity with aliphatic hydrocarbons, such as ethane and propane and with benzene, leading to a direct amination with high efficiency. However, the reactivity of $Fe(NH)^+$ towards methane turned out to be surprisingly low, the reaction efficiency being only 0.002. It has been mentioned already that the PtO^+ ion **78** can oxidise methane to methanol. Of the other metal oxide ions studied, FeO^+ is of particular interest. This ion reacts with an efficiency of 0.2 with methane to give the product ions $FeOH^+$ (57%), $FeCH_2^+$ (2%) and Fe^+ (41%) by liberating $CH_3\cdot$, H_2O and CH_3OH, respectively. A host of computational studies on the methanol formation in this reaction has led eventually to the concept of two-state reactivity with which a number of mechanistic puzzles in organometallic transformations could be explained. The essence of the two-state reactivity is that the reactants and products belong to one spin ground-state surface, whereas the intermediates have a different spin multiplicity by spin inversion at the crossing points of the ground-state surface with that of the different spin multiplicity surface. In this way, lower barriers become available in going from reactants to products, thus providing an energetically more favourable reaction pathway. Note that in the two-state reactivity concept no initial excitation of the reactants is involved, which is therefore essentially different from the configuration mixing model discussed in the "Aromatic radical cation and arenium ion chemistry" section above.

Before presenting a few other catalytic cycles reported by the group, the interesting stoichiometric coupling of the greenhouse gases methane and carbon dioxide by use of Ta^+ should be mentioned. This metal ion efficiently forms $Ta(CH_2)^+$ by dehydrogenation of methane, which subsequently reacts with carbon dioxide to give, by liberation of CO, the $OTa(CH_2)^+$ ion which reacts with another carbon dioxide molecule to yield TaO_2^+ and ketene.

Two other catalytic cycles to be mentioned from the group concern the oxidation of ethylene and benzene. The first is the fully catalytic cycle presented in Scheme 22, where ethylene is oxidised and the reactions **79 → 80** and **80 → 79** each occur with unit efficiency.

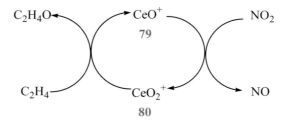

Scheme 22

Although this process is fully catalytic, the turnover number per CeO_2^+ ion appeared to be limited to 8, which was predominantly caused by reaction of CeO_2^+ with contaminating hydrocarbons leading to the formation of the unreactive CeO_2H^+ ion. The second is the oxidation of benzene to phenol again in a fully catalytic cycle, given in Scheme 23.

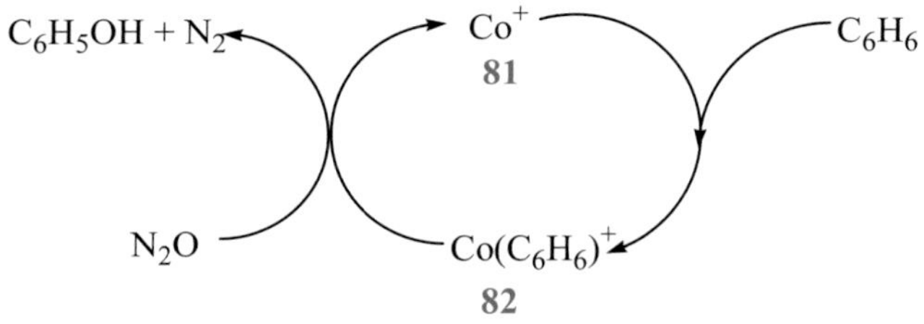

$$C_6H_5OH + N_2 \quad Co^+ \quad \mathbf{81} \quad C_6H_6$$

$$N_2O \quad Co(C_6H_6)^+ \quad \mathbf{82}$$

Scheme 23

In this case, the relatively large turnover number of ~18 per Co^+ ion was achieved under the conditions used, the limitation being due to a sink in the cycle because of the competing complexation of $Co(C_6H_6)^+$ with benzene.

This section concludes by stating that H. Schwarz and his group have contributed enormously to a very detailed insight into, and a much deeper understanding of, elementary steps in catalytic processes and have thereby provided a solid basis for future studies in this exciting area of chemistry.

NEGATIVE IONS

In general, negative ions have received much less research interest in mass spectrometry than positive ions and relatively few groups have worked in this area. Two groups that were very active in this field were those of K.R. Jennings and of the author during his career at the University of Amsterdam, The Netherlands. The former group had shown, by use of ICR, that $O^{\bullet-}$ formally abstracts $H_2^{\bullet+}$ from a single carbon atom of a variety of organic molecules, if not aromatic. This abstraction occurs in a stepwise fashion, that is, in most cases it starts with a hydrogen atom abstraction to give OH^- that, within the collision complex formed, reacts further by proton abstraction to give the final radical anion product. A notable example was ethylene, where these reaction steps led to the formation of the vinylidene radical anion $CH_2=C^{\bullet-}$. Of course, one can assume that $O^{\bullet-}$ also abstracts $H_2^{\bullet+}$ from the two carbon atoms of ethylene, but this would lead to the radical anion of acetylene which is unstable with respect to electron detachment. The author's group then showed that $H_2^{\bullet+}$ abstraction from different carbon atoms could readily result in the formation of stable radical anions. Examples were propyne and acetone, the radical anions from the latter being given in Scheme 24.

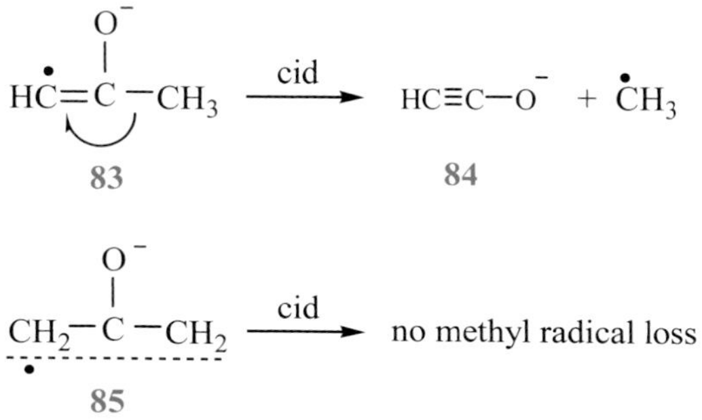

Scheme 24

The ion **83** generated by 1,1-$H_2^{\bullet+}$ abstraction in this Scheme did eliminate a methyl radical upon CID to give the deprotonated ketene species **84**. Such elimination was not observed for the ion **85** formed by a 1,3-$H_2^{\bullet+}$ abstraction. Many reactions of negative ions with neutral molecules were studied later on by the author's group using the home-built Fourier transform (FT) ICR mass spectrometer that became operational in April 1980.

Radical anions, generated by reaction of $O^{\bullet-}$ with a variety of organic molecules, formed the basis for gas-phase acidity measurements of the corresponding radicals by performing bracketing experiments. In this way, it was found that very frequently the radical was more acidic than its parent molecule, such as the phenyl radical and its mono-substituted F-, Cl- and CN-analogues, the nitrogen radical of hydrazobenzene and the isocyanomethyl and halo-methyl radicals. Generally the higher acidity of the radicals $R^{\bullet}$ is due to the higher electron affinity of their corresponding neutral (R–H) species. Another interesting reaction of $O^{\bullet-}$ was that with methylamine, ethylamine and dimethylamine. It gave rise to a peak at m/z 18 in the FT-ICR spectrum with an intensity higher than could be accounted for by natural isotopes of lower mass ions. ^{18}O- and deuterium labelling together with accurate mass measurements were in agreement with the elemental composition of H_2O so that the authors were forced to assume that $H_2O^{\bullet-}$ can exist as a stable species in the gas phase. Its chemical behaviour suggested that this ion could best be described as a hydroxide ion–hydrogen atom complex. Other species observed in the author's group that were at first sight unusual were H_3O^- and NH_4^-. The former ion was generated by reaction of OH^- with formaldehyde in successive proton abstraction and hydride transfer reactions in the encounter complex followed by

elimination of carbon monoxide to give the hydride solvated water molecule as proven by
deuterium and ^{18}O-labelling experiments and pictured in Scheme 25.

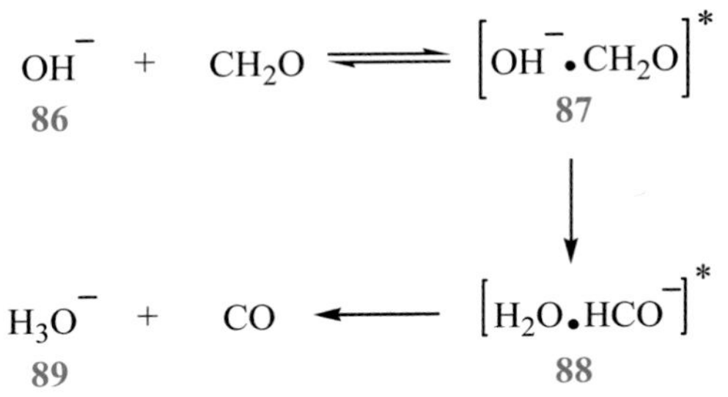

$$OH^- \ + \ CH_2O \ \rightleftharpoons \ \left[OH^- \bullet CH_2O\right]^*$$

$$\begin{array}{ccccc} 86 & & & & 87 \end{array}$$

$$H_3O^- \ + \ CO \ \longleftarrow \ \left[H_2O \bullet HCO^-\right]^*$$

$$\begin{array}{ccccc} 89 & & & & 88 \end{array}$$

Scheme 25

It should be noted here that, fully independently and practically simultaneously, this ion had
also been observed by J.F. Paulson's group at the Air Force Research Laboratory, Hanscom
AFB, Massachusetts, USA, as a product from collision between $OH^-.H_2O$ and H_2 in a
longitudinal double mass spectrometer. After the successful generation of the H_3O^-, a year
later the long-lived NH_4^- ion was also generated for the first time. To this end, a proton
was abstracted from formaldehyde by NH_2^- in an exothermic reaction to give HCO^-, which
subsequently reacted by hydride transfer to an ammonia molecule with expulsion of carbon
monoxide to give the hydride solvated ammonia molecule. The last two examples from the
author's group to be mentioned concern H/D exchange of the $(M-H)^-$ ions of 2,2-dimeth-
ylpropionaldehyde and N,N-dimethylformamide, deuterated at the formyl position. The
former anion unexpectedly exchanged all hydrogen atoms, implying the formation of a primary carbanion known to be unstable with respect to electron detachment with very few
exceptions. The two anion structures 90 and 91 were suggested to account for the stability
of the primary carbanion. Ion 90 would derive its stability from interaction of the dipole of
the aldehyde group with the negative charge of the sp^3-orbital of the primary carbon atom.
Ion 91 would be stabilised by homoconjugation which was made possible by rehybridisation
of the sp^3-orbital to a p-orbital, so as to overlap with the π-system of the aldehyde group.

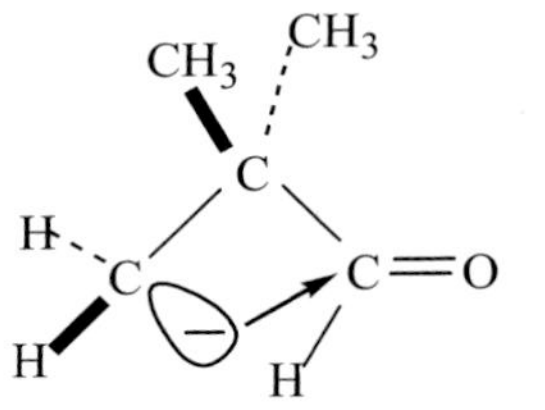

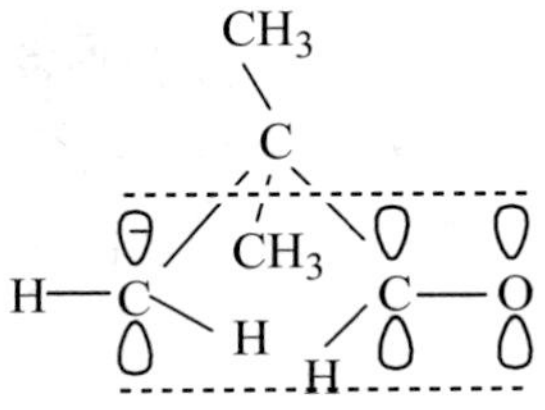

In the case of formyl deuterated N,N-dimethylformamide, the interesting observation was
made that its $(M-H)^-$ ion exchanges two of its hydrogen atoms rapidly with ND_3 while the
exchange of a third hydrogen atom was very slow and minor.

This was explained by use of Scheme 26, where the deprotonated methyl group in anti-
position with respect to the carbonyl group exchanges its hydrogen atoms unlike the methyl
group in the syn-position with respect to the carbonyl group because of the large barrier
for rotation around the C–N bond and the significant difference in acidity calculated for the
anti- and syn-methyl group.

90

91

EPILOGUE

This chapter hopefully gives a sufficiently adequate coverage of the fundamental contributions of European scientists to mass spectrometry in the past 60 to 70 years. In addition to

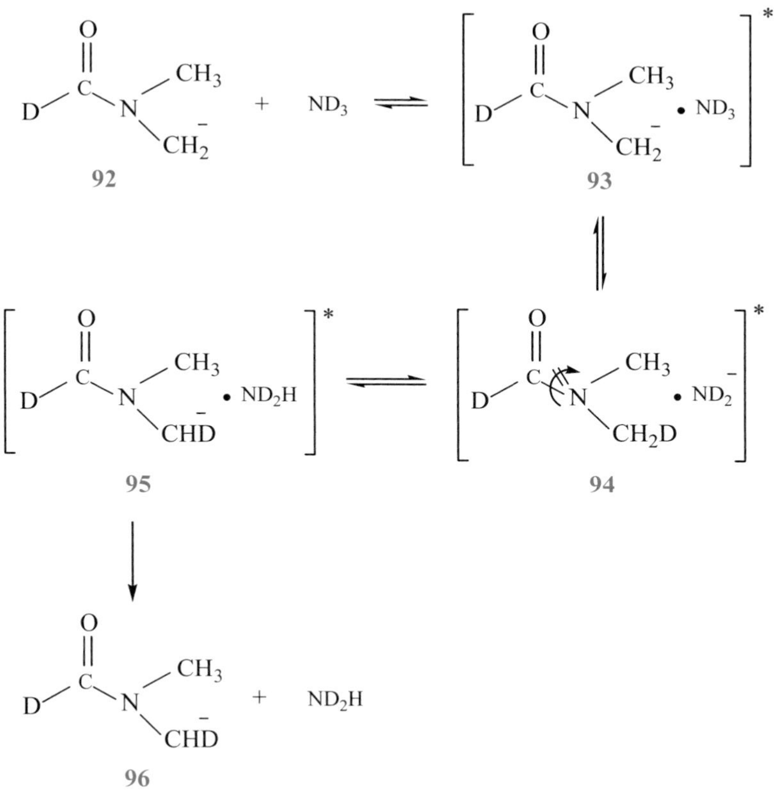

Scheme 26

the topics described, numerous publications have appeared on chemically very interesting and frequently very complex rearrangements of ions that occur in the gas phase. Nowadays, the potential energy surfaces associated with these rearrangements and also other gas-phase ion reactions can be explored computationally with high precision by virtue of the enormous progress made in theoretical chemistry. Finally, the quantitative determination of thermochemical and thermodynamic properties, such as the heats of formation of ions and neutrals and the intrinsic gas-phase acidities and basicities of organic molecules in the absence of solvent molecules, has reached an unprecedented accuracy. For information on all these mentioned issues the reader is referred to the literature.

LITERATURE FOR FURTHER READING

1. K. Adamczyk, M. Prémont-Schwarz, D. Pines, E. Pines and E.T.J. Nibbering, "Real-time observation of carbonic acid formation in aqueous solution", *Science* **326,** 1690–1694 (2009).

2. R.D. Bowen, "Ion–neutral complexes", *Acc. Chem. Res.* **24,** 364–371 (1991).

3. H. Budzikiewicz, "Structure elucidation by ion–molecule reactions in the gas phase: the location of C,C-double and triple bonds", *Fresenius Z. Anal. Chem.* **321,** 150–158 (1985).

4. K. Eller and H. Schwarz, "Organometallic chemistry in the gas phase", *Chem. Rev.* **91,** 1121–1177 (1991).

5. N. Goldberg and H. Schwarz, "Neutralization–reionization mass spectrometry: a powerful "laboratory" to generate and probe elusive neutral molecules", *Acc. Chem. Res.* **27,** 347–352 (1994).

6. H.-F. Grützmacher, "Intra- and intermolecular reactions of aromatic radical cations: an account of mechanistic concepts and methods in mass spectrometry", *Org. Mass Spectrom.* **28,** 1375–1387 (1993).

7. S. Hammerum, "Distonic radical cations in gaseous and condensed phase", *Mass Spectrom. Rev.* **7,** 123–202 (1988).

8. D. Kuck, "Half a century of scrambling in organic ions: complete, incomplete, progressive and composite atom interchange", *Int. J. Mass Spectrom.* **213,** 101–144 (2002).

9. K. Levsen, *Fundamental Aspects of Organic Mass Spectrometry.* Verlag Chemie, Weinheim, Germany (1978).

10. P. Longevialle, "Ion–neutral complexes in the unimolecular reactivity of organic cations in the gas phase", *Mass Spectrom. Rev.* **11,** 157–192 (1992).

11. N.M.M. Nibbering, "Four decades of joy in mass spectrometry", *Mass Spectrom. Rev.* **25,** 962–1017 (2006).

12. D. Schröder and H. Schwarz, "Intrinsic mechanisms of oxidation reactions as revealed by gas-phase experiments", *Top. Organomet. Chem.* **22,** 1–15 (2007).

13. H. Schwarz, "Radical eliminations from gaseous cation radicals via multistep pathways—the concept of "hidden" hydrogen rearrangements", *Topics in Current Chemistry* **97,** 1–31 (1981).

14. H. Schwarz, "Remote functionalization of C–H and C–C bonds by "naked" transition metal ions", *Acc. Chem. Res.* **22,** 282–287 (1989).

15. H. Schwarz and D. Schröder, "Concepts of metal-mediated methane functionalization. An intersection of experiment and theory", *Pure Appl. Chem.* **72,** 2319–2332 (2000).

16. M. Speranza, "Kinetics and mechanisms in gas-phase ion chemistry by radiolytic methods". *Mass Spectrom. Rev.* **11,** 73–117 (1992).

17. M. Speranza, "Enantioselectivity in gas-phase ion-molecule reactions", *Int. J. Mass Spectrom.* **232,** 277–317 (2004).

18. M. Speranza, "Gas-phase enantioselective reactions in non-covalent ion–molecule complexes", *Chirality* **21,** 69–86 (2009).

19. J.K. Terlouw and H. Schwarz, "The generation and characterization of molecules by neutralization–reionization mass spectrometry (NRMS)", *Angew. Chem. Int. Ed. Engl.* **26,** 805–815 (1987).

20. C. Wentrup and R. Flammang, "Studies of reactive intermediates using matrix and gas phase techniques", *J. Phys. Org. Chem.* **11,** 350–355 (1998).

21. D.H. Williams and J.H. Beynon, "The concept and role of charge localization in mass spectrometry", *Org. Mass Spectrom.* **11,** 103–116 (1976).

22. D.H. Williams, "A transition-state probe", *Acc. Chem. Res.* **10,** 280–286 (1977).

GC/MS and LC/MS

Andries Bruins
University of Groningen

GAS CHROMATOGRAPHY-MASS SPECTROMETRY

For the present users of mass spectrometers, it is difficult to envisage how limited the technique was prior to about 1960. Mass spectrometry (MS) was dominated by relatively slow scanning magnetic sector mass spectrometers. The direct insertion probe was just under development. Electron ionisation (EI) was the only technique available to the majority of users, and the interpretation of EI mass spectra of organic molecules was in its infancy. For example, the McLafferty rearrangement observed in the EI spectra of carbonyl compounds was first described in 1958.

EI mass spectrometry requires a sample to be in the vapour state prior to ionisation. Batch inlet systems, such as the all glass heated inlet system (AGHIS), were used for the introduction of a volatile sample into the ion source. Purity of a sample is always of major concern in EI mass spectrometry because it was and remains a difficult task to unravel spectra consisting of the many fragment ions generated from a mixture. A separation system that could deliver samples as a vapour to the mass spectrometer would be a major step toward handling of mixtures.

Gas chromatography (GC) had only been invented relatively recently, however, in 1952, by Martin and James, in Britain. As soon as GC was developed further and became more generally available, the need for identification of individual components became apparent. Consequently, there was a need to solve two problems in one system: the recording of spectra of pure samples separated by GC and the identification of unknown components in complex mixtures.

In spite of all limitations of primitive GC and slow scanning mass spectrometers, on-line GC/MS was first described in 1959. In contrast to common practice in mass spectrometry, a Bendix time-of-flight (TOF) mass spectrometer was chosen for this first GC/MS experiment, and the GC was a home-made apparatus made up of individual components. Mass spectra were recorded at a rate of 2000 spectra per second with spectra being observed on an oscilloscope screen and hard copy output provided by photographing the oscilloscope display.

These early results were followed by work in two directions: improved instrumentation for gas chromatography and development of interfaces between GC and MS. Increasing the performance of GC separations was not in the hands of mass spectrometrists, of course. The GC community undertook research into open tubular capillary GC columns. Originally, these columns were known as Golay columns, since pioneering research was carried out by Golay and Desty at Perkin-Elmer. These columns were originally made of metal tubing. Desty introduced glass capillary columns and, in the mid-1960s, deactivated glass capillary columns were made by K. Grob in Switzerland. Capillary columns were not widely used until around 1980, when flexible fused silica columns were introduced.

Some pioneering groups in Europe made almost immediate use of capillary columns. Henneberg and Schomburg in Germany demonstrated the capability of a capillary column

Opposite: Home made DLI interface constructed in 1982 by the author.

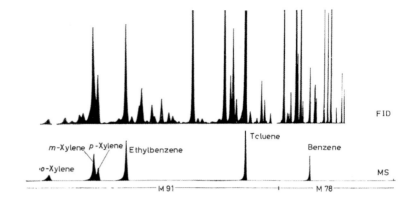

Figure 1. GC/MS with a capillary GC column and a CEC 21-620 mass spectrometer. Selected ion monitoring of *m/z* 78 and 91 together with flame ionisation detection. Reproduced with permission from D. Henneberg and G. Schomburg, in *Gas chromatography*, Ed by M. van Swaay. Copyright Butterworths, London (1962).

coupled to a mass spectrometer in a presentation at a conference in Hamburg in 1962. It was a little ironic that, at the same conference, questions were asked about the actual necessity of on-line coupling of GC with MS. Was it not better to collect fractions and measure individual mass spectra, instead of spending precious mass spectrometer time on an hour long GC run? This was one of the examples where new developments are faced with scepticism. In fact, the same question arose during workshops about on-line LC/MS 20 years later.

There is a need for fast scans in GC/MS and the older magnetic sector instruments were not capable of scanning and recording full mass spectra within a few seconds. During further development of GC/MS, it was recognised that the recording of selected ions is a definite advantage in trace analysis of targeted compounds. Henneberg and Schomburg realised that their CEC 21-620 cycloidal MS was not capable of carrying out fast scans and so, because of the limitations imposed by their instrument, they were among the pioneers of selected ion monitoring (SIM) by showing characteristic traces of classes of aliphatic, unsaturated and aromatic hydrocarbons at *m/z* 85, *m/z* 83, *m/z* 78 and *m/z* 91.

The interface used by Henneberg and Schomburg was a capillary restrictor between the GC column and ion source. In 1962, Brunnée and co-workers (Atlas Mess und Analysen-technik, Bremen) used an open split interface between a capillary column and the ion source of an Atlas CH4 mass spectrometer. This was borne out of necessity, since the pumping system of the CH4 could only handle 1% of the gas flow exiting the GC column. It is interesting to note that Brunnée *et al.* used their GC/MS set-up to demonstrate fundamental limitations in the relationship between signal-to-noise in full-scan spectra and a number of practical parameters: MS resolution, amplifier time constant, scan speed and sample size. Brunnée listed the advantages and disadvantages of recording full scan spectra and monitoring selected ions.

In the early days of GC/MS, selected ion monitoring was often done on abundant fragment ions in EI spectra. It was therefore called mass fragmentography. Selection of a limited number of ions in a magnetic sector mass spectrometer was done by switching the accelerating

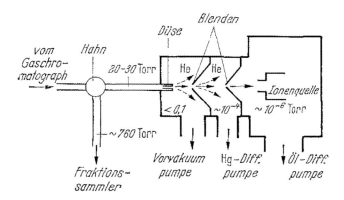

Figure 2. Schematic diagram of a Becker–Ryhage two-stage jet separator for GC/MS. Reproduced with permission from E. Stenhagen, "Jetziger Stand der Massenspektrometrie in der organischen Analyse", *Fresenius Z. Anal. Chem.* **205,** 109–123 (1964). Copyright Springer, 1964.

voltage. On LKB instruments, manufactured in Sweden, this technique was known as AVA, accelerating voltage alternator. For practical reasons, the masses of the ions were not spread out over too wide a mass range, a limitation that does not exist in quadrupole mass spectrometers. Now that mass spectrometers are fully computer-controlled, and limitations in instrumentation have been removed, either method can be chosen, each having its own merits: full scan for identification and structure elucidation and SIM for trace analysis and low level quantitation of targeted compounds.

Before it was common practice in GC to employ capillary columns, packed columns that are operated at gas flow rates of 20 mL min^{-1} and above were in general use. A splitter interface was used during first attempts at connecting the GC to a mass spectrometer. Because of the substantial loss of sensitivity, several devices were developed for the enrichment of the analytes relative to the carrier gas. The first enrichment interface in Europe was the jet-separator developed by Ryhage in Stockholm, Sweden and published in 1964. Its design was patterned after the isotope separator by E.W. Becker and co-workers in Germany. It was attached to an Atlas CH4 mass spectrometer, modified for fast scanning (1–2 s per spectrum from *m/z* 12 to *m/z* 500) so that a sufficient number of mass spectra could be recorded during the elution of a component from the GC. For a long time, this separator, incorporated into LKB mass spectrometers, was considered state-of-the art in GC/MS with packed GC columns.

When the vacuum systems of mass spectrometers were fitted with bigger oil diffusion pumps, it became apparent that the direct coupling of open tubular columns with the ion source was within reach. Glass capillary columns were awkward to use. The installation in the injector and column oven required a skilled operator. I remember it was no fun to straighten the inlet part of the column for insertion into the GC injector. The connection to the ion source was often via a metal capillary (for example, platinum, as proposed by Neuner-Jehle in Switzerland), but connection by means of a union or by heat-shrinkable Teflon was not easy. All these drawbacks were overcome by the advent of flexible fused silica columns, around 1980.

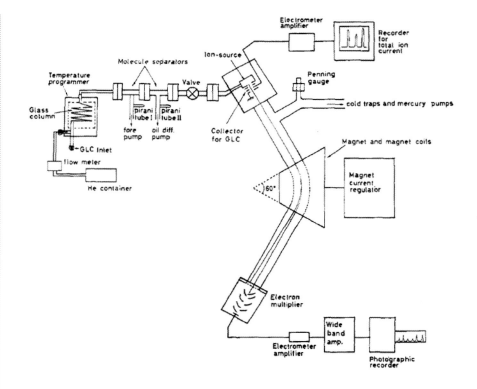

Figure 3. Schematic diagram of a gas chromatograph/ mass spectrometer combination. Two-stage jet separator and Atlas CH4 (Bremen). Reproduced with permission from R. Ryhage, *Anal. Chem.* **36,** 759–764 (1964). Copyright American Chemical Society 1964.

Connection to the injector was easy and coupling to the ion source was done in one of two ways: either by open-split coupling with a separated capillary to the source, or by direct insertion into the ion source. The open-split coupling had two advantages. As the outlet of the column was at ambient pressure, retention times in GC/MS are identical to retention times obtained with standard GC detectors (flame ionisation, electron capture etc.) and, also, there would be no degradation of GC column performance that might occur due to vacuum applied to its outlet. The latter problem was shown to be very minor. Leclerq and co-workers at the University of Eindhoven in the Netherlands made a thorough theoretical and experimental investigation of GC column performance under various outlet pressure conditions, and found that loss of performance was very small, while speed of analysis was increased significantly. At this point, it was safe to state that the best GC/MS interface is no interface.

In the 1980s, GC/MS had become a mature technique. The use of capillary columns was common practice and packed columns gradually became obsolete for most GC/MS applica-tions. On the MS side, the quadrupole mass spectrometer was the most widely used for routine GC/MS, together with the quadrupole ion trap. Low-resolution magnetic sector instruments had largely ceased to be used but high-resolution MS, with selected ion moni-toring, had a firm place in very selective targeted analysis of chlorinated dioxins.

On the GC side, there was continuing development of injection systems and several European researchers and companies made their contributions. Splitless injection and solvent effects were investigated by Grob and Grob in Switzerland and the programmed temperature vaporiser injector was developed by Poy at the DANI GC company in Italy. Another Italian company, Carlo Erba, made a significant contribution to on-column injection into open tubular GC columns. Schomburg's group in Germany was one of the most prominent GC research laboratories. New equipment and methods were presented at a series of conferences in Hindelang and Riva del Garda.

Speaking of manufacturers, the LKB company in Sweden made its mark by means of the early industry standard LKB9000 mass spectrometer with Becker–Ryhage separator. This very successful model was followed by the LKB 2091, which had good features such as a mechanically switchable EI-chemical ionisation (CI) source. In the mid-1970s there was increasing competition from quadrupole GC/MS instruments and, as a result, LKB stopped further development of GC/MS instruments. Other routine, magnetic sector instruments were the Kratos MS25 and MS 80 and the Varian MAT CH5. Higher end sector machines were the MAT 90 and 900 series (now Finnigan MAT) VG 70–70, VG Autospec and Kratos MS50.

The first European quadrupole GC/MS systems were built by Varian MAT in Germany, the MAT 44 introduced in 1979 and by Ribermag in France, which later became NERMAG. The MAT 44 made use of hyperbolic quadrupole rods. After the American company Finnigan acquired MAT, these rods were installed in the Finnigan 4500 series.

Fast GC separations on short capillary columns have to be complemented with very fast scanning mass spectrometers. In Europe, this was taken up by HD Technologies in Manchester in the UK. The company developed TOF mass spectrometers for fast GC/MS: the HyperJet bench-top and the SprinT, which is a more compact bench-top instrument. HD Technologies is now part of Thermo Fisher Scientific. Other TOF options are the GC/TOF by Micromass (now a Waters subsidiary) and Kronus GC/TOF by SAI, also in Manchester.

The need for more specific detection in GC/MS (and also LC/MS) can be fulfilled by high-resolution MS and by tandem mass spectrometry (MS/MS). VG/Micromass in Manchester and Finnigan-MAT in Bremen have built a number of hybrid instruments for this purpose, including sector-TOF, sector-quad, sector-ion-trap and quadrupole-TOF instruments, but because of decreasing interest in magnetic sector mass spectrometers, the sector hybrids have largely lost their importance in the GC/MS field. For the trace analysis of dioxins, on the other hand, high-resolution magnetic sector mass spectrometers built in Manchester and Bremen are prevalent. The most important TCDD disaster in Europe was the explosion in Seveso (Italy) in 1976.

Tandem mass spectrometry is now mostly carried out on triple quadrupole instruments or on ion trap mass spectrometers and has become a widely-used technique. It is interesting to note that Simon Gaskell (formerly at the University of Manchester) demonstrated maybe the first GC/MS/MS application in his presentations and publications about first and second field-free region metastable peak monitoring in the late 1970s.

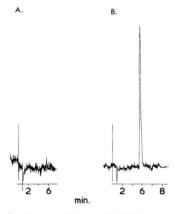

Figure 4. S. Gaskell: GC/MS with selected metastable peak monitoring of m/z 347→271 in the first field-free region of the VG 70-70F. *tert*-Butyldimethylsilyl derivative of 5-alpha-dihydrotestosterone. a: blank; b: 100 pg of steroid derivatised and injected. Reproduced with permission from A.P. de Leenheer, R.R. Roncucci and C. van Petegem (Eds), *Quantitative mass spectrometry in the life sciences II*, p. 138. Copyright Elsevier (1978)

Pioneers and early adopters of GC/MS in Europe were Charles Brooks in Glasgow and Herman Adlercreutz in Helsinki, both working on the analysis of steroids. Siekmann in Germany demonstrated the use of GC/MS as a definitive method in clinical chemistry. Egil Jellum in Oslo was one of the pioneers in the identification of inborn errors of metabolism by GC/MS. Hans Brandenberger in Switzerland was a proponent of the use of negative ions for GC/MS in toxicology. The Karolinska Institute in Stockholm, Sweden had a strong position in the GC/MS analysis of neurotransmitters. There were many publications on GC/MS of essential oils and flavour components. In Belgium, André de Leenheer and Magda Claeys were pioneers of quantitation by GC/MS. At present, the majority of papers on essential oils, found through *Chemical Abstracts* are by authors from China.

Hans Maurer in Saarland, Germany, made a strong contribution to libraries of drugs and other compounds of toxicological interest. In the UK, the work by Lawson in clinical chemistry and by the late Brian Millard on quantitative mass spectrometry was well known. Theory and equations for quantitation by isotope dilution mass spectrometry were published by Pickup and McPherson (Harrow, UK, 1976), and cited in many papers on quantitative GC/MS. The conferences on quantitative MS in Ghent, Belgium, organised by de Leenheer and Frigerio were a great opportunity for meeting the practitioners in this new field.

LIQUID CHROMATOGRAPHY-MASS SPECTROMETRY

Considering the successful development of on-line GC/MS, it was no surprise that the combination of liquid chromatography (LC) with mass spectrometry was the next project in the series of connections between separation methods and mass spectrometry. But it was no surprise either that the question about off-line versus on-line separation should come up again. Even when the interfaces for LC/MS where commercially available, there was still opposition against on-line LC/MS, and pros and cons were heavily debated at the first LC/MS workshop in Montreux, Switzerland in 1981. Fraction collection from a liquid chromatograph is easy, but the recording of mass spectra of individual fractions by means of solids probe sample introduction is too time-consuming for a large number of fractions. Even today, however, it can be a method of choice for an important component that can then be analysed with different ionisation techniques, ionisation polarities and ion-fragmentation conditions.

Let us first have a look at the birth of LC/MS. Victor Talroze in Moscow, in the former Soviet Union, can be considered to be the father of LC/MS. His group experimented with the introduction of a liquid into an EI source via a very narrow capillary instead of from a heated batch inlet system. Liquid flow rates were extremely low, because of the limited vacuum pumping capacity of the EI mass spectrometer. The aim was to record EI spectra of a liquid, not of solutes in a solvent from a liquid chromatograph. This liquid introduction was picked up by Mike Baldwin and Patrick Arpino in McLafferty's group at Cornell University in the USA. They realised that a larger amount of liquid or solvent could be handled by a chemical ionisation source and its vacuum pumps. By using solvent vapour as reactant gas, they were able to record mass spectra of solutes, including small peptides. The door to LC/MS by direct liquid introduction (DLI) was opened. It did not take long for mass spectrometer

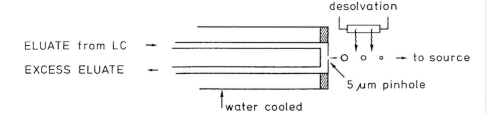

Figure 5. Schematic
diagram of a direct
liquid introduction (DLI)
interface for LC/MS.

manufacturers to start making this primitive system more reliable. The original Arpino/
McLafferty system consisted of a glass capillary tube inserted into the source of a magnetic
sector mass spectrometer. There were considerable difficulties due to the high accelerating
voltage of the MS ion source.

Commercial systems obviated the high voltage problem by the use of quadrupole mass
spectrometers. Another modification was the use of an inlet probe closed off with a thin
metal disk, in which a small pinhole of less than 10 μm diameter was drilled. A pressurised
liquid stream from the LC column would create a jet of liquid that would evaporate and
thus provide reagent gas for CI and neutral sample vapour to be ionised by ion–molecule
reactions. Attilio Melera worked on this method at Hewlett Packard laboratories in the
USA while Patrick Arpino carried out similar studies in Paris, together with Ribermag (later
called NERMAG). Data were presented in Europe at the International Mass Spectrometry
Conference in Oslo, Norway in 1979. At around the same time, the first overview article on
LC/MS was published by Arpino and Guiochon in the A-pages of *Analytical Chemistry*.

A disadvantage of the DLI system is the splitting away of 99% of the eluent. Jack Henion in
the USA and Paul Krien at NERMAG started to use microbore LC columns that operate
at lower flow rates and allow a more favourable split ratio and, hence, improved sensitivity.

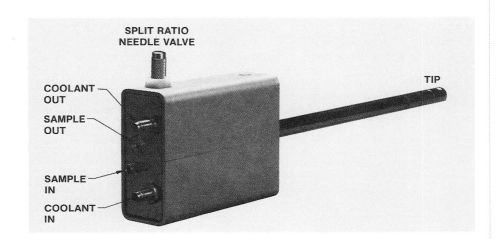

Figure 6. DLI interface
manufactured by Hewlett-
Packard.

The heart of a DLI system is a laser-drilled pinhole in a metal disk. Plugging of this tiny 5–10 μm orifice can be minimised by the use of a filter between the LC column and the DLI probe. Since frequent replacement of this laser-drilled disk was costly, Patrick Arpino and Claude Beaugrand at NERMAG started to use very short pieces of narrow bore fused silica tubing. An improvement to the vacuum pumping speed of a DLI mass spectrometer was the incorporation of a cold trap around the ion source, inside the vacuum envelope. Again, this was done by both Hewlett-Packard in the USA and Patrick Arpino in Paris. In this way, the liquid flow into the MS can be increased, giving improved sensitivity.

The DLI probe produces a jet of liquid that has to evaporate inside the ion source. Arpino and Dedieu designed a desolvation chamber, consisting of a conical converging/diverging tube installed between the tip of the DLI probe and the ion source. Patrick Arpino wrote a number of papers in the *Journal of Chromatography* about the requirements of a vacuum system for LC/MS, on LC conditions and on "Why the solvent should not be removed in LC/MS coupling". All these improvements to DLI took place in the early 1980s, when thermospray was around the corner (see below) and started to be commercialised. Frank Pullen in the UK presented a low-pressure discharge ionisation version of DLI in 1989. A similar system was patented in 1990 by Edward Ramsey of CarloErba in Italy. By that year, however, LC/MS by means of atmospheric pressure ionistion (API) sources started its breakthrough, making both DLI and thermospray obsolete.

In the same early days of LC/MS there was the other option: remove the solvent and introduce the sample into the ion source. In its first automated incorporation, the moving wire transport system was used by R.P.W. Scott. The LC eluent dripped on the wire, solvent evaporated and the sample on the wire was fed into the source by continuous movement, via vacuum reducing locks. Since it was clear that the amount of sample deposited on a wire was small, the next step was the use of a moving belt instead of a moving wire. McFadden, at Finningan in the USA, demonstrated its use and a commercial version was born. The first few years of LC/MS, and discussions at the first LC/MS workshops in Montreux, saw serious competition between DLI and moving belt, with sometimes heated discussions between proponents of the two LC/MS interfaces.

The moving belt allowed freedom of choice of ionisation technique (EI or CI), and choice of reactant gas for CI. Since the sample had to be evaporated from the belt, however, there

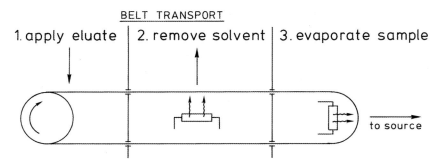

Figure 7. Schematic diagram of a moving belt interface.

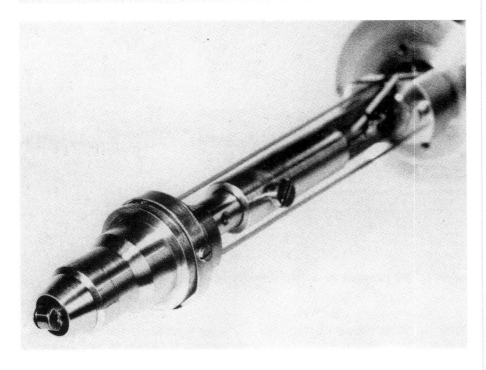

Figure 8. Moving belt interface manufactured by Finnigan MAT (Bremen, Germany); top: complete interface removed from the vacuum locks; bottom: detail of the front end of the belt positioned inside the ion source.

was always a chance of thermal degradation of a sample prior to ionisation. VG/Micromass in Manchester adopted the moving belt interface design and Finnigan MAT in Bremen made the belt suitable for their magnetic sector mass spectrometers. A significant advantage of the VG and MAT designs was the introduction of the belt all the way into the ion source, so that the distance between the sites of sample evaporation and ionisation was reduced. Indeed, the two newer designs fared better with respect to labile compounds than the original Finnigan belt, built for the Finnigan quadrupole instruments.

Dai Games, originally in Cardiff, later in Swansea in the UK, was an early adopter of moving belt LC/MS. His group published a large number of papers, demonstrating the versatility of the moving belt in natural products research, detection of pesticides and a number of other areas. Games emphasised the advantage of library searchable EI spectra. The deposition of an eluent containing a high percentage of water produces irregular beads of liquid, instead of a smooth film. The result is noisy total ion current and extracted ion current traces. Reduction of the eluent flow rate alleviates this problem. Therefore, Games' group promoted the combination of microbore HPLC with the moving belt. The comparison of moving belts of different designs was carried out in Games' group.

Evaporation of a sample from the belt was not easy in the case of more polar samples. For this reason, Jan van der Greef in the Netherlands in 1985 used deactivation of the belt by means of a solution of Carbowax 20M, a polyethylene glycol that was applied very often for deactivation of glass capillaries and other materials that are in contact with samples in GC and GC/MS. Karsten Levsen and co-workers in Germany, in the previous year had demostrated a successful application of the moving belt and negative chemical ionisation with chloride anions in the analysis of glycosides. In 1988, Verhey and Van der Greef, working in Leiden, in the Netherlands, designed a post-column extraction system that changed the solvent from being highly aqueous from a reversed-phase column into highly organic solvent, that gave a smooth layer on the belt. The organic solvent was easy to evaporate and the sample could be desorbed efficiently into the ion source. This "phase system switching" method was very suitable for targeted analysis of particular components but not for complete MS analysis of an entire LC run. At the Montreux conference in 1988, Niessen and Van der Greef demonstrated that belt speed programming affords a higher sensitivity in targeted compound analysis.

In 1980, a very different application of the moving belt had been demonstrated by Benninghoven in Germany, who used the belt as a sample introduction system for secondary ion mass spectrometry (SIMS). Another incorporation of a transport system was the rotating disk by Jungclas et al. working in Marburg, Germany, which made use of ^{252}Cf fission fragment ionisation but it was never turned into a commercial product. ^{252}Cf fission fragment ionisation, first published by McFarlane in the USA, and called plasma desorption, was a simple system for the ionisation of peptides. At the time, this was considered "ionisation of high mass materials", but in about 1990, matrix-assisted laser desorption/ionisation (MALDI) and electrospray ionisation (ESI) made this ionisation technique obsolete.

In 1989, the development, applications and demise of the moving belt were reviewed by Patrick Arpino. Atmospheric pressure ionisation techniques made the moving belt obsolete for the majority of LC/MS applications.

Driven by lack of funds, researchers were looking for alternatives for the two commercially available interfaces, DLI and the moving belt. Since a home-made transport system is mechanically complex, the simple and desirable home-made LC/MS interface is a type of DLI. Patrick Arpino's work on a capillary interface and CI was followed up by Jack Henion at Cornell University, in the USA. After the use of a splitter for regular HPLC, he turned to microbore HPLC, with the commercially available Jasco FAMILIC 100, used earlier by Susan Rottschaeffer at SmithKline in the USA. The Jasco instrument was a syringe pump and columns were made of 0.5 mm i.d. Teflon tubing. The eluent flow rate was approximately

Figure 9. Home made DLI interface constructed in 1982 by the author of this chapter; a fused silica capillary is connected to a microbore HPLC, and is slid into the probe, inside the copper cylinder; during LC/MS operation the copper cylinder is located inside the inlet port of the heated ion source block, so that heat is transferred to the eluent, to support stable evaporation.

$10\,\mu L\,min^{-1}$, which generates about $10\,mL\,min^{-1}$ of solvent vapour, which is about the right amount for use as a reagent gas in chemical ionisation.

My personal recollection is that I followed in Jack Henion's steps, and tried to use a glass capillary, sliding it through the direct insertion probe inlet of a Finnigan 3300 quadrupole MS. The original goal was to try to produce a jet of liquid, as in the HP and NERMAG DLI probes. It was not possible to get a stable ion source pressure in this way. Six months later I obtained funds for purchase of the Jasco FAMILIC and had 50 μm i.d. fused silica tubing to hand. During several stages of experiments, it became clear that the eluent evaporates inside the capillary and that heat transfer to the tip of the capillary was necessary to support steady evaporation and produce a stable ion source pressure. In 1982, together with my colleague Ben Drenth, calculations on the rate of evaporation of the eluent and theoretical limitations supported this experimental result. Thus it became clear that a home-made capillary inlet for the LC eluent was compatible with fairly volatile samples, but salts and other non-volatile analytes would block the tip of the capillary immediately.

Experiments along similar lines were carried out by Nigel Evans at British Gas, who used the MAT44 quadrupole MS, by Wilfried Niessen in Amsterdam, in the Netherlands, who worked on the connection of open tubular LC with MS, by the group of Rob Tijssen and André Smit at the Shell Research Laboratories in Amsterdam, and by Alex Appfel in the LC group of Udo Brinkman and Roland Frei at the Free University in Amsterdam. Appfel tried to turn the capillary into a pneumatically-assisted nebuliser inside the vacuum system and, a little later, his design was constructed and made available for sale by Hositrad Holland. Further efforts on the generation of a jet was made by Kientz et al. at TNO in Rijswijk, in the Netherlands, in 1996. In spite of all this hard work, but because of inherent limitations, the capillary design was not adopted by a large group of research workers. Kratos in

Manchester, in the UK, showed results of a prototype capillary interface at the International Mass Spectrometry Conference in Vienna in 1982, but it never became a product.

The LC/MS workshops in Montreux, organised by the late Roland Frei, were a good opportunity for the presentation of new, unusual and home-made LC/MS interfaces. Alborn and Stenhagen, Göteborg University (Sweden) experimented with packed capillary columns that were installed inside a transfer tube in the ion source housing of a home made magnetic sector mass spectrometer with which they managed to obtain EI mass spectra. The research group at the Free University in Amsterdam, supervised by Udo Brinkman and Roland Frei was active in pre-column and post-column extraction methods for LC/MS. Patrick Arpino gave an overview of the status of LC/MS in 1981, with emphasis on liquid introduction systems. He commented on electrospray, which was a failure at that time, and wrote:

> "Up to now we were embarrassed to answer such frequently asked questions from potential LC/MS users: how do you deal with polar molecules?; can you accommodate salts, buffers or ion-pairing reagents...?; can you introduce polar solvents? From now on, we may have to answer that these are the conditions we like best".

This statement was bold in 1981 but, as we shall see, it has become true since ESI has become a reality.

PARTICLE BEAM

The moving belt interface offers the distinct advantage of information-rich, library-searchable EI mass spectra and free choice of reagent ions in chemical ionisation. Due to the mechanical complexity of moving parts and the kapton belt that might break in the middle of an important LC run, there was a search for other methods that can separate a sample from the LC eluent. The particle beam interface serves this purpose. It was developed by Ross Willoughby in Richard Browner's group at Georgia Tech, Atlanta, USA in 1984. The original name was "monodisperse aerosol generation interface for chromatography" (MAGIC). In principle, it works like the jet separator for GC/MS and separates

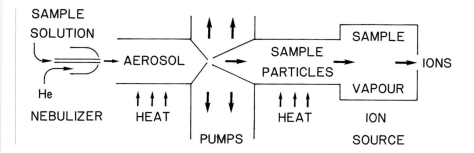

Figure 10. Schematic diagram of a particle beam interface for LC/MS.

Figure 11. Particle beam interface manufactured by Hewlett-Packard.

pneumatically-generated droplets and chunks of dried analyte (particles) from evaporating solvent and nebulising gas. Dry particles hit the inside of the ion source and the sample evaporates and is ionised by EI or CI.

The first commercial version of particle beam LC/MS was developed by Hewlett-Packard. Other manufacturers, such as Micromass in the UK, built their own versions.

A particle beam interface only offers moderate sensitivity. As with all gas-phase ionisation techniques in LC/MS, thermally-labile molecules will decompose prior to ionisation. In a number of laboratories and mass spectrometry facilities, flow injection coupled with particle beam was used as an automated alternative to solids probe sample introduction.

In 1993, a particle beam interface was modified for hyperthermal surface ionisation by Tinke, under supervision of Wilfried Niessen in Leiden, in the Netherlands. Achille Cappiello of the University of Urbino, Italy, started working with micro-LC and nano-LC columns coupled with particle beam interfaces at about the same time and, over the years, he redesigned the nebuliser and managed a significant improvement in sensitivity when the LC eluent contains nearly 100% water. A further development was the elimination of the pneumatic nebuliser, and insertion of a fused-silica transfer line into the EI source. The eluent flow rate was below 1 μL min^{-1} and a restriction at the source end of the fused-silica capillary prevented premature evaporation of the eluent inside the capillary.

THERMOSPRAY

At the 1980 ASMS conference in New York, there were two presentations of major importance to those who worked on the direct coupling of HPLC with MS. One was by Iribarne on ion evaporation (see below under Electrospray) and the other was by Marvin

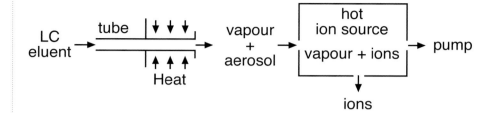

Figure 12. Schematic diagram of a thermospray interface for LC/MS.

Vestal on a new ionisation technique for introduction of an LC eluent at "normal" flow rates (1 mL min⁻¹). Vestal and co-workers discovered that a sample dissolved in an ammonium acetate solution can be ionised when the solution is nebulised by the application of heat to the end of a capillary tube, inside the ion source in a vacuum. Most surprising was the unexpected finding that no external means of ionisation, such as electrons from a filament, was needed to generate sample ions. The principle of operation is shown in Figure 12. When the eluent stream comes in contact with the heated section of the tube, approximately 95% is evaporated and the remaining liquid is dispersed into an aerosol that is propelled by steam into the ion source. There is no small orifice that is prone to being plugged, as in DLI, and moreover, the full effluent from a 4.6 mm i.d. column (1 mL min⁻¹) could be introduced into the ion source, so this new LC/MS technique was applauded as a major step forward.

After the presentation of thermospray at the ASMS conference, Marvin Vestal started the Vestec company for manufacturing complete thermospray mass spectrometers. Other manufacturers introduced thermospray on their mass spectrometers, either by the purchase of a customised thermospray source from Vestec (for example, NERMAG, Paris, France), or by building their own version (VG/Micromass and Kratos, Manchester, UK).

The mechanism of thermospray ionisation is, for the most part, a gas-phase reaction of ammonium ions with neutral sample molecules for positive ions and reactions of acetate anions for the formation of negative sample ions. Thermospray is, therefore, a mild CI process that is not suitable for the ionisation of weakly basic or weakly acidic sample molecules. By using a filament or discharge for ionisation, the addition of ammonium acetate can be eliminated and the chemical ionisation process can be extended to more reactive reagent ions and less polar samples. The discharge version of thermospray manufactured by Micromass was called Plasmaspray.

The liberation of ammonium ions from an ammonium acetate solution was not surprising, in view of the publications by Iribarne and Thomson (Toronto, Canada) in 1977 and 1979 about the "evaporation" of ions from solution. Röllgen and co-workers in Bonn, Germany, demonstrated that sample ions can be liberated from solution in thermospray. The best conditions for sample ion liberation, however, were a low concentration of other electrolytes and a high concentration of organic solvent, while the generation of ammonium ions for CI was favoured at a high concentration (0.1 M) of ammonium acetate and a high concentration of water in the eluent mixture. A few years later, the conditions formulated by Röllgen's group would find application in the optimisation of ion yield in ESI. Since ion yield

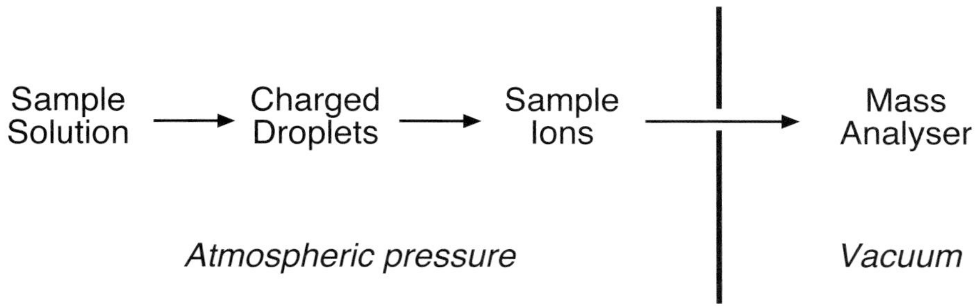

Sample → Charged → Sample → Mass
Solution   Droplets   Ions   Analyser

Atmospheric pressure   *Vacuum*

Figure 13. Operating principle of electrospray ionisation in an ion source operating at atmospheric pressure.

in thermospray was strongly dependent on eluent composition, a dual beam vapouriser was developed by the Röllgen group, in order to decouple reagent ion generation from sample evaporation.

In spite of its attractive features and promises, thermospray suffered from drawbacks: ionisation efficiency was strongly dependent on fine tuning of the interface temperature which, in turn, depends on solvent composition. Thus, gradient elution in HPLC was not easily accommodated by thermospray. A practical problem was the collection of large amounts of solvent in a cold trap, to protect the rotary vacuum pump connected to the ion source. Nevertheless, thermospray convinced many mass spectrometrists that LC/MS had finally become a reality.

For 10 to 15 years a large number of papers have been published about thermospray, all over the world, and European scientists made their mark. Christine Eckers and Timothy Blake at Smith, Kline & French in the UK worked on drug and endogenous compounds and their metabolites and conjugates. Seppo Auriola in Kuopio in Finland investigated a series of alkaloids. Hostettmann and coworkers in Lausanne in Switzerland used thermospray in their work on many kinds of natural products. Wils and Hulst in Rijswijk, The Netherlands, have investigated chemical warfare agents and their degradation products. In Barcelona in Spain, the group of Emilio Gelpí worked on neurochemistry and prostaglandins, while Damiá Barceló made extensive use of thermospray in his work on pollutants in the environment. The group led by Wilfried Niessen and Jan van der Greef in Leiden, The Netherlands, took a close look at anion exchange chromatography combined with thermospray MS. Röllgen's group in Bonn, Germany, published extensive studies on the mechanism of thermospray. This list is far from complete, and is based on publications that caught my attention during the first years of thermospray, and on personal contacts with the authors at the LC/MS conferences in Montreux.

CONTINUOUS FLOW FAST ATOM BOMBARDMENT

The first publication of the continuous flow fast atom bombardment (cfFAB) interface for LC/MS was by Ito, Ishi and co-workers in Japan in 1985. Richard Caprioli's group in the USA followed soon afterwards and made major contributions to its development and range of applications. In Europe, cfFAB interfaces were built by, among others, VG/Micromass, Kratos and Finnigan MAT. The JEOL (Japan) frit-FAB was probably the best among the commercialised interfaces. Although Jan van der Greef's group cooperated with Finnigan MAT in the optimisation of cfFAB conditions, the number of publications on cfFAB from European groups has been very limited and there was more interest in the subject in the USA and Japan.

IONISATION AT ATMOSPHERIC PRESSURE FOR LC/MS

Until 1985, the field of LC/MS showed a lively picture of new developments and competition between interfaces, between research groups and between manufacturers. Thermospray seemed the way to go, with particle beam as a runner-up.

Uncommon methods, such as atmospheric pressure chemical ionisation (APCI) by the Horning group at Baylor College, Texas, in 1974 and ion evaporation by Iribarne and Thomson in Toronto in 1980 did not catch enough attention. Both systems made use of ionisation at atmospheric pressure, for which equipment was not readily available from the manufacturers. The results from ion evaporation, a system that makes use of pneumatic nebulisation at atmospheric pressure with a high-voltage induction electrode for droplet charging, were impressive in the presentation by Iribarne at the ASMS conference in New York in 1980. At one of the following ASMS conferences, Bruce Thomson showed doubly- and triply charged negative ions for adenosine triphosphate, a result that could not be matched by any other ionisation and sample introduction technique. The Sciex mass spectrometer used by Thomson, however, was unknown to the community of organic and analytical mass spectrometrists, and Marvin Vestal was able to catch full attention for his thermospray technique.

Nevertheless, the importance of ionisation at atmospheric pressure was recognised by Jack Henion, who teamed up with Bruce Thomson and tried to use his Hewlett-Packard DLI probe in the APCI source of the Sciex mass spectrometer. This led to the birth of the heated nebuliser interface for APCI. There had been other attempts at the generation of ions from electrically-charged droplets. Prior to the ion evaporation experiments, there was the work by Dole and co-workers in the USA on the use of electrospray for the generation of beams of macro-ions from a polystyrene solution in benzene/acetone solution. Unfortunately, the Dole group could not record meaningful mass spectra.

Fenn's group, working at Yale University in the USA, revisited Dole's work. He was very experienced in the study of molecular beams and his group built a mass spectrometer with a free jet expansion from atmospheric pressure into the vacuum of the spectrometer with which they obtained the first good quality electrospray mass spectra, published in 1984. At about the same time, the group around Lidya Gall in Leningrad, in the USSR, reported mass spectra of ions from solutions at atmospheric pressure. Their original paper in 1984 was an outgrowth of their work on electrohydrodynamic ionisation *in vacuo*. Further work from this group was made public in Western Europe at the International Mass Spectrometry Conferences in Bordeaux in 1988 and in Amsterdam in 1991. The article describing electrospray mass spectrometry by the Fenn group in *Analytical Chemistry* in 1985 brought electrospray MS to the attention of a broader group in the analytical mass spectrometry community.

There was no breakthrough yet, because thermospray received almost all the attention from users and manufacturers of mass spectrometers.

Two factors would turn out to be crucial: the demonstration of real LC/MS and LC/MS/MS of difficult samples and the generation of multiply charged ions of proteins. Jack Henion's group at Cornell and Fenn's group at Yale played a decisive role in the breakthrough of ESI for LC/MS.

After Henion and Thomson completed their experiments with DLI on the Sciex TAGA, Jack realised the potential of APCI, and he took the risk of purchasing a Sciex TAGA 6000 triple quad. At that time, the TAGA (Trace Atmospheric Gas Analyzer) was an instrument for monitoring air quality and was controlled by a primitive data system that was not designed for ease of use and handling of data from a LC/MS experiment. Its strong design feature was the ion source and vacuum system, equipped with a gas curtain to prevent the formation of ion-solvent clusters and very fast ($100,000\,L\,s^{-1}$) cryogenic pumping of the mass analyser. This hardware was eminently suitable for the use of the heated nebuliser with APCI, as demonstrated by the publication of high-speed quantitative LC/MS/MS (60 injections in 60 minutes) in 1986.

I happened to play a role in the early use of this instrument, after arriving at Cornell in the summer of 1985 to work as visiting scientist in Henion's group. It turned out to be a combination of the right place, right moment and right instrument. I had been impressed by ion evaporation by Iribarne and Thomson in 1980 and by Fenn's work in 1984/1985, so why not give electrospray a try on the Sciex? We positioned an electrospray capillary in front of the Sciex ion sampling orifice, and it worked right away on a solution of ammonium acetate. We had also tried Thomson's ion evaporation system, but found it very insensitive. This was mainly due to the selection of conditions, a solution of a sample in 0.1 M ammonium acetate in water/acetonitrile, as was customary for thermospray. Soon, it was found that a high concentration of ammonium acetate gives a strong reduction in the yield of sample ions. In a further refinement of the electrospray experiment, a gentle flow of air was passed over the spray tip, in order to improve stability for negative ion formation, as recommended by Fenn's group. It was only a small step to increase the flow rate to the velocity required for pneumatic nebulisation. In this way, it was possible to increase the liquid flow rate to at least $50\,\mu L\,min^{-1}$, compatible with the elution of 1 mm i.d. HPLC columns. The name Ionspray was coined, a contraction of "ion evaporation" and "electrospray", to highlight the regime in which the interface operated: pneumatic nebulisation with assistance from an electric field, for the generation of electrically-charged droplets. At the ASMS conference in Cincinnati (1986), the Henion group presented data on LC/MS and LC/MS/MS with the "IonSpray" interface on the Sciex TAGA.

Although this was a promising result, the breakthrough of electrospray needed another major step forward. This was the discovery by Fenn's group that electrospray can generate a consistent and reproducible series of multiply charged ions of proteins, which allowed the determination of the molecular weight of a protein by the use of a fairly simple quadrupole mass spectrometer with a limited m/z range. Fenn made his presentation at the ASMS

Fugure 14. Home built atmospheric pressure ion source on a modified NERMAG R3010 triple quadrupole mass spectrometer. An RF-only transfer quadrupole is located inside the original ion source vacuum envelope. Photo taken in the laboratory of the author.

conference in San Francisco in May1988, followed by more examples shown by Fenn, by Tom Covey (Sciex) and by Dick Smith (Batelle Labs, USA) at the LC/MS workshop in Freiburg in the fall of 1988. Until then, high mass ions were generated by FAB or field desorption and detected with extended mass range magnetic sector mass spectrometers. The opportunities for mass spectrometry of proteins aroused the interest of all manufacturers of mass spectrometers, such as VG/Fisons/Micromass, who constructed the BioQ.

In the small molecule world, there had been slow progress since 1986. Tom Covey and others in Henion's group demonstrated how useful IonSpray LC/MS could be for the analysis of drugs, contaminants in the environment and other compound classes. Finally, Sciex decided to overhaul the design of the TAGA and, in 1989, the API3 was launched at the Pittsburg Conference and the pharmaceutical industries were quick to adopt this instrument. In Europe Paul Macrae at Pfizer in Sandwich in the UK was one of these early proponents, soon followed by scientists at Hoffman La Roche and Sandoz in Basel, Dreher at BASF and others. The pharmaceutical companies could now run and quantitate polar and thermolabile drugs, metabolites and conjugates, which was impossible, or at least very difficult, with thermospray.

Back in 1986, after my return home, I was convinced about the power of electrospray/ionspray, but there was no instrument that could be equipped with an atmospheric pressure ion source. During a tour around European MS manufacturers, it appeared that NERMAG

(Paris, France) had converted a standard R1010 to a prototype inductively-coupled plasma (ICP) mass spectrometer. Since ICP-MS makes use of ionisation at atmospheric pressure, transferring ions through pressure reduction stages into the mass analyser, the NERMAG was considered a good starting point for the modification of the ICP-MS to a room-temperature atmospheric pressure ionisation MS. It worked out all right and, in April 1988, I had the first electrospray mass spectrometer in Western Europe. I adopted the curtain gas principle as used and patented by Sciex, which was allowed since there was no intention of selling the source design.

Manufacturers of API sources had to circumvent the curtain gas patent. In the early API instruments that were built to run ESI spectra of proteins, the gas dynamics of the transition from atmosphere to high vacuum were far from perfect, but with the help of moderate voltage drops, declustering of $MH_n^{n+}(H_2O)_x$ ions worked well enough to get a reasonable ion transmission. At the time, the Sciex API3 was far superior, thanks to its original design, as a small molecule detector. Through the evolution of design, other manufacturers caught up. For example, the VG/Fisons/Micromass (now Waters) ion source evolved from the BioQ via the Platform to the Z-spray arrangement. Finnigan (USA and Bremen, Germany) worked with the Analytica of Branford source (headed by Fenn's PhD student Craig Whitehouse) for some time, but changed to the heated capillary for ion transfer into the vacuum, a system designed and patented by Brian Chait's group at Rockefeller University (New York, USA). Mark Allen and Ivor Lewis (London, UK) ported the electrospray source to a magnetic sector mass spectrometer and Finnigan MAT (Bremen) followed, some time later, on the MAT 900, as did VG and Kratos in the UK.

Electrospray is the method of choice for LC/MS of thermolabile samples and biomacromolecules. But electrospray shows a very different behaviour from EI and CI. It is not mass flow sensitive but, on the contrary, ion signals change very little if the rate of infusion of a sample solution is increased or decreased. This apparent concentration-sensitive behaviour was taken advantage of by Matthias Wilm and Matthias Mann (who got his PhD in Fenn's group) at EMBL in Heidelberg, Germany. The common liquid flow rate of several $\mu L\,min^{-1}$ was reduced to tens of $nL\,min^{-1}$. A 1 μL sample placed in a short capillary, drawn out to a fine few μm i.d. tip, would thus create electrospray for several tens of minutes. During this time, a series of different MS and MS/MS experiments could be performed on a sample. The apparent concentration sensitivity of electrospray gave a strong impetus to the combination of capillary ($\ll$1 mm i.d.) HPLC columns with mass spectrometry. This combination has now been widely adopted for the analysis and identification of proteins. The Wilm+Mann design was commercialised by the Danish company Protana around 1997. In hindsight, it is interesting to observe that micro LC, which was an escape route in the early development of LC/MS, became main stream for sample-limited applications such as proteomics. LC Packings (founded by Jean-Pierre Chervet, a former PhD student from the Free University in Amsterdam) was the first company to supply equipment for micro and nano LC, using a flow splitter in order to accommodate a regular LC pump and their FAMOS autosampler, developed in cooperation with Spark Holland (Emmen, the Netherlands). LC Packings is now part of Thermo Fisher Scientific. Competition in the low-flow LC area is, among

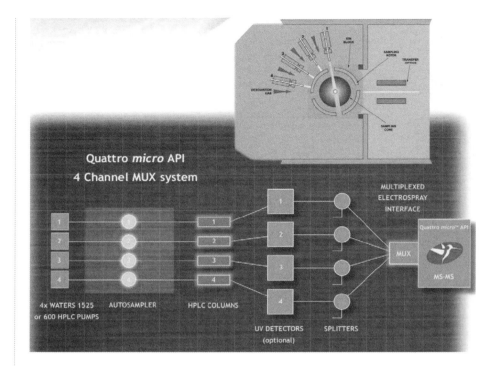

Figure 15. Micromass MUX arrangement for coupling four liquid chromatographs to one electrospray ion source.

others, from the Danish company Proxeon, now part of Thermo Fisher Scientific, and from a number of companies in the US and Canada.

It thus seemed that electrospray was best combined with capillary and nano LC columns. However, the intricacies of work with such columns are incompatible with the requirements of high-throughput, robust HPLC for pharmaceutical and biomedical analyses. Nebuliser-assisted electrospray started at $10–50\,\mu L\,min^{-1}$. Flow rates of up to $1\,mL\,min^{-1}$ can be handled, but sensitivity gets poorer, since sample concentration in the LC eluent decreases when the column i.d. is increased. Due to incomplete desolvation of sprayed droplets at high flow rate, many sample ions are lost in droplets deposited on the walls of the ion source. So improvement of performance in the high-flow region requires better desolvation of sprayed droplets, which requires heat. The entire source can be heated, but it turned out that mixing the plume of sprayed droplets with a flow of hot gas does the job. Tom Covey at Sciex achieved a dramatic gain in sensitivity with his first generation TurboIonSpray source in 1994. One heat gun was sufficient for $200\,\mu L\,min^{-1}$ from a 2 mm i.d. column and, later, two heat guns in the TurboV source pushed the level of performance to $1\,mL\,min^{-1}$ from standard 4.6 mm i.d. columns. The other manufacturers constructed their own versions of high-flow electrospray.

Figure 16. Prototype atmospheric pressure photoionisation source constructed in the laboratory of the author, built inside a Sciex heated nebuliser APCI source housing. Photo courtesy of Peter Jacobs, Oss, The Netherlands.

Quantitative LC/MS/MS of a large number of samples requires short cycle time between injections. Short columns, small particle diameter columns, higher-pressure HPLC pumps afford fast separations. HPLC cycle time is the sum of column equilibration time, injection time and elution time. Since relevant MS information is collected during part of the elution time, the sum of other times is wasted time. To minimise this wasted time, parallel operation of two or more columns in front of one mass spectrometer makes more efficient use of data acquisition time of the MS. The Micromass MUX was designed for the combination of two or more HPLCs with one electrospray mass spectrometer, by means of multiple sprayers together with a rotating mechanical shutter, for the successive selection of the sample ions from each HPLC.

After the success of ESI in general, and the success of the Sciex APCI in bioanalysis, all manufacturers implemented APCI on their instruments. For the user there was, and is, choice between ESI for ionisation from the liquid phase and APCI for ionisation in the gas phase. This is of particular importance in LC/MS of small molecules, where ESI and APCI may offer different selectivity and sensitivity. Ionisation suppression by matrix components has turned out to be a major problem in bioanalysis but APCI is affected much less than ESI by this problem.

When LC/MS started, EI and CI seemed the way to go. By 1998, it was almost impossible to combine LC/MS with EI. The moving belt and particle beam interfaces had become obsolete, ESI and APCI dominated, but there was still a need for the ionisation of "apolar" samples. Less polar samples can be ionised in ESI and APCI by the attachment of NH_4^+, Na^+ or Li^+ ions to lone pair electrons on oxygen and nitrogen atoms present in the sample molecule. In 1998, Ernst Bayer in Tübingen, Germany, demonstrated that transition metal ions such as Ag^+ can be attached to C=C double bonds, with no need for the presence of heteroatoms. An amazing range of samples such as unsaturated terpene hydrocarbons could be analysed by LC/MS.

In 2000, Achille Cappiello in Urbino, Italy went back to EI and combined very low flow nano LC with an EI source. Amirav in Israel used a molecular beam interface for recording EI spectra of molecules cooled in the free jet expansion. Now that API sources were the way to go for LC/MS, why not try an API method for the generation of molecular ions from samples having low ionisation energy? It had been demonstrated around 1990 by Revelskii in Russia that photoionisation in an API source is feasible for the effluent from a gas chromatograph. Reference to these publications in Russian journals was found in *Chemical Abstracts*. For LC, selective ionisation of sample molecules should be feasible, since most LC solvents have an ionisation energy of more than 10 eV, while that of most analytes is less than 10 eV.

Fortunately, a krypton-filled gas discharge lamp for GC with PI detection could be purchased off the shelf at a low cost from Cathodeon (now Hereaus Noble Light, Cambridge, UK). My personal experience in this field was through a scientific cooperation with Sciex. They provided an API365 triple quadrupole instrument and funds for postdoc Damon Robb who started in the fall of 1998. One year later, we had a working system, a provisional US patent and, at the same time, it appeared that the US company Syagen had been working along the same lines, starting with a low-pressure PI source. The result for MS users in the field was the introduction of the Photospray source by Sciex, while Syagen provided OEM sources for Agilent, Finnigan/Thermo, Micromass/Waters and other manufacturers.

The chemistry of the APPI source was not as simple as expected. It was surprising to observe MH^+ ions instead of $M^{+\bullet}$ for many samples. It took some time to find out where the proton came from. It turned out that ionised toluene, used as a dopant (an intermediate in the ionisation of samples), can protonate $(acetonitrile)_2$ and $(methanol)_3$ clusters and thus generate reactant ions for chemical ionisation. So APPI is, for the most part, photon initiated APCI! Later, it appeared that anisole does not act as a proton donor. Anisole, chlorobenzene and bromobenzene are good dopants for $M^{+\bullet}$ formation by charge exchange. Damon Robb (Vancouver, Canada) has worked this out further to other dopants. First time users of APPI were the beta testers of prototype sources built in Groningen, under the research contract with Sciex.

Risto Kostiainen's group in Helsinki studied the effect of LC eluent composition and investigated negative ion formation in the APPI source. Agilent cooperated with the Govert Somsen group and G.J. (Ad) de Jong at the University of Utrecht, The Netherlands, who made major steps forward in an unexpected direction: the combination of micellar electrokinetic chromatography (MEKC) and capillary electrophoresis (CE) with APPI. Thorston Benter's group (University of Wuppertal, Germany) has introduced atmospheric pressure laser ionisation (APLI), which makes use of energy transfer from two or more less energetic photons (248 nm, 5 eV) to aromatic analyte molecules. This group is very active in exploring the scope of APLI for LC/MS making thorough investigations of spatial distribution ion generation and transportation in both APLI and APCI sources.

In many cases, APPI shows better sensitivity than APCI and, in some cases, it is superior to ESI. It has been reported that APPI is less sensitive to ionisation suppression than ESI and APCI for a number of LC/MS/MS assays. Finally, the molecular ions (positive or negative) give different fragment ions from those given by quasi-molecular ions in MS/MS. Thus, different selectivity is expected which can be useful in a particular analysis.

If one considers methods of achieving more selectivity, possible routes include selection of ionisation, fragmentation and higher mass resolution. Hybrid sector-TOF, sector-quadrupole and sector-ion trap instruments were constructed by VG/Fisons/Micromass and Finnigan MAT. The quadrupole-TOF hybrid built by Micromass, in close cooperation with Howard Morris, was much better suited to ESI and LC/MS/MS than the hybrid sector instruments, since there is no high accelerating voltage on elements of the atmospheric pressure ion source. The Q-TOF affords a much better duty cycle than a triple quadrupole instrument for full-scan product ion spectra. The high resolution offered by the TOF section made LC-QTOF a very desirable option for fragmentation studies of peptides and for drug molecules. Peptide mass fingerprinting and metabolite identification are probably the most important applications of the QTOF. Sciex, followed later by Bruker, introduced their versions of the QTOF. The full width half maximum (FWHM) resolution of the original QTOFs was about 10,000.

In 2005, Thermo introduced the Orbitrap mass analyser, developed by Makarov. This was a major technological achievement, since the original idea was formulated in 1999. Makarov started his work within the small company HD Technologies, which is now part of Thermo. The Orbitrab offers high resolution (60,000 FWHM under standard conditions) which is better than the resolution obtained with a TOF, but not as good as the resolution of Fourier transform ion cyclotron resonance (FT-ICR). The Orbitrap does not use a superconducting magnet, so the cost of ownership is lower than for an FT-ICR. The hybrid linear ion trap Orbitrap was an instant success, in proteomics, in drug research and many other areas of LC/MS applications. The TOF manufacturers realised the challenge and started to improve their mass analysers.

Ion mobility is a very different method for making distinction between ions. Mobility is a function of charge and shape. Isobaric, isomeric ions that cannot be distinguished by (high resolution) mass spectrometry, can be separated according to their mobility. Ion mobility at atmospheric pressure, combined with quadrupole mass spectrometry was used by Kostiainen's group in Helsinki. A commercially available variation on this theme is field asymmetric ion mobility spectrometry (FAIMS) from Ionalytics (now part of Thermo), developed in Canada by Guevremont and co-workers. Ion mobility spectrometry at low pressure has been studied by several groups, amongst other by Mike Bowers, David Clemmer and Dave Russell in the US. In Europe, Micromass/Waters implemented a travelling wave version in their Synapt LC/MS/MS instruments in 2007. Ion mobility offers a new option for increased selectivity in LC/MS. Separation takes place according to charge and shape in the IM section, followed by separation according to charge and mass in the mass analysers.

With the increasing demand for mass spectra and LC/MS, and since computer-controlled instruments can be set up and tuned by an expert, but be operated by non-experts in a routine mode, VG/Micromass introduced an automated open-access quadrupole mass spectrometer, first for flow injection of sample solutions and later for complete walk-up LC/MS.

On-line LC/MS had become an enormous success. Discussions about on-line versus off-line would seem to be a waste of time. Nevertheless, fraction collection has returned. Fraction collection for MALDI can be done with an automated spotter for micro or nano LC that deposits a droplet of eluent mixed with MALDI matrix solution every one or few seconds on a MALDI target plate. MALDI with a high repetition rate laser (1000 Hz) is then run in automated mode. Reconstruction of total ion and extracted ion chromatograms is a first pass analysis. Next, the plate is rerun for recording of MS/MS spectra of components of interest. This procedure has found application in the field of proteomics. As an alternative, fractions can be collected and kept in solution in a fraction collector, for re-injection in an automated chip-based nanospray, again for recording of MS/MS spectra by TOF/TOF or QTOF.

It is amazing that LC/MS is back where it started!

The development of LC/MS as described above could be followed in Europe by attending the Montreux LC/MS workshops in 1981, 1982, 1984 and every even year thereafter. In the beginning, the workshops were dominated by new developments presented by manufacturers and academics from universities. Scientists and managers from the pharmaceutical companies looked at all this "playing around" and were amused. In 1981, 1982 and 1984, the subjects of the papers in the conference proceedings were: ionisation methods (presented by Nico Nibbering), arguments for using DLI by Patrick Arpino, developments and applications of DLI presented by NERMAG researchers and HP DLI users, and the use of microbore HPLC. In 1984, the first research and applications of thermospray were presented. In 1986 and 1988, emphasis was on cfFAB, optimisation and applications of thermospray. From 1981 through to 1988, the moving belt received major attention and there was mention of supercritical fluid chromatography/MS and capillary electrophoresis/MS. 1988 saw the presentation by John Fenn and others on electrospray and multiply charged ions of proteins. In the 1990s this picture changed drastically. Industry started to purchase newly-developed API-MS equipment and showed applications, mostly in the pharmaceutical field. Academia could not afford the new instruments, such as the Sciex API3. Thermospray continued to be the most widely used technique in 1990, 1992 and 1994. cfFAB was applied by some groups in Europe, but mostly outside Europe. Particle beam made its inroads and the moving belt and DLI disappeared gradually. In 1996 and 1998 nearly all presentations made use of API techniques ESI and APCI; thermospray was almost absent. The year 2000 saw the introduction of APPI prototypes, and in 2004 there were the first APPI applications using commercial APPI sources. Since 1990, the workshop has changed from an instrumentation-development event to an applications-oriented conference.

At the Montreux conferences there were the optional LC/MS courses taught by Jack Henion and Dai Games and, more recently, Jack Henion and Bob Voyksner. Since 1989, the LC/MS workshop has been held in the USA, organised by Jack Henion and Bob Voyksner in the odd years and in Montreux, organised by Jan van der Greef in the even years. Roland Frei, who organised the workshops from 1981 through 1988, passed away in January 1989.

In 1993, Janet Oxford and Christine Eckers started the series of LC/MS courses and conferences, held every other year, one week before Christmas. The College of Pharmacy in London was the first location, but since 1995, the venue has been Robinson College in Cambridge. The course was, and is, taught by a number of scientists specialising in different aspects of LC, MS and LC/MS interfacing and ionisation.

SELECTED READING

M.L. Gross and R.M. Caprioli (Eds), "Ionization Methods", Volume 6 *Encyclopedia of Mass Spectrometry*. Elsevier, Amsterdam, The Netherlands (2007).

W.M.A. Niessen (Ed.), "Hyphenated Methods", Volume 8 *Encyclopedia of Mass Spectrometry*. Elsevier, Amsterdam, The Netherlands (2006).

R. Willoughby, E. Sheehan and S. Mitrovich, *A Global View of LC/MS*, 2nd Edition. Global View Publishing, Pittsburgh, Pennsylvania, USA (2002).

W.M.A. Niessen, *Liquid Chromatography-Mass Spectrometry*, 3rd Edition. CRC Press, Boca Raton, Florida, USA (2006).

A. Cappliello (Ed.), *Advances in LC-MS Instrumentation*, Journal of Chromatography Library Volume 72. Elsevier, Amsterdam, The Netherlands (2007).

R.K. Boyd, C. Basic and R.A. Bethem, *Trace Quantitative Analysis by Mass Spectrometry*. John Wiley & Sons, Chichester, UK (2008).

From field desorption to MALDI and to the resurgence of time-of-flight mass spectrometry

Michael Karas
University of Münster, Münster, Germany

INTRODUCTION

Viewed from today's perspective, the 1970s and early 1980s were exciting times when the different lines of development in new ionisation techniques finally grew together from their various origins and the whole field picked up momentum. The major obstacle for the expansion of mass spectrometry for the analysis of bioorganic compounds and biopolymers was the fact that common ionisation techniques such as electron impact and chemical ionisation relied on the transfer of intact analyte molecules from the condensed phase, either from their liquid state or solution, or directly from the solid crystalline state to the vacuum of the ion source. Clearly, simple (i.e. slow) thermal heating of labile compounds could not be a very useful method since even small polar amino acids were not accessible because of their thermal degradation. Looking back at the developments, two main pathways were followed to solve the problem. Either ionisation of the analytes would have to be carried out directly from their solution—which was first realised in thermospray ionisation and finally resulted in electrospray ionisation or, alternatively, release of analyte neutrals and their ionisation would have to be carried in one step *in vacuo* in the ion source of the mass spectrometer. This "desorption/ionisation" step was most successfully achieved by subjecting the sample to a sudden impact of energy. This could be achieved by bombardment of the sample with ions, either of intermediate energy in the keV range in secondary ion mass spectrometry (SIMS) or of high energy in the MeV range from accelerators, or by nuclear fission in plasma desorption (PD), or by a pulse of intense light from a laser (LDI).

It is, however, always easy to point out a rationale for the scientific progress from the endpoint. First, the actual scientific steps are taken by individual scientists within distinct boundary conditions and progress or even breakthrough may not be immediately visible or obvious either to the inventor or to the community. This is especially true when progress occurs outside a scientific community, such as the analytical/organic mass spectrometry community. Adoption of new concepts is made much more difficult by discrepancies that typically exist between the instrumental performance in the laboratory of the inventor and the standards established in the community and especially by the lack of commercially available instruments of adequate performance. It is for this reason that PD, SIMS and finally MALDI were not widely adopted immediately since they are all techniques that needed the development of time-of-flight mass spectrometers to show their full potential. On the other hand, if progress is made within an established scientific community, such as organic mass spectrometrists, the adoption, commercialisation and dissemination of a successful idea may be very rapid, as was the case, for example, for fast atom bombardment (FAB).

Second, progress achieved—especially outside a particular community—is typically based on an unexpected observation made in the course of routine experiments rather than as a result of a planned series of investigations, and PD and SIMS are clear examples of this type of development. The inventor's act is then first to perceive the implications of the experimental findings and second and more importantly to "sell" the invention by showing (and publishing) something truly spectacular. In that respect, the first insulin mass spectrum yielded by PD was more important than the best and analytically useful peptide mass spectrum reported earlier, as was the first ugly and analytically meaningless protein mass

Opposite: The matrix–analyte crystals formed after drying for a 2,5-dihydroxybenzoic acid matrix.

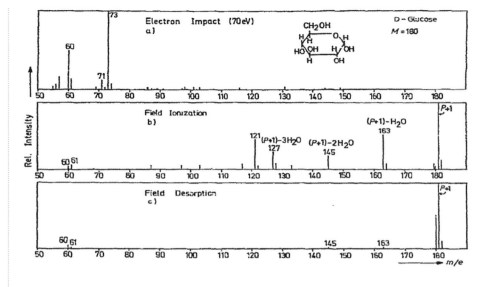

Figure 1. Electron impact, field ionisation and field desorption mass spectra of glucose. Reprinted with permission from Reference 1, Copyright (1969), with permission from Elsevier.

spectrum above 100 kDa which defined the breakthrough for MALDI. The important role of these spectacular events is to tear down thought barriers which they do much more efficiently than is possible by the presentation and discussion of new conceptual ideas.

FIELD DESORPTION

Field desorption—introduced in 1969 by Beckey and coworkers at the University of Bonn, Germany, as the first successful technique for the mass spectrometry of large labile biomolecules—delivered the generic term for this class of new techniques, which were called "desorption" and later "desorption/ionisation" techniques. Field ionisation had overcome one problem of electron-impact ionisation, i.e. the low intensity or complete lack of molecular ions in EI mass spectra and thus "*became known as a 'soft' method of ionization*":[1] but in that respect it was not unique since this is also achieved by chemical ionisation (CI). An extra step was needed to avoid decomposition of labile organic compounds induced by their heating for their transfer into the vacuum/gas phase of the ion source. This was achieved when the sample was directly loaded onto the special emitters used in field ionisation consisting of a forest of carbonaceous whiskers. These so-called "activated field anodes" were loaded with a small droplet of the sample solution—and the solvent was removed by evaporation in the ion source. When heated to a particular temperature well below that typically required for their thermal vaporisation, strong and stable ion signals of thermally labile compounds such as glucose could be recorded in magnetic sector instruments. The theoretical concept for this "field desorption" was developed by E.W. Müller[2] for the ionisation of adsorbed metal atoms or gases such as oxygen at extremely high electric fields on ultrafine metallic tips in a field ion microscope by analogy to field evaporation of ions of the tip material. It was assumed that these conceptual ideas can be transferred to the situation of individual absorbed analyte molecules. For these molecules the energy barrier to desorption made up by van der Waals binding to the surface—and thus the temperature needed for their evaporation—is reduced in the presence of a high electric field which also induces ionisation. This model, however, would predict the formation of radical molecular ion species whereas even-electron ions such as (de)protonated or cationised molecules dominated the FD mass spectra. The lively discussion of the fundamental FD processes is also reflected in the *IUPAC Compendium of Chemical Terminology*:

> "field desorption (in mass spectrometry) A term used to describe the formation of ions in the gas phase from a material deposited on a solid surface (known as an 'emitter') in the presence of a high electrical field. 'Field desorption' is an ambiguous term because it implies that the electric field desorbs a material as an ion from some kind of emitter on which the material is deposited. There is growing evidence that some of the ions formed are due to thermal ionization and some to field ionization of vapour evaporated from material on the emitter. Because there is generally little or no ionization unless the emitter is heated by an electric current, 'field desorption' is a misnomer. The term is, however, firmly implanted in the literature and most users understand what is going on regardless of the implications of the term. In addition, no better simple term has been suggested to take its place and so, reluctantly, it is recommended that it be retained. 1991, 63, 1547"

The conclusion that "field desorption is a misnomer", because little ionisation occurs unless the emitter is heated, is a biased summary of the discussion started by a paper suggesting an alternative "model for ionization mechanisms in field desorption mass spectrometry"[3] and the subsequent lively discussions under the title "field desorption without fields".[4] The reverse is also true, however, for FD of true non-volatile samples, i.e. that pure thermal heating without applying an strong electric field does not lead to ion formation. Later investigations which used thin bare metal wires loaded with the sample rather than activated field anodes revealed by optical microscopy and mass spectrometry that an electro-hydro-dynamic disintegration and ionisation of the sample occurs from a viscous glassy state under the influence of both temperature and electric field.[5] This led to the conclusion that ions are formed in a desolvation mechanism, which from today's viewpoint shows some relation to the electrospray ionisation process.

A number of contributing factors were responsible for the dominance of the Beckey group for field ionisation and field desorption. In addition to Beckey's group there were three more research groups in the Institute of Physical Chemistry at the University of Bonn, which covered all aspects from the physical chemistry of ionisation (F.W. Röllgen), the energetics of ions and their fragmentation (K. Levsen) to broad analytical application of FD (H.R. Schulten). Moreover, the institute had a well-equipped and experienced mechanical (and

Figure 2. Loading of the analyte solution to an activated FD emitter. Reproduced from H.R. Schulten and H.M. Schiebel, "Principle and techniques of field desorption mass spectrometry", *Naturwissenschaften* **65,** 223–230 (1978) with kind permission from Springer Science and Business Media.

electronic) workshop which made it possible to construct and manufacture the mechanical components necessary to convert conventional EI magnetic sector mass spectrometers into FI/FD mass spectrometers. The acknowledged importance of this is also reflected in the fact that the head of the workshop (A. Heindrichs) is co-author in one of the early FD papers. An impressive selection of manufactured parts and journeyman's pieces was displayed in the entrance hall of the institute in Bonn.

As early as 1972, the first FD mass spectra of unprotected peptides were reported extending up to a nonamer. In 1978 the FD mass spectrum of vitamin B12 was reported, a compound which at that time became a standard by which the high-mass capability of a new ionisation technique was judged. The first ten years of applications were reviewed by H.R. Schulten in 1983 and covered nearly all classes of (bio)analytes from small synthetic drugs to peptides, oligosaccharides and oligonucleotides up to about 2000 Daltons.[6] However, FD never became the method of choice in a larger analytical community. This is most probably due to the need for a constant supply of reproducibly working activated field anodes—one per sample to be analysed. Further, with regard to the fundamental processes described above, it was often difficult to find or ever to reach the so-called "best anode temperature" to yield a stable ion emission for the time needed to acquire a mass spectrum. Simultaneous detection of ions in order to acquire mass spectra from a burst of ions by photo-plate sector instruments was a possible means to overcome those problems, but was not widely accessible to all potential users of FD. As a consequence, field desorption was quickly replaced by the new technique of fast atom bombardment in the developing bio-organic mass spectrometry community and has been used only for relatively few specific applications since then. One area of application was the field of technical polymers[7,8] where field desorption yielded superior results especially for non-polar polymers; again, however, it was finally replaced in this case mainly by MALDI-MS.[9]

The advent of field desorption which led to the successful generation of mass spectra from increasingly thermally labile compounds of increasing mass stimulated the search for other ionisation methods which were characterised by the term "desorption" and made use of alternative means of desorption/ionisation. This did not mean, however, that there was a standstill within the EI and CI community. The obvious limitation, i.e. the required transfer of the sample from the solid or liquid state into intact and stable molecules in the gas phase, was addressed by the introduction of new ideas on how to extend the capabilities of conventional EI and CI sources. The first of these was the reduction of the energy required for vaporisation by deposition of the sample onto inert substrates. A second approach was the concept of "rapid heating",[10] based on the idea that, provided the rate at which energy is transferred to the sample is sufficiently high, vaporisation can kinetically overcome thermal decomposition. In order to facilitate ionisation, the sample was positioned either very close to the electron beam in an EI source (in-beam EI) or inserted into a CI source [in-beam CI, desorption or direct CI (DCI)]. Such experiments had been carried out much earlier by Reed et al.[11] in Britain. Over the next few years, discussions on the mechanisms of these processes continued and posed the question as to whether thermal processes can lead to the desired progress and, indeed, was the progress that had been achieved explicable in terms of thermal processes. As far as practical applications were concerned, there was only modest progress in the use of in-beam or direct EI/CI techniques since the short burst of ions typically produced limited their wider use and impact, due at least in part to the use of scanning mass analysers available at the time.

SECONDARY ION MASS SPECTROMETRY

The major developments in the field of ionisation techniques occurred, however, outside the organic mass spectrometry community. The bombardment of solid surfaces with keV ions results in a sputtering process and the emission of "secondary" ions. This process was and is still widely used in SIMS for elemental analysis of metals and semiconductors with the capabilities both of depth profiling by the sputtering/erosion process and of microscopic analysis due to the possibility of focussing the primary ion beam by ion optical means. When, however, the analytical goal changed to the investigation of the surface, e.g. for the investigation of catalysts, the flux of the incident ions had to be greatly reduced, since every impinging ion induces an impact cascade by transferring energy and momentum to the target atoms, resulting in a large damaged surface area that is much larger than the size of the impinging atom. The flux of ions had thus to be reduced to about 10^{12} ions/cm^2 for the whole experiment in order to guarantee that no ion hits a previously damaged area within one experiment. This approach became known as "static" SIMS and was reported by Benninghoven in 1969.[12] When applying this static SIMS for surface characterisation, it became obvious that not only the atomic constituents of the surface were detected but also contaminants from chemical pretreatment, such as anions from inorganic acids. Shortly afterwards, organic fragment and molecule ions were also detected which, at that time and level of understanding of the sputtering process, was completely unexpected. Subsequently, this was extended to amino acids and small peptides,[13] but it was not more widely adopted because the scanning mass spectrometers used at the time were not suited to the single-event process. Only at the end of the 1970s were time-of-flight (TOF) analysers coupled to a static ion bombardment source by Standing's group in Canada and by the Benninghoven group in Europe.[14,15] Almost immediately afterwards, however, the attention of the mass spectrometric community turned to the next big development, i.e. the introduction of FAB.

^{252}CF PLASMA DESORPTION IONISATION

In parallel with the gradual development of organic SIMS, however, another unexpected observation was made by nuclear physicists using a time-of-flight mass spectrometer in an experiment aimed at investigating the β-decay recoil of short-lived nuclei from the surface of a monolayer source. Macfarlane and coworkers at Texas A&M University, USA realised that the peaks occurring in the mass spectrum originated from ions generated from organic impurities which were produced by the ionising radiation. In a key experiment, they located the radioactive nuclei on the backside of a thin foil coated with an organic sample and the so-called ^{252}Cf plasma desorption technique was born.[16] Almost immediately, a very active group of European scientists, including Bo Sundqvist from Uppsala, Sweden, Yvon LeBeyec

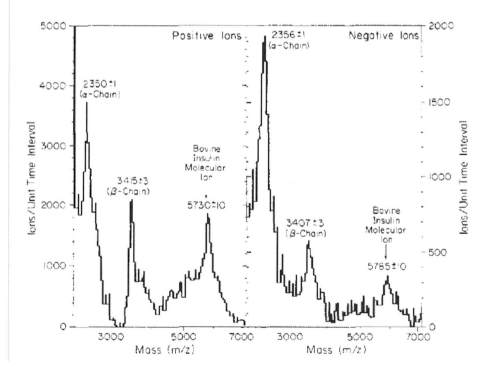

Figure 3. First mass spectrum of insulin. Reprinted with permission from Reference 19. Copyright (1982) American Chemical Society.

from Orsay, France and Karl Wien from Darmstadt, Germany and their research groups, began collaborative work on this technique. Dedicated research in the fundamental processes leading to the formation of quasimolecular ions of compounds of increasingly higher mass was carried out using the capabilities of nuclear physics institutes and ion accelerators. It became clear that the high-energy (around 100 MeV) recoil particles of the ^{252}Cf nuclear fission (e.g. ^{142}Ba and ^{106}Tc) penetrate the thin aluminium foil and the sample creating a high-energy track in which a plasma is formed and only atoms can persist. This infra track is surrounded by an outer cylinder in which the energy per unit volume is constantly decaying. At some distance from the infra track, a shower of slow electrons is released resulting in an efficient electronic excitation of the sample and the erosion of material and formation of a crater around the infra track. The sample was electrosprayed from an aqueous solution on to the substrate foil.[17,18] Even though this was far away from being optimal and was later replaced by using nitrocellulose as an additive, plasma desorption had the privilege of setting the milestone for the future. In 1981, during a visit of Ron Macfarlane and Catherine McNeal to Uppsala, Sweden, an attempt was made to obtain a spectrum of insulin and a weak but clearly detectable signal on a large background was recorded and published in 1982.[19] This was a true breakthrough since it clearly demonstrated for the first time that it was possible to generate intact ions of proteins in the gas phase which forms the basis of modern protein MS. In their conclusion, the authors state:

> "An important milestone in mass spectrometry development has been realised with the detection of gas-phase molecular ions of insulin. This is not only because it is an important molecule for biomedical applications, but also because it is near that semantic boundary in mass space beyond which a peptide becomes a protein".

Even though the mass range was constantly extended in the following years to small proteins, PD never became widely used in the growing biological mass spectrometry community. The PD TOF MS systems were strikingly simple instruments—once the sample was loaded, the production of the mass spectrum could be followed on screen. They were in a sense an anticipation of modern benchtop MS systems but their performance with respect to mass resolution and mass determination accuracy never reached a level for them to be fully accepted by the established mass spectrometry community. Big improvements were achieved by the development of optimised sample preparation. The use of nitrocellulose as a sample backing allowed for an on-stage clean-up of samples from salts and contaminants and greatly improved the performance.[20] Since TOF mass analysers and data accumulation techniques were technologies which were not offered by the major manufacturers, a commercial PDMS machine became available only from a small start-up company in close cooperation with the Uppsala group. Bio-Ion Nordic AB in Uppsala, Sweden started in 1983 and the first BioIon Bin-10K instrument was delivered to Peter Roepstorff's group in Odense, Denmark in 1984. About 50 PDMS instruments were built, sold and in use in the 1980s and 1990s, but MALDI had already appeared on the scene and finally took over.

FAST ATOM BOMBARDMENT IONISATION

Towards the end of the 1970s and early 1980s, another big step was made by the introduction of FAB. Since this step was achieved within the organic MS community using quadrupole instruments and soon commercial sector instruments in a close relation to instrument manufacturers in Manchester, it immediately attracted wide interest and made a major impact. Towards the end of the 1960s, Alfred Benninghoven had suggested that by using a very low flux primary ion beam so as not to damage a substance present on a surface, it was possible to obtain a mass spectrum of the substance, including both molecular and fragment ions. Many surface scientists considered that Static Secondary Ion Mass Spectrometry (SSIMS) the technique, and John Vickerman and Mickey Barber at the University of Manchester Institute of Science and Technology decided to investigate this further by use of a simple argon ion gun attached to a small quadrupole instrument. Initial results obtained by John Wolstenholme in 1976 were encouraging. Bob Bordoli, supported by a grant from Pilkington Glass, began work for his doctorate with Vickerman on the use of SIMS to investigate the surface chemistry of glass, but it soon became apparent that the continuous bombardment of a sample on a glass surface by argon ions caused charging up which led to the loss of the spectrum. He therefore constructed a fast atom argon beam by passing the ions through a charge exchange chamber which overcame the charging problem and also allowed the gun to be interfaced to a sector instrument. In 1978, in the absence of Vickerman on sabbatical leave, he joined Don Sedgwick's group working with Barber and interfaced the atom gun to the source of a somewhat elderly MS902 instrument of uncertain reliability. Samples were introduced on a modified field desorption sample probe, with the emitter assembly replaced with an angled copper tip, upon which the sample for analysis was placed, and which was etched in nitric acid between samples. Spectra were recorded on a pen and ink chart recorder, and spectral calibration was obtained by manually counting the spectra. The problems of damage and the transient nature of the spectra remained, however. The use of the "fast atom" gun was published in two back-to-back papers in *J.C.S. Chemical Communications* submitted in January 1981.[21,22]

The breakthrough came when it was realised that samples could be dissolved in a viscous, involatile solvent such as glycerol which eliminated the detrimental effects of sample damage and so allowed prolonged observation of the spectrum. Barber had attended a lecture in which the use of glycerol to slow down the tumbling motion of proteins in solution was discussed. This suggested to him that glycerol would be a useful solvent for FAB samples and the following day, FAB spectra of two simple tripeptides were obtained for the first time. For various reasons, partly concerned with possible patenting of the technique, commercial exploitation and the wish to obtain increasingly impressive spectra which would not immediately be bettered by others, full details of the technique were not made public for some time and details of sample preparation were not revealed to early visitors to the laboratory. In the first *Nature* paper (submitted in February 1981, appearing in the September issue) Barber and colleagues remained cryptic, e.g. in their choice of title, "Fast atom bombardment of solids as an ion source in mass spectrometry",[23] this title was also chosen for the paper which is typically used as the first FAB citation.[21] The description of the experiments stays vague: "We have, however, largely overcome this effect by judicious use of solvent and

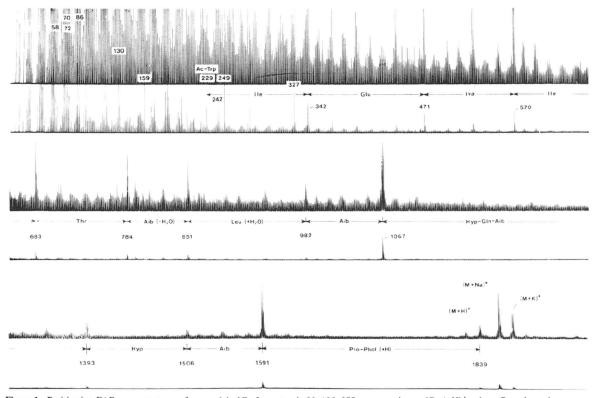

Figure 1. Positive ion FAB mass spectrum of zervamicin IC. Ions at m/z 93, 185, 277, etc., are due to $(G_n + H)^+$, where G = glycerol.

support systems, paying particular attention to the viscosity and volatility of the medium from which the sample is deposited on the stage".[23] The first explicit mention of glycerol can be found in a *Biochem. J.* paper submitted in late February 1981[24] and two months later by another group using the FAB technique—obviously the news on the key role of glycerol had become more widely known.[25]

After preliminary work at UMIST in the summer of 1980 during which a number of "difficult" samples had been run for Brian Green, a joint venture with Vacuum Generators began and a commercial version of the FAB gun was fitted to a ZAB mass spectrometer. During this period, Ken Reinhart visited the company and over a three-hour period, Andrew Tyler obtained the FAB spectra of thirteen peptide antibiotics which Reinhart counted and interpreted as fast as they were produced and these formed the basis of a publication later in 1981.[26] By then, the use of glycerol was generally known and the technique was finally launched in public at the ASMS meeting in Minneapolis earlier in the year by which time many laboratories were using the technique.

Figure 4. Positive fast atom bombardment mass spectrum of zervamicin—please note the discussion of the glyerol cluster ions in the figure caption. Reprinted with permission from Reference 26. Copyright (1981) American Chemical Society.

The development of FAB provides a good example of team work. Micky Barber was very good at producing ideas, many of which first appeared over lunch in a local hostelry, "The Swinging Sporran", when the group discussed the results of the morning's work and planned the work for the afternoon. He had absolutely no interest in any aspect of administration, however, and he was fortunate to have John Vickerman initially and Don Sedgwick later to deal with such mundane matters as raising financial support for the group. Much credit must also go to his co-workers, such as Bob Bordoli and Andrew Tyler, who put his ideas into practice and finally to Brian Green and his colleagues at Vacuum Generators for producing the first commercial version of a FAB source.

With the introduction of the liquid matrix—and not by the use of an atom gun which was nevertheless giving name to the technique—high primary atom beam currents could be used and strong signals from involatile and thermally labile compounds could be recorded over minutes or even tens of minutes enabling one to use scanning sector instruments and quadrupole mass analysers. Since FAB sources could be hooked up without major problems to existing EI/CI instruments, FAB sources became commercially available relatively rapidly and were widely adopted, resulting in numerous applications within a field which had not been previously accessible. In the following years, ion beams were also used to effect ion production and some improvements could be achieved by using heavier primary ions, such as Cs^+, and higher impact energies. As a result, the term "liquid" SIMS was introduced as a more suitable acronym. An intense discussion of the fundamental processes and on the role of the matrix started, again focussing on the role of thermal and non-thermal effects within the desorption ionisation process; however, it became soon clear that the major practical effect of the liquid matrix was to prevent the accumulation of radiation damage on the sample by the removal of the affected volume and a constant renewal of the exposed surface.

FAB became the major mass spectrometric tool for the analysis of bioorganic compounds for the next ten years—until ESI and MALDI took over—and biological mass spectrometry became a growing field in analytical mass spectrometry. Very early after its introduction—shortly after the report of the insulin detection by PDMS—a mass spectrum of insulin could also be obtained using FAB MS, and in 1984, isotopically resolved signals of insulin molecular ions were reported. FAB was not the first desorption ionisation technique to use a matrix but the *liquid* matrix defined the first real breakthrough. The beneficial role of a matrix was attributed to the isolation of the analyte reducing analyte–analyte interactions, the emission of larger pieces of material, the entrainment of analyte molecules and a cooling effect by evaporation of matrix molecules in addition to its having a role in the ionisation process.

LASER DESORPTION IONISATION AND MATRIX-ASSISTED LDI

The desorption ionisation technique completing the experimental approaches to generate ions from solid samples was laser desorption ionisation (LDI). The use of lasers to generate ions dates back to the time shortly after lasers were developed and became available in the 1960s. Several groups used lasers for the analysis of inorganic samples, but little attention was paid to organic samples until the mid-1970s. Most widely used were CO_2 lasers emitting at 10.6 μm in the infrared, either pulsed to about 150 ns or in continuous-wave operation mode. The wavelength of the lasers was not of great concern for a LDI experimental set-up, since the laser was primarily regarded as a tool to achieve very fast heating and the energy transfer was considered to occur typically via the metallic substrate. A pulsed CO_2 laser was used by Kistemaker and coworkers in Amsterdam, Netherlands, and they could successfully measure an underivatised glycoside (digitonin) as cationised species using a magnetic sector instrument equipped with a dedicated detection system.[27] Further investigations demonstrated that fast evaporation even of thermally labile compounds, such as sucrose, occurs, and a separate source of cations made it possible to induce and promote ionisation by cationisation in the gas phase.[28] However, direct laser desorption (ionisation) of the same compound and other non-volatiles had been shown earlier by Röllgen and his group in Bonn, Germany using a continuous-wave CO_2 laser, their conclusion was: "The above experiments also show that the phenomenon of laser induced desorption of quasimolecular ions cannot be explained by thermal heating of the sample alone".[29] Nevertheless, the use of a laser for desorption ionisation was essentially viewed from the standpoint of the fast heating approach. Scepticism would have been justified for this simplistic view, however, since the various experimental parameters used in laser desorption ionisation varied over a wide range. Depending on the type of laser wavelengths ranged from the ultraviolet to the far infrared, light emission was either pulsed (with a few ns for Q-switched Nd:YAG) or continuous and depending on the laser and focussing conditions used in the particular experiment the laser power generated at the sample surface (irradiance in $W\,cm^{-2}$) varied over many orders of magnitude.

A second development took place that once again was outside the (bio)organic mass spectrometric community. This was the development of the LAMMA (laser microprobe mass analyser) instruments which combined a laser, a UV-optical microscope for laser focussing and sample observation and—for the first time since the Bendix instrument of the 1960s—a TOF analyser. The LAMMA instruments were conceptualised by Franz Hillenkamp and Raimund Kaufmann at their universities in Frankfurt and Düsseldorf, Germany. They were constructed and commercialised by Leybold-Heraeus in Cologne, Germany, in two versions. The first was the LAMMA 500 in which the sample was a thin section of a biological tissue spread on an electron microscopic copper grid. The laser beam was focussed by the microscope optics outside the vacuum and perforated the sample directly located on the vacuum side of a microscope quartz plate which also served to seal the vacuum of the ion source. The goal of this instrument was to determine the local distribution of elements in biological samples at the resolution of an optical microscope of about 0.5 µm and under optical control of the experimentalist.[30,31] For that purpose a short-pulse high-power laser was used to ignite a plasma and to evaporate completely and atomise the sample. At first, a ruby laser emitting in the red at 694 nm was used, but later, this was replaced by a Q-switched Nd:YAG laser using the frequency tripled or quadrupled wavelength of 355 nm or 266 nm, respectively. The decision to move to the UV was on the one hand based on the better focussing of shorter wavelengths, but on the other hand promoted by the observation that the recorded mass spectra became more reproducible when switching to shorter wavelengths. This LAMMA concept was improved in a second version, the LAMMA 1000, in which the sample was irradiated from the front *in vacuo*. A part of the microscope focussing system had to be arranged in the vacuum system: the laser was focussed on to the

Figure 5. Picture of the
LAMMA 1000 Laser
Microprobe Mass Analyser
(Leybold Heraeus Köln,
Germany).

surface by the objective lens at an angle of about 30° at a working distance of about 10 mm, located on top of the ion extraction optics, which enabled one to analyse the surface of any solid with an optical resolution of about 2–3 µm.[32]

Prototypes of both systems were the equipment in Franz Hillenkamp's laboratory in the Institute of Biophysics at the Goethe University of Frankfurt, when I joined Franz Hillenkamp's group in January 1983 as a postdoctoral research assistant. The LAMMA instruments were designed and marketed for elemental/physical analysis of biological specimens and for surface analysis of bulk samples of any origin, but—like the other DI techniques—the observation of molecular ions had initiated discussions on the mechanisms of laser desorption ionisation and the possible use of pulsed UV-laser DI as tool for organic analysis.[33] In particular, the microscopic control of the sample spot irradiated by the laser turned out to be of extreme benefit for investigations of the UV-LDI processes and the role of the sample state and sample preparation in the near future. On the other hand, the instrumental concept to have the sample at ground potential and to focus on the detection of atomic ions limited the accessible ion energy to a few keV and posed severe limitations for the detection of higher-mass ions.

When I joined Franz Hillenkamp's group, my first task was to investigate the effect of the UV-laser wavelength on the generation of ions from amino acids and small peptides with the idea that the UV absorption should have some influence. The Nd:YAG laser of the LAMMA 1000 instrument offered two options, i.e. the use of the frequency-quadrupled laser at a wavelength of 266 nm—the normal wavelength used in the instrument—and the frequency-tripled laser output at 355 nm. For the amino acids investigated, this enabled one to differentiate between samples that absorbed to different extents at the laser wavelength of 266 nm and the lack of classical UV absorption for all samples at 355 nm. The important role of the sample absorption soon became clear. Samples were prepared by drying droplets of a sample solution on a metallic substrate. While highly reproducible LDI mass spectra of protonated molecule ion species and some specific fragment ions were obtained for tryptophane, tyrosine and phenyalanine, and dipeptides containing Trp or Tyr at 266 nm for laser pulses with adjusted laser energy, much higher laser irradiances were required for non-absorbing samples and much more at 355 nm. For non-absorbing samples and at 355 nm, it was much more difficult to find a good laser shot and it was sometimes easier to use thick samples thus excluding the influence of the metallic substrate.

The LDI mass spectra yielded intense fragment ions and molecule ions appeared also as cationised species. In all these experiments, single laser shot mass spectra were recorded, printed and interpreted, since computers to accumulate and average mass spectra were just becoming available but were not yet in common use at this time. When, however, attempts were made to produce mass spectra of, for example, vitamin B12 or larger peptides, even when they contained Trp or Tyr residues, all efforts failed. For vitamin B12 intense fragment ions due to the corrin dye system were detected. We concluded that despite the strong absorption of the dye, fragmentation is induced within the molecule without reaching the necessary energy per unit volume to induce a successful LDI, a situation also given for larger peptides with only one absorbing side chain. These considerations were based on the fundamental hypothesis that UV-LDI is a volume process induced by energy deposition of the laser light into the solid, either readily controlled by adjusting the laser energy if the sample shows a strong absorption at the wavelength or by non-linear processes if the sample is non-absorbing. Indirect excitation of the sample by using the metallic substrate as the absorber was even less reproducible and reliable. Only the first of these processes may result in the reproducible ablation of a small sample volume provided an adequate energy per unit volume is reached. Indeed small and smooth craters on a tryptophane sample were detected using electron microscopy.

As for the broader use of UV-LDI, these observations and their rationalisation were disappointing. Even the choice of the right wavelength for an analyte compound would not be sufficient, since even a high molar absorption coefficient would not automatically lead to a sufficiently high energy deposition per sample volume. At the same time, highly absorbing chromophore groups within a larger molecule would imply that there was the danger of intense photofragmentation. The search for a general solution of the problem drew on the vigorous discussion of the role of glycerol in FAB and of the fundamental processes implied by a matrix in desorption ionisation and resulted in the simple question arising: "What could be a suitable matrix for UV-LDI?". The answer was: "A small organic compound which strongly absorbs at the laser wavelength used and exhibits a soft ionisation." Within the group of amino acids the highly absorbing tryptophane should thus work as a matrix for a non-absorbing amino acid such as alanine. The experiment was a success and summarised in an *Analytical Chemistry* paper in 1985 also coining the new name: *'Matrix-Assisted' Laser Desorption.* The mass spectrum of a mixture of alanine (Ala) and Trp taken at Trp threshold irradiance is shown in Figure 6. A strong signal of the Ala quasi-molecular ion was observed in addition to that of Trp. It is important to note that its desorption took place at

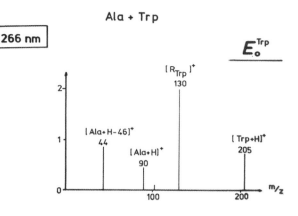

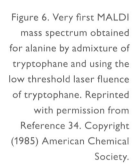

Figure 6. Very first MALDI mass spectrum obtained for alanine by admixture of tryptophane and using the low threshold laser fluence of tryptophane. Reprinted with permission from Reference 34. Copyright (1985) American Chemical Society.

an irradiance of about a tenth of that necessary for obtaining spectra of alanine alone". The final sentence of the paper was: "The data and the interpretation presented in this paper promise to be of considerable value for future practical applications of laser desorption mass spectrometry.... the use of a strongly absorbing matrix at a fixed laser wavelength offers a more controllable energy deposition and thus 'soft' ionisation and enhanced ion yield for organic samples independent of their individual absorption characteristics".[34] In the same year, the first mass spectra of small peptides were presented at the IMSC conference in Swansea. In the following two years our work concentrated on fundamental issues of the MALDI process, the finding of further usable matrices, i.e. nicotinic acid and non-volatile liquids also used in FAB, 3-nitrobenzyl alcohol (NOBA) and 2-nitrophenyl octyl ether (NPOE).[35] Moreover, we tried to define the limits with respect to the accessible mass range; the peptide melittin with a mass of 2845 Da was the largest compound which could be measured. In a 1987 paper, the current understanding was summarised including the idea of chemical ionisation processes via matrix photoionisation promoting analyte ionisation by proton transfer. Experiments were also carried out using a (non-absorbing) mixture of sucrose and CsI. It was speculated that the formation of preformed ionic clusters of $(CsI)_n Cs^+$ in the heterogenous sucrose/CsI mixture facilitated the detection of very large CsI clusters with masses up to m/z of 15,000. These experiments were also undertaken to test the principal ability of the LAMMA system for the detection of larger ions, since until then ions with masses exceeding m/z of 3000 had not been detected. A major limitation was the low ion energy of 3 keV used which was also the energy with which the ions were impinging on the first dynode of the secondary electron multiplier or the front of the double channel plate detector. This energy is too low for large singly charged ions to induce efficient conversion into the first electron(s) to be multiplied in the SEM cascade. In addition, the limited performance of our TOF system with respect to mass resolution—even though it had been improved in the meantime by the implementation of a home-built two-stage Mamyrin reflector—and the inferiority of the acquired data in comparison to the numerous FAB spectra appearing in the literature obscured the perspective for the future of MALDI in bioanalytical mass spectrometry.

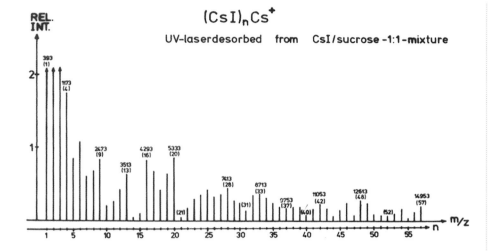

Figure 7. First high mass ions (CsI cluster ions) detected on a LAMMA 1000 instrument from CsI mixed with sucrose. Reprinted from Reference 35, Copyright (1987), with permission from Elsevier.

In 1987, the IFOS (Ion Formation from Organic Solids) IV meeting was held in Münster, bringing together a small group of scientists from Europe and the USA involved and interested in the elucidation of fundamental processes occurring in desorption ionisation and the development of DI techniques for future applications. Franz Hillenkamp's group had just moved to Münster and we had reinstalled the laboratory in the Institute of Medical Physics and Biophysics at the University of Münster after a long renovation phase; Dr Ute Bahr and Dr Bernhard Spengler were the further members of the group at the restart. At this meeting, rumours were afloat that a Japanese group had succeeded in producing protein ions by LDI and had presented data at a Chinese–Japanese meeting, which later turned out to be the work of Koichi Tanaka at Shimadzu finally published in *Rapid Communications in Mass Spectrometry*.[36] Even though we did not know any details, it was enough to boost our efforts. The first step was to raise the potential at the front of the channel plate, i.e. to redesign the detector system with a capacitor to decouple the collector signal from a high electric potential. The LAMMA system was equipped with high-voltage BNC connectors which were specified for use up to 6 kV. We tested the voltage stability towards arcing and found that 9 kV was still safe in the connected state. Thus we could lift the front end of the channel plate up to 9 kV, so that the total ion energy impinging on the detector surface was also raised to 9 keV. Using nicotinic acid as a matrix and insulin and small proteins as test analytes we were immediately successful. Even though single shot signals just yielded a slight elevation of the base line or just the observation of an elevated noise level in the molecule ion mass region, the computer-based data acquisition now available made possible the accumulation of numerous single laser shot mass spectra, resulting in the first MALDI mass spectra of small proteins with masses exceeding 10 kDa.[37]

The following months were filled with considerable efforts to extend the mass range—we were also in competition with PDMS and ESI and under distinct time pressure, since we had announced an oral presentation for the IMSC Bordeaux meeting at the end of August in 1988. In late 1988 we were able to implement a new post-acceleration detector in the

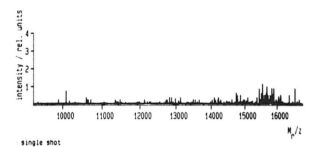

Figure 8. One of the very first protein MALDI mass spectra, top: single laser shot, down: 20 laser shots summed up.

LAMMA 1000 which was the first result of a cooperation started with Finnigan MAT in Bremen and Dr U. Giessmann. This detector comprised an EMI secondary electron multiplier with one extra front dynode lifted to a post-acceleration potential of 20 kV (−20 kV for positive ions). Secondary electrons and secondary ions were accelerated to the SEM yielding an impressive improvement in ion detection efficiency, single laser shots yielded readily-detectable protein signals and accumulation or averaging was only needed to improve the signal's S/N ratio. With this detector, emphasis could be shifted to the optimisation of sample preparation and the search for new matrix compounds. Even though it sacrificed mass resolution by introducing flight path differences due to the use of Venetian blind geometry and introduced additional time spreads of the ion signal by the parallel use of secondary electrons and ions, it was a great improvement in enabling us to elucidate the capabilities of MALDI for protein analysis. The detector made it possible within the limitations of the LAMMA instrument to shift the borders to above 100 kDa. The first example of a protein above 100 kDa was β-D-Galactosidase yielding a very broad but high-intensity molecule ion signal. This made it possible that the first transparency in my oral presentation at the Bordeaux meeting was a replacement of the announced title of "MALDI above 10,000 Da" by "MALDI above 100,000 Da".

Clearly, the ability to generate mass spectra of large proteins was the major issue which attracted the attention of the analytical community and was the driving force of the early

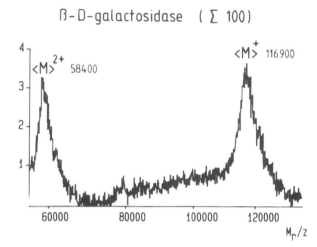

ß-D-galactosidase (∑ 100)

Figure 9. First MALDI mass spectrum of a protein above 100 kDa using 266 nm and nicotinic acid as matrix accumulated from 100 laser shots.

days of MALDI (and ESI), even though the analytical usefulness of delivering a protein mass with an undefined accuracy from broad ion signals was questionable. Whereas ESI—because of the multiple charging of the analytes—could straightforwardly be coupled to existing mass analysers and soon stood to benefit from advanced instruments making it possible to carry out accurate mass analysis and MS/MS experiments, the evolution of MALDI MS suffered from the lack of specific expertise for time-of-flight analysers within the major manufacturers of MS instruments. ESI-MS was further pushed forward, since it became immediately obvious that ESI is the ideal ionisation method to couple HPLC to mass spectrometry, a technological development which defined another major goal of mass spectrometric development which had not yet been achieved. MALDI, moreover, suffered at least until the end of the 1980s from its need for specialised electronic equipment, i.e. fast A/D converters or transient recorders/digital oscilloscope, respectively, which were able to record the single-shot MALDI mass spectra with sufficient time resolution and storage length. The Gould Biomation transient recorder used in the LAMMA systems operated

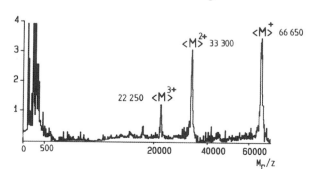

bovine serum albumin (single shot)

Figure 10. Single laser shot MALDI mass spectrum of bovine serum albumin after installation of a post-acceleration detector.

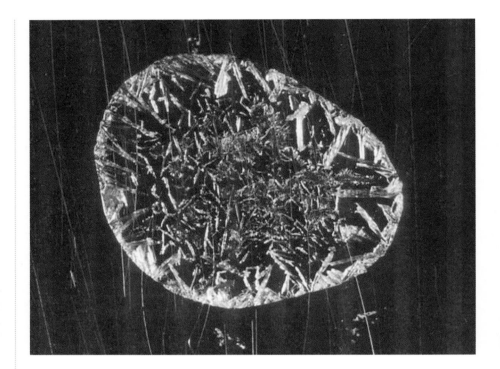

Figure 11. The matrix–
analyte crystals formed
after drying for a
2,5-dihydroxybenzoic acid
matrix.

at only 100 MHz, i.e. a maximum time resolution of 10 ns, and only 2048 channels, which
gave a small time and mass range to be recorded at high time resolution—and nevertheless
was a major cost factor for a TOF system. Around 1990, progress in the electronic industry
made accessible a new generation of digital oscilloscopes with constantly improving time
resolution and performance still at a high, but affordable price. Today these stand-alone
instruments are replaced by computer modules integrating both data acquisition and data
accumulation and allowing for fast data transfer from the transient recorder module to the
data evaluation software. Modern PC-board transient recorders now have a time resolution of down to 0.25 ns (4 GHz sampling rate) and up to 16 M points per channel storage
memory. The next critical issue was the laser. Clearly, an advanced MALDI mass spectrometer should integrate the laser into a fully computer-controlled system and should not
demand any expertise in laser physics from the user. The first step into this direction was
the use of nitrogen lasers replacing the Nd:YAG lasers, at the same time the costs for the
laser dropped considerably—since an adequate small nitrogen laser was on the market.

With respect to MALDI-TOF instruments, there was only a slow growth. The Rockefeller
mass spectrometry group of Brian Chait and Ron Beavis decided to build their MALDI
instrument using a linear TOF system with a high acceleration potential of up to 30 kV.
They could soon reproduce the Münster results and started their own investigations into
new superior matrix compounds, also at higher wavelengths. They used a tripled Nd:YAG
laser at 355 nm and introduced cinnamic acid derivatives, such as sinapinic acid and later

α-cyano-4-hydroxycinnamic acid.[38,39] Both matrices are still widely used today and the latter is still a standard matrix for peptide MS and MS/MS analyses in proteomics applications. At the same time the LAMMA 1000 system in Münster was equipped with a N_2 laser, 2,5-dihy-droxybenzoic acid was found to be superior matrix at 337 nm, again a matrix compound still widely used today, e.g. for large proteins, oligosaccharides or phosphopeptides.[40] It is striking that nearly all of the matrix compounds used today were discovered in the early days of MALDI; only recently, after more than 15 years of controversial discussion of the funda-mental MALDI processes was a rational approach developed by the author's group which allowed us to predict a superior matrix, namely 4-chloro-α-cyano cinnamic acid.[41] With respect to the acceptance of MALDI as an analytical tool, an important contribution of the Rockefeller group was to show that the level of 100 ppm accuracy is obtainable when using MALDI and TOF mass analysers in protein analyses,[42] thus the acceptance for MALDI in the mass spectrometric community which had quickly adopted ESI was considerably raised. The cooperation and sporting competition between the Münster and the Rockefeller group was reflected in the first MALDI review paper appearing in the A pages of *Anal. Chem.* in 1991.[44]

The Rockefeller high-voltage linear TOF instrument served as the prototype for the first commercially available MALDI instrument which was manufactured by Marvin Vestal's com-pany, Vestec, in Texas, USA. Within Finnigan MAT, two instrumental developments were running in parallel, the first of which was the conception and production of a low-accelera-tion voltage reflectron system in cooperation between the Münster group and the Finnigan MAT division in Bremen—the Vision 2000 which was presented at the manufacturer's exhibition at the IMSC meeting in Amsterdam in 1991. At the same time, the English Finni-gan MAT division had brought to market a benchtop small linear system—the Lasermat—using a concept based on the Biolon PDMS system, i.e. a small protein-mass-determination instrument. Further small benchtop MALDI TOF systems were commercialised by Kratos/Shimadzu, but as time passed, the concept of benchtop dedicated protein-mass-determina-tion instruments did not prove to be sustainable. Despite the big impression made by the measurement of large proteins by mass spectroemtry, the whole field, which in the middle of the 1990s was given additional momentum by the start and rapid establishment of prot-eomics, moved back from protein to peptide analysis for which all the benefits and tools of mass spectrometry, such as accurate mass determination for the monoisotopic signals and MS/MS techniques, could be applied.

For MALDI two important contributions formed the base for its survival in competition with ESI and for its growth into a high-throughput bioanalytical tool. This was first the introduction of delayed-extraction or time-lag focussing for MALDI and its implementation into the existing TOF technology, which raised the performance of today's MALDI TOF systems to an unforeseen level.[44–46] It is one of the few cases for which the implementation of a one-step technical tool converts a limitation into a virtue. Due to the MALDI ablation process and the dense material cloud formed and expanding in the first few nanoseconds, the major prerequisite for a high-quality TOF mass analysis, i.e. the best possible defini-tion of starting point and ion energy after acceleration, is no longer met. Ions leaving the MALDI plume have a broad initial velocity and directional distribution, which—aggravated by collisions upon their acceleration in the applied electric field—results in energy and time spreads making it impossible even by the use of a reflectron system to exceed a mass resolution of a few thousand. Moreover, a good mass resolution can only be obtained close to the threshold fluence, i.e. with a limited number of ions. By introducing a delay between the laser pulse and the ion extraction, the ion cloud expands into the vacuum above the sample and dilutes. Ions are distributed in space according to their initial velocity, so that when the acceleration field is switched on after a delay of typically a few hundred ns, those ions having the highest initial velocity gain less kinetic energy from the electric field. These ions will still leave the ion source first, but with a lower total ion energy and will thus be caught up by the ions which were originally slower. This is only completely possible for two ions, but practically modern delayed-extraction sources create a well-defined time (for one m/z value) and spatial focus outside the ion source, for which the detrimental initial properties of the ions are essentially transferred into an ion energy spread. In a linear DE system voltages and delay times have to be adjusted to shift this focus to the detector, in a reflectron system this focus is adjusted to be close to the ion source. The electrostatic mirror or reflectron is then able to achieve a time focus for ions of even a considerable energy spread at the detector surface. All advanced MALDI TOF systems use this technique—together with a high-acceleration energy—and routinely reach mass resolutions above 10,000 and higher. Although the time and space focussing of the ions is necessarily not perfect, it became clear within the evolution of MALDI-TOF instruments that this was not the limitation for the mass resolution achievable. When the channel plates serving as SEM detectors were replaced by the next generation channel plates having a smaller channel diameter the TOF resolution grew considerably. The steps were from originally 25 μm to 12 μm and to 6 μm, and instantly the mass resolution doubled, proving that the spread in time-of-flight path length induced by the different penetration depths into the tilted channels before ions hit the walls was the major reason for the limitation in mass resolution.

Nevertheless, a second development was needed to maintain the interest of the mass spectrometric community in MALDI as an ionisation technique. This is the ability to carry out MS/MS analyses and obtain structural information on selected ions. The prerequisites for this were created by Raimund Kaufmann and Bernhard Spengler at the University of Düsseldorf, Germany, by the detection of a substantial metastable decay of ions generated by MALDI.[47] This was first done on protein ions in a retarding field linear TOF MS and this also explained the deterioration of signal quality with increasing mass or in reflectron instruments. They termed the fragmentation process "post-source decay PSD" and then proposed a technical solution to generate fragment-ion mass spectra in a reflectron system by stepping down the reflectron voltages.[48] Thereby, an MS/MS spectrum is generated in about 10 energy steps or mass windows, for each window the reflectron is able to compensate for the energy spread. These MS/MS spectral pieces are stitched together by the computer software. This is not a very convenient way to generate a MS/MS mass spectrum and takes time and a large amount of laser shots. This technique has been replaced in both commercially-available TOF/TOF instruments (Applied Biosystems and Bruker) by combining two TOF systems, in which a delayed-extraction low-acceleration-energy first TOF is used to select precursor ions by fast switching of an ion gate and to provide time for an efficient metastable decay. The (metastable) fragment ions from a selected precursor ion are then lifted to a high electrical potential and further accelerated into the analytical TOF analyser using the DE technique, thereby enabling a one-step analysis of all fragment ions to be obtained, since their energy spread is considerably reduced and hence can now be compensated. Modern advanced MALDI TOF systems are constructed in this way but they can also be used as "simple" TOF MS instruments. For the construction and marketing of these instruments and their major use in proteomic studies the aspect of the speed of analysis and high-throughput became important so that, as a result, these instruments are now equipped with modern diode-pumped solid-state (Nd:YAG) lasers emitting at 355 nm at constantly increasing frequency up to 2000 Hz. This still leaves a flight time through the system of 500 μs which is far more than is needed to finalise a single-shot MALDI spectrum even in the high mass range and still gives room for further enhancement of speed of analysis. MALDI TOF/TOF instruments form the majority of the MALDI machines manufactured and in use today, supplemented by two alternative approaches. The first is produced and marketed by Shimadzu which is a hybrid MS/MS system combining a quadrupole ion trap and a reflectron TOF system, the second is the MALDI orbitrap by Thermo which delivers the high-mass-accuracy of an orbitrap system, however, at the expense of a limited mass range.

NANO-ELECTROSPRAY-IONISATION

While the above discussion dealt exclusively with the "sudden energy" desorption ionisation techniques, European contributions have also had a strong impact in the field of electrospray ionisation. This may be traced back to the very beginning, when almost simultaneously with Fenn's group, Russian scientists worked and reported on the use of what they called "extraction of dissolved ions under atmospheric pressure (EDIAP)" in a sector instrument. This was nothing but electrospray ionisation—for further information please refer to *Rapid Commun. Mass Spectrom.* **22,** Editorial and 267–270 (2008)—however, it was only reported in Russian in a Russian journal and so was largely overlooked in the West. When moving back to the early days of ESI, the set-up generally used comprised a metal capillary and a syringe pump with a pumping rate of a few μL min⁻¹. Under optimised experimental conditions (voltage and solvent) this allowed the experimenter to produce a stable and visible electrospray mist. From this two major developments moved in opposite directions. The first was to make it possible to electrospray at a considerably larger flow rate driven by the goal to use ESI as the coupling device between MS and HPLC which at that time used flow rates of mL min⁻¹. A number of successful efforts were made to facilitate a stable and robust electrospray at high flow rates; depending of the manufacturers, different brand names were used, but the key issue always was to get rid of the majority of the ESI mist comprising droplets that are too large. Usually, the first step was to arrange for the jet not to hit the entrance orifice of the mass spectrometer by introducing an angle between the ESI needle and the MS axis. The second development was addressing the topic of sensitivity. Even though the sensitivity in ESI experiments was impressive when compared to the pre-ESI (and-MALDI) world, the numbers given were, however, usually based on a calculation of the consumed liquid while accumulating a mass spectrum and not on the total sample volume loaded to the syringe pump. When looking at the electrospray the first loss of sample was immediately obvious, i.e. only a small part of the ESI mist, or droplets, is able to pass through the first orifice of the atmospheric-pressure-vacuum differential pumping interface which is necessarily very small. Efforts to miniaturise the set-up by using smaller capillaries formed the straightforward approach, but the introduction of nano-electrospray ionisation added a new dimension. Matthias Wilm joined Matthias Mann's group at the EMBL in Heidelberg, Germany, as a PhD student with the idea to abandon completely the forced-flow concept based on a theoretical model for a more efficient dispersion of the liquid.[49] Instead of an open metal capillary which—however small the diameter—always needs a considerable wall thickness to be mechanically stable and therefore results in a large emitting front surface, they used pulled glass capillaries with tiny openings in the 1 μm range. These glass (or quartz) capillaries were covered with thin layers of sputtered gold to make them electrically conductive to apply the spray voltage. When raising the voltage the electrospray process occurred at much lower voltages and the flow of liquid was maintained by the electrospray itself. The practical aspect immediately apparent was the dramatic increase in sensitivity, now at typical flow rates of a few tens of nL, a few μL of solution suffice to carry out elaborate MS and MS/MS experiments. When using the Finnigan (Thermo) transfer-capillary AP-vacuum interface, the tip could be positioned inside the capillary orifice thereby permitting 100% of the nanospray to be transmitted to the mass spectrometer. Moreover, nanospray is much more stable than conventional ESI and, for example, also affords the stable spray of aqueous solutions. In an effort to demonstrate the practical advantages of nanospray, my group showed that solutions containing high concentrations of salt can be stably electrosprayed.[50] Moreover, we could show that when reducing the capillary opening to less than 2 μm the visible spray mist vanished and the ESI mass spectra change qualitatively:[51] for a test solution containing a peptide, a sugar and a cationic detergent typical suppression effects promoting the detection of surface active components vanish at flow rates below 20 nL min^{-1} and all analytes show up. This agrees well with the picture of initial droplets of decreasing size which are fully accessible to the ESI droplet fission and desolvation process. Even though nanoESI is the method of choice for measuring individual samples, most of today's applications in biochemical/biomedical or proteomics research are carried out using nanoHPLC at typical flow rates of a few 100 nL min^{-1} and thus outside the "true" nanoESI scheme. The TriVersa NanoMate® by Advion which is a commercially available system for automated (off-line) ESI measurements of multiple samples appears to have maintained some of the beneficial properties of "true" nanoESI by the construction of the nozzles in their ESI chip.

REFERENCES

1. H.D. Beckey, "Field desorption mass spectometry: A technique for the study of thermally unstabie substances of low volatility", *J. Mass Spectrom. Ion Phys.* **2,** 500–503 (1969).

2. E.W. Müller, "Field desorption", *Phys. Rev.* **102,** 618–624 (1956).

3. J.F. Holland, B. Soltmann and C.C. Sweeley, "A model for ionization mechanisms in field desorption mass spectrometry", *Biomed. Mass Spectrom.* **3,** 340–345 (1976).

4. H.D. Beckey and F.W. Röllgen, "Field desorption 'without fields'", *Org. Mass Spectrom.* **14,** 188–190 (1979).

5. S.S. Wong, U. Giessmann, M. Karas and F.W. Röggen, "Field desorption of sucrose studies by combined optical microscopy and mass spectrometry", *Int. J. Mass Spectrom. Ion Proc.* **56,** 139–150 (1984).

6. H.R. Schulten, U. Bahr and P.B. Monkhouse, "Biochemical applications of field desorption mass spectrometry", *J. Biochem. Biophys. Meth.* **8,** 239–269 (1983).

7. K. Rollins, J.H. Scrivens and M.J. Taylor, "The characterization of polystyrene oligomers by field-desorption mass spectrometry", *Rapid Comm. Mass Spectrom.* **4,** 355 (1990).

8. H.R. Schulten and R.P. Lattimer, "Application of mass spectrometry to polymers", *Mass Spec. Rev.* **3,** 231–315 (1984).

9. J.H. Scrivens and A.T. Jackson, "Characterisation of synthetic polymer systems", *Int. J. Mass Spectrom.* **200,** 261–276 (2000).

10. R. Beuhler, E. Flanigan, L.J. Greene and L. Friedman, "Proton transfer mass spectrometry of peptides. A rapid heating technique for underivatized peptides containing arginine", *J. Am. Chem. Soc.* **96,** 3990–3999 (1974).

11. R. Reed and W.K. Reid, *J. Chem. Soc.* 5933 (1963).

12. A. Benninghoven, "Analysis of submonolayers on silver by negative secondary ion emission", *Phys. Stat. Sol.* **34,** K169 (1969).

13. A. Benninghoven and W. Sichtermnann, "Secondary ion mass spectrometry: A new analytical technique for biologically important compounds", *Org. Mass Spectrom.* **12,** 595–597 (1977).

14. B.T. Chait and K.G. Standing, "A time-of-flight mass spectrometer for measurement of secondary ion mass spectra", *Int. J. Mass Spectrom. Ion Phys.* **40,** 185–193 (1981).

15. A. Benninghoven, "Some aspects of secondary ion mass spectrometry of organic compounds", *Int. J. Mass Spectrom. Ion Phys.* **53,** 85–89 (1983).

16. D.F. Torgerson, R.P. Skowronski and R.D. Macfarlane, "A new approach to the mass spectrometry of non-volatile compounds", *Biochem. Biophys. Res. Commun.* **60,** 616–621 (1974).

17. B. Sundqvist and R.D. Macfarlane, "^{252}Cf-Plasma desorption mass spectrometry", *Mass Spectrom Rev.* **4,** 421–460 (1985).

18. J. Bergquist, P. Hakannson, B. Sundqvist and R. Zubarev, "Mass spectrometry of proteins—Uppsala perspectives on past and present", *Int. J. Mass Spectrom.* **268,** 73–82 (2007).

19. P. Hakansson, I. Kamensky, B. Sundqvist, J. Fohlmann, P. Peterson, C.J. McNeal and R.D. Macfarlane, "Iodine-127-plasma desorption mass spectrometry of insulin", *J. Am. Chem. Soc.* **104,** 2948–2949 (1982).

20. P. Roepstorff, "Plasma desorption mass spectrometry of peptides and proteins", *Acc. Chem. Res.* **22,** 421–427 (1989).

21. M. Barber, R.S. Bordoli, R.D. Sedgwick and A.N. Tyler, "Fast atom bombardment of solids (F.A.B.): A new ion source for mass spectrometry", *J.C.S. Chem. Commun.* 325–327 (1981).

22. D.J. Surman and J.C. Vickerman, "Fast atom bombardment quadrupole mass spectrometry", *J.C.S. Chem. Commun.* 325–327 (1981).

23. M. Barber, R.S. Bordoli, R.D. Sedgwick and A.N. Tyler, "Fast atom bombardment of solids as an ion source in mass spectrometry", *Nature* **293,** 270–275 (1981).

24. M. Barber, R.S. Bordoli, G.V. Garner, D.B. Gordon, R.D. Sedgwick, L.W. Tetler and A.N. Tyler, "Fast-atom-bombardment mass spectra of enkephalins", *Biochem. J.* **197,** 401–404 (1981).

25. D.H. Williams, C. Bradley, G. Bojesen, S. Santikarn and L.C.E. Taylor, "Fast atom bombardment; a powerful technique for the study of polar molecules", *J. Am. Chem. Soc.* **103,** 5700–5704 (1981).

26. K.L. Rinehart Jr, L.A. Gaudioso, M.L. Moore, R.C. Pandey, J.C. Cook Jr, M. Barber, R.D. Sedgwick, R.S. Bordoli, A.N. Tyler and B.N. Green, "Structures of eleven zervamicin and two emerimicin peptide antibiotics studied by fast atom bombardment mass spectrometry", *J. Am. Chem. Soc.* **103,** 6517–6520 (1981).

27. M.A. Posthumus, P.G. Kistemaker, H.L.C. Meuzelaar and M.C. Ten Noever de Brauw, "Laser desorption-mass spectrometry of polar nonvolatile bio-organic molecules", *Anal. Chem.* **50,** 985–991 (1978).

28. G.J.Q. van der Peyl, K. Isa, J. Haverkamp and P.G. Kistemaker, "Gas phase ion/molecule reactions in laser desorption mass spectrometry", *Org. Mass Spectrom.* **16,** 416–420 (1981).

29. R. Stoll and F.W. Röllgen, "Laser desorption mass spectrometry of thermally labile compounds using a continous wave CO_2 laser", *Org. Mass Spectrom.* **14,** 642–645 (1979).

30. F. Hillenkamp, E. Unsöld, R. Kaufmann and R. Nitsche, "A high-sensitivity laser microprobe mass analyzer", *Appl. Phys.* **8,** 341–348 (1975).

31. H. Vogt, H.J. Heinen, S. Meier and R. Wechsung, "LAMMA 500 principle and technical description of the instrument", *Fres. Z. Anal. Chem.* **308,** 195–200 (1981).

32. P. Feigl, B. Schueler and F. Hillenkamp, "LAMMA 1000, a new instrument for bulk microprobe mass analysis by pulsed laser irradiation", *Int. J. Mass Spectrom. Ion Phys.* **47,** 15–18 (1983).

33. H.J. Heinen, "On ion formation in laser desorption mass spectrometry with LAMMA", *Int. J. Mass Spectrom. Ion Phys.* **38,** 309–321 (1981).

34. M. Karas, D. Bachmann and F. Hillenkamp, "The influence of the wavelength in high irradiance ultraviolet laser desorption mass spectrometry of organic molecules", *Anal. Chem.* **57,** 2935-2939 (1985).

35. M. Karas, D. Bachmann, U. Bahr and F. Hillenkamp, "Matrix-assisted ultraviolet laser desorption of non-volatile compounds", *Int. J. Mass Spectrom. Ion Proc.* **78,** 53-68 (1987).

36. K. Tanaka, H. Waki, Y. Ido, S. Akita, Y. Yoshida and T. Yoshida, "Protein and polymer analyses up to *m/z* 100 000 by laser ionization time-of-flight mass spectrometry", *Rapid Commun. Mass Spectrom.* **2,** 151–153 (1988).

37. M. Karas and F. Hillenkamp, "Laser desorption ionization of proteins with molecular masses exceeding 10000 dalton", *Anal. Chem.* **60,** 2299-2301 (1988).

38. R.C. Beavis and B.T. Chait, "Cinnamic acid derivatives as matrices for ultraviolet laser desorption mass spectrometry of proteins", *Rapid Commun. Mass Spectrom.* **3,** 233–237 (1989).

39. R.C. Beavis, T. Chaudhary and B.T. Chait, "α-Cyano-4hydroxycinnamic acid as a matrix for matrix-assisted laser desorption mass-spectrometry", *Org. Mass Spectrom.* **27,** 156–158 (1992).

40. K. Strupat, M. Karas and F. Hillenkamp, "2,5 Dihydroxybenzoic acid: A new matrix for laser desorption/ionization mass spectrometry", *Int. J. Mass Spectrom. Ion Proc.* **111,** 89–102 (1991).

41. T.W. Jaskolla, W.D. Lehmann and M. Karas, "4-Chloro-α-cyanocinnamic acid is an advanced, rationally designed MALDI matrix", *Proc. Natl. Acad. Sci. USA* **105,** 12,200–12,205 (2008).

42. R.C. Beavis and B.T. Chait, "High-accuracy molecular mass determination of proteins using matrix-assisted laser desorption mass spectrometry", *Anal. Chem.* **62,** 1836–1840 (1990).

43. F. Hillenkamp, M. Karas, R.C. Beavis and B.T. Chait, "Matrix-assisted laser desorption/ionization mass spectrometry of biopolymers", *Anal. Chem.* **63,** 1193A–1203A (1991).

44. R.S. Brown and J.J. Lennon, "Mass resolution improvement by incorporation of pulsed ion extraction in a matrix-assisted laser desorption/ionization linear time-of-flight mass spectrometer", *Anal. Chem.* **67,** 1998–2003 (1995).

45. M.L. Vestal, P. Juhasz and S.A. Martin, "Delayed extraction matrix-assisted laser desorption time-of-flight mass spectrometry", *Rapid Commun. Mass Spectrom.* **9,** 1044–1050 (1995).

46. M.L. Vestal, "Modern MALDI time-of-flight mass spectrometry", *J. Mass Spectrom.* **44,** 303–317 (2009).

47. B. Spengler, D. Kirsch and R. Kaufmann, "Fundamental aspects of postsource decay in matrix-assisted laser desorption mass spectrometry. 1. Residual gas effects", *J. Phys. Chem.* **96,** 9678–9684 (1992).

48. B. Spengler, "Post-source decay analysis in matrix-assisted laser desorption/ionization mass spectrometry of biomolecules", *J. Mass Spectrom.* **32,** 1019–1036 (1997).

49. M.S. Wilm and M. Mann, "Electrospray and Taylor-Cone theory, Dole's beam of macromolecules at last?", *Int. J. Mass Spectrom. Ion Proc.* **136,** 167–180 (1994).

50. R. Juraschek, T. Dülcks and M. Karas, "Nanoelectrospray—more than just a minimized-flow electrospray ionization source", *J. Am. Soc. Mass Spectrom.* **10,** 300–308 (1999).

51. A. Schmidt, T. Dülcks and M. Karas, "Effect of different solution flow rates on analyte ion signals in nano-ESI MS, or: when does ESI turn into nano-ESI?", *J. Am. Soc. Mass Spectrom.* **14,** 492–500 (2003).

Mass spectrometry
in Manchester

Bob Bateman

Waters Corporation, Manchester, UK

MANCHESTER'S INDUSTRIAL HISTORY

Much of Manchester's history is concerned with the cotton industry and textile manufacturing during the time of the Industrial Revolution. At this time the great majority of cotton spinning took place in Manchester and surrounding towns, and Manchester was for a time the world's most productive centre of cotton processing, and later the world's largest marketplace for cotton goods.

Manchester's damp climate is well suited to cotton processing, and its damp climate and geographical terrain provides an abundance of water power. Mechanisation of the cotton industry began with inventors such as Richard Arkwright (1732–1792) who built Manchester's first cotton mill. His "water frame" (1769) was the first powered means of producing cotton yarn in abundance. Ten years later Samuel Crompton (1753–1827) produced the "spinning mule" which allowed the mechanical production of many types of yarn. Manchester began expanding at a remarkable rate. The number of cotton mills in and around Manchester continued to grow throughout the first half of the 19th century, during which time Lancashire cotton accounted for a half of all British exports.

The latter half of the 19th century saw the rise of the city as the region's financial centre. Manchester continued to process cotton, and by the start of World War I two-thirds of the world's cotton was processed in the area. Engineering firms in Manchester initially made machines for the cotton trade before diversifying into general manufacture. Similarly, the chemical industry in the area started by producing bleaches and dyes for the textile industry before expanding into other areas.

In 1833 Joseph Whitworth (1803–1887), born in Stockport, Manchester, set up as a manufacturer of machine tools, serving the cotton industry and mechanical engineering in general. He developed measuring equipment, including a screw gauge capable of measuring to one ten-thousandth of an inch. But perhaps Whitworth's greatest contribution to mechanical engineering was the standardisation of screw threads throughout the industry. At this time different workshops worked to different thread specifications. Gathering in screws from as many workshops as possible, Whitworth devised a standard for screw threads with a fixed thread angle of 55° and having a standard pitch for a given diameter. This soon became the first nationally standardised system, the "British Standard Whitworth", and was the standard in British engineering until 1948. Whitworth Street in Manchester is so named in tribute to his contribution to mechanical engineering.

Similarly, John Dalton Street in Manchester is named in tribute to John Dalton (1766–1844), an English philosopher and schoolteacher who lived and worked in Manchester. Dalton is best known for his pioneering work on the development of modern atomic theory. He shaped the vague ideas about chemical combination into a precise science of atoms and molecules and, in 1803, he presented these ideas before the Manchester Literary and Philosophical Society in a paper entitled "On the Absorption of Gases by Water and other Liquids". This was published in 1805, to which he appended a table of the relative weights of the elementary particles. In 1808, in his book *A New System of Chemical Philosophy*, he

Opposite: Shipping note for the first MS1, serial number 1.

concluded that the elementary particles, or atoms, of one element are all alike in weight and are different from atoms of another element, and he set out rules that when atoms combine they do so in simple and constant ratios.

Dalton, and his gifted pupil James Prescott Joule (1818–1889), a physicist who established the mechanical theory of heat and discovered the first law of thermodynamics, were both Manchester scientists of international repute. Others with close links to Manchester were to follow.

Sir Joseph John Thomson, better known as J.J. Thomson (1846–1940), was born in Cheetham Hill, Manchester. In 1870 he studied engineering at Owens College, forerunner to the University of Manchester, and in 1884 he became Professor of Physics at the Cavendish Laboratory, Cambridge, where he carried out his famous experiments leading to the discovery of the electron and of isotopes. In 1906 he was awarded the Nobel Prize in Physics for the discovery of the electron.

Ernest Rutherford (1871–1937), born in New Zealand, studied at McGill University in Canada where his work on radioactive decay led to his Nobel Prize in Chemistry in 1908. In 1907 he was appointed to the chair of Physics at Manchester University where, with his students Hans Geiger (1882–1945) and Ernest Marsden (1889–1970), he demonstrated the nuclear nature of atoms and formulated the Rutherford model of the atom consisting of a very small positively charged nucleus orbited by electrons. In 1919 he succeeded J.J. Thomson as Director of Research at the Cavendish Laboratory in Cambridge where, with his students John Cockcroft (1897–1967) and Ernest Walton (1903–1995), he carried out the first experiment to "split the atom" in a controlled manner using a particle accelerator.

James Chadwick (1891–1974) was born in Bollington, Cheshire, a few miles from Manchester. At Manchester University he carried out research into radioactivity under Ernest Rutherford. He subsequently joined Rutherford at the Cavendish Laboratory in Cambridge where, in 1923, he became Assistant Director of Research. Here he carried out experiments that led to his discovery of the neutron in 1932 and for which he was awarded the Nobel Prize for Physics. In 1935 he was appointed to the Chair of Physics at Liverpool University where he was to play an important role in the events leading to the establishment of a commercial mass spectrometry business in Manchester.

As a major trading centre, Manchester's location some 35 miles inland from the Irish Sea is far from ideal and much effort was expended in establishing an effective transport and distribution infrastructure. The Rivers Mersey and Irwell only provided navigation for small boats, and during dry spells there was not always sufficient draft for a fully laden boat. With the onset of the Industrial Revolution and the growing use of steam power there was a rapid increase in demand for coal. The Duke of Bridgewater's mines in Worsley, Manchester, were among those that supplied the surrounding districts with coal. The Duke's solution to the transportation problems was to build a canal, the "Bridgewater" Canal, generally recognised to be the first "true" canal, from Worsley to Manchester. The canal, the first stage of which is underground, headed south from Worsley to cross the River Irwell over the Barton Aqueduct before turning east into Manchester. The canal opened in 1761 and led to a rapid fall in the price of coal in Manchester. The canal was extended in 1776 from Manchester to the River Mersey estuary at Runcorn, providing a solution to the problem of transporting cotton and textile products from and to the Port of Liverpool.

By the start of 19th century huge tonnages of textile raw material were imported through Liverpool and carried to the textile mills near Manchester, most of which was transported via the Bridgewater Canal. It was felt the canal company was making excessive profits and throttling the growth of Manchester. In 1830 the world's first intercity passenger railway, in which trains were timetabled and hauled by steam locomotives, was opened between Liverpool and Manchester. The railway provided faster and cheaper transport of raw materials and finished goods between the Port of Liverpool and Manchester.

Towards the latter part of the 19th century Manchester's economy was moving into decline. The dues now being charged by the Port of Liverpool and the railway charges were perceived as excessive; it had become cheaper to import goods from Hull on the east coast of England than it was from Liverpool. A ship canal was proposed as a way to reverse Manchester's economic decline by giving the city direct access to the sea for its imports and exports. The 36 mile long Manchester Ship Canal between the River Mersey estuary and Manchester, capable of accommodating medium sized inter-continental cargo liners, was opened in 1894, and in its day was the largest navigation canal in the world. The newly created "Port of Manchester" became Britain's fourth largest port.

The ship canal did not immediately produce the boost in trade that was hoped for, however, and an industrial estate, then a radically new concept, was proposed to help promote traffic on the canal. A timbered deer park in an area, known as Trafford Park, was seen as a prime site for this estate. Trafford Park lies between the Manchester Ship Canal on its northern border and the Bridgewater Canal on its southern border. Occupying an area of almost two square miles, it is the largest industrial estate in Europe. At its peak in 1945 there were an estimated 75,000 workers employed in the estate.

In 1899 the American entrepreneur and engineer George Westinghouse acquired a site in Trafford Park and set up the British Westinghouse Electric Company, a subsidiary to the Westinghouse Electrical Company in Pittsburgh, USA. Building work started in 1900 and the factory was laid out on American lines to accommodate American production methods. The factory began production in 1903, making turbines and electric generators. Westinghouse also built housing for the workforce near to the factory. The road layout was based on the American grid pattern, with streets and avenues identified by numbers rather than names.

US control of British Westinghouse had proved to be a hindrance to the company gaining government contracts during World War I and so, in 1917, control of the holding company was acquired by the Metropolitan Finance Company and Vickers Ltd. In 1919 Vickers purchased the Metropolitan shares in the holding company and changed the name of the company to Metropolitan Vickers Electrical Company (MV), commonly referred to as

"Metrovick" or "Metrovicks". The immediate post-war years were difficult, but its fortunes changed in 1926 with the formation of the Central Electricity Generating Board which standardised electrical supply and led to a massive expansion of electrical distribution and installations, the national "grid", and to a massive growth in the use of domestic appliances.

In 1928 MV merged with its Rugby-based rival British Thomson-Houston (BTH), a company of similar size and with a similar product range. The next year the combined company was purchased by Associated Electrical Industries (AEI), a holding group that already owned several other manufacturers of electrical components and appliances. However, MV and BTH continued to trade under their own names, and to compete against each other.

MV became highly diversified, manufacturing turbines, generators, switchgear, transformers, electronics, railway traction motors, electrical appliances and scientific apparatus. During World War II Metrovick assembled the "Manchester", "Lancaster" and "Lincoln" bombers for A.V. Roe at Trafford Park. Metrovick and BTH became the first two firms in the world to construct jet engines (independently from each other).

THE FIRST MASS SPECTROMETER

The Director of Research and Education at MV until 1951 was A.P.M. Fleming (1881–1960), who had trained at Westinghouse in the USA before joining British Westinghouse in 1902. During his time at Metrovicks, Fleming established the Research Department and oversaw important innovations in engineering education. The policy pursued by Fleming was to employ people who were themselves capable of generating ideas relevant to the company's needs, rather than to employ people just to carry out ideas handed down from above.

In 1928 a member of the MV Research Department, C.R. Burch (1901–1983), experimented with purifying transformer oil by distillation and in so doing discovered that certain high-boiling petroleum derivatives could be used effectively in vacuum diffusion pumps as a replacement for mercury. He had discovered the Apiezon oils and greases (manufactured by MV and marketed by Shell) that have contributed so much to vacuum technology. The oil was much cheaper and easier to handle than mercury, but best of all it did not need the liquid air traps necessary with mercury pumps. MV proceeded to design and manufacture a range of all-metal, water-cooled vacuum diffusion pumps in which petroleum hydrocarbons (Apiezons A and B) were used.

At this time in the Cavendish Laboratory in Cambridge, Cockcroft and Walton, under the direction of Rutherford, were building their particle accelerator that led to the first controlled "splitting of the atom", as mentioned above. Cockcroft had previously studied at Manchester College of Technology and then worked at MV where his potential was recognised and, with the company's help, he took up studies at Cambridge University. Through his contacts at Metrovick he had already been able to persuade the company to provide a purpose built 350,000 volt transformer for the particle accelerator. By 1929 Metrovicks was half-way towards the commercial production of the Apiezon vacuum pumps and Cockcroft, getting wind of this development, was quick to snap up a couple of prototypes for the bargain price of £5. The pumps were used successfully, without liquid air traps, to evacuate the particle accelerator.

As a result of these developments MV had become relatively expert in high vacuum technology and was awarded the first contract to build radar equipment in the late 1930s. All the radar stations in the crucial year 1940 were powered by MV continuously pumped thermionic valves. Nevertheless, Metrovick's vacuum pump business led to the need for further research and development into vacuum technology, including the need for an ionisation gauge that did not need "baking and bombarding" in order to determine the lowest pressure that could be produced by an oil diffusion pump. In 1943 J. Blears (1912–2000), a member of the Vacuum Physics section in the MV Research Department, sketched out a design for a new steel flange-mounted gauge to be bolted directly onto the body of any vessel where pressure was to be measured. He built a mock-up of this gauge for testing in a bell jar, specifically to check the electrode dimensions were satisfactory and to determine the optimum operating voltages. He decided to compare this gauge with the ion gauge he normally used, and also with an Alpert type "nude gauge". This led to the astonishing and alarming discovery that the Alpert type gauge gave a pressure reading approximately ten times higher than that of the gauge they had previously used.

It now became apparent that if the "nude gauge" gave the correct pressure reading then all measurements made over the previous 20 years were in error by a factor of 10 or thereabouts. Furthermore, the ultimate pressure produced by the oil diffusion pump was ten times higher than had been advertised, and therefore further work on Apiezon oils would be necessary. For one night a week during the war Blears served in a volunteer fire crew and on one of these nights, when there was little to do, he sat in the air raid shelter and read Nier's 1936 paper on mass spectrometry. He had "been fascinated by the concept of being able to steer a stream of ions through such a long distance with such precision, and he became fired with enthusiasm to build a mass spectrometer when the war was over". Following his discovery about the ultimate pressure produced by the oil diffusion pump he realised that little was known about the nature of the residual gases in the high vacuum, and perhaps a mass spectrometer might be useful to improve the understanding of these gases.

Blears was given approval to go ahead with the building of an experimental mass spectrometer, not only for studies of the nature of a vacuum, but also as an instrument that could be sold for isotope assay and hydrocarbon analysis. In those days licences were necessary for the building of any equipment not directly related to the war effort. Accordingly, in April 1944, Blears wrote to the Department of Scientific and Industrial Research (DSIR) requesting permission to use one ton of steel and five hundredweight of copper for the purpose of building a mass spectrometer. By chance this coincided with the UK Government's decision to develop its own atomic bomb, for which it would need mass spectrometers to investigate its success in separating the uranium 235 and 238 isotopes. In June 1944 the MV Research Department was approached by the DSIR to quote for three mass spectrometers to a specification then in the hands of Chadwick at Liverpool University.

The Metropolitan Vickers MS1 built in 1946 in the MV Research Department in Trafford Park, Manchester. The MS1 was the first commercial mass spectrometer built outside the USA. It was used to measure the isotope ratios of uranium in uranium hexafluoride contained in the gas cylinders on the side of the instrument. The instrument is being operated by Anne Mettrick, a mathematician who worked in the Vacuum Physics Section in MV's Research Department.

Blears later wrote "that the determining events are more often *chance* and *coincidence* rather than logical planning. This was the coincidence. The UK Government had made its decision on atomic weapons and mass spectrometers would be essential for uranium enrichment assays. MV was already known for its continuously evacuated vacuum plant, and was also known for its work in high energy physics, having recently constructed cyclotron accelerators for Cockcroft at the Cavendish Laboratory and for Chadwick at Liverpool. Now it was known to be interested in mass spectrometers. This made MV an obvious choice as collaborator. This was the determining factor in the type of machine to be developed, and research on the nature of a vacuum had to wait for more propitious times."

Chadwick had moved from Cambridge in 1935 when he was elected to the Chair of Physics in the University of Liverpool. Between 1943 and 1946 he also spent time in the United States as Head of the British Mission attached to the Manhattan Project for the development of the atomic bomb. Chadwick's team at Liverpool had built a prototype instrument based on information provided by General Electric in Schenectady. This was discussed with Blears at a meeting in Liverpool in September 1944 and MV was asked to provide an instrument with equivalent performance, making whatever improvements it could safely and expeditiously incorporate. The formal contract for three instruments was placed by the Ministry of Aircraft Production in January 1945.

The mass spectrometer, known as the MS1, had an electron impact (EI) ion source, an accelerating voltage of 2 kV, and a magnetic sector with six inch radius and 90° sector angle. It included means for connecting uranium hexafluoride (UF_6) gas cylinders. The first instrument was delivered to Chadwick and C.A. McDowell at Liverpool University in March 1946, and the second and third instruments were installed at the UKAERE, Harwell, in mid-1946. These instruments were the first mass spectrometers to be built commercially outside the USA. A fourth instrument was built and retained at MV before it was eventually acquired by the Medical Research Council.

EARLY MASS SPECTOMETERS

In 1946 work started on a replacement for the MS1. It needed to be as good as the MS1 for uranium isotope assay, but in addition, and to satisfy potential industrial and university requirements, it needed to deal with isotope assay of all the gaseous elements, with organic

MV factory shipping note for MS1, serial number 1, (dated 13th March 1946) to Professor Sir James Chadwick at the Physics Department in the University of Liverpool.

The Metropolitan Vickers MS2 general purpose mass spectrometer, in production from 1950 until the early 1960s.

and inorganic gas analysis, with both positive and negative ions and with the measurement of appearance potentials. Moreover, all the glass vacuum envelopes, used in the MS1 for the source and collector regions, were replaced by an all-metal analyser tube to which the source and collector housings, the diffusion pump and cold-trap were attached by rubber-gasketed metal flanges. The new instrument, the MS2, had the same ion optical arrangement and the same magnet as the MS1, although many of the electronic supplies were improved or replaced. An improved signal amplifier was designed using surplus military electrical components that were becoming available after the end of the war. However, the quality of the vacuum produced by oil diffusion pumps was not good enough and band heaters were added to allow baking of the instrument. This in turn exposed the limitations of the rubber gaskets which outgassed severely when baked.

Time was required to overcome these problems. The situation was helped, however, by the fact that there was an embargo on shipments of mass spectrometers from the USA, the only other source of supply for what had by that time become an essential instrument. A prototype MS2 was first exhibited in 1948, but it was not until 1950 that the first shipments were made. The first order was from J. Danby at the Physical Chemistry Laboratory, Oxford, and was closely followed by orders from ICI, Shell, BP and the UKAEA.

Later refinements in the design of the MS2 made it suitable for the routine analysis of mixtures of hydrocarbon gases. A high molecular weight version became available using a higher field strength magnet to increase the mass range to m/z 700, and with a resolving power of 600 to 700. It was also fitted with a heated inlet system which allowed liquids and some organic solids to be presented to the ion source for analysis. Other versions were produced, for example an MS2S for the isotopic analysis of metals by thermal ionisation.

By 1948 it had become clear that at least half the mass spectrometers likely to be sold in the future would be used for applications that were essentially chemical in nature. MV was not a chemical company and employed no-one who was likely to be able to discuss chemical applications on equal terms with those who would be buying its mass spectrometers. Consequently, in 1949, the physical chemist J.D. Waldron (1928–2001) was recruited, and whose work was to be crucial to the development and communication of applications of mass spectrometry. In 1950 the physicist R.D. Craig was recruited, whose work was to be key to the development of the ion optics of mass spectrometers. Waldron and Craig were to be central figures in the evolution of the mass spectrometry (MS) businesses in Manchester in the years to come.

Members of the Research Department photographed (c. 1956) on the roof of MetroVick's Research Department. Amongst the group are several scientists and engineers from the Mass Spectrometry Section. These include on the back row Robert Craig (far left), Ernie Potter (third from left), John Waldron (fourth from left) and Alan Errock (fifth from left), and on the front row Martin Elliott (second from left) and Nigel Prosser (second from right).

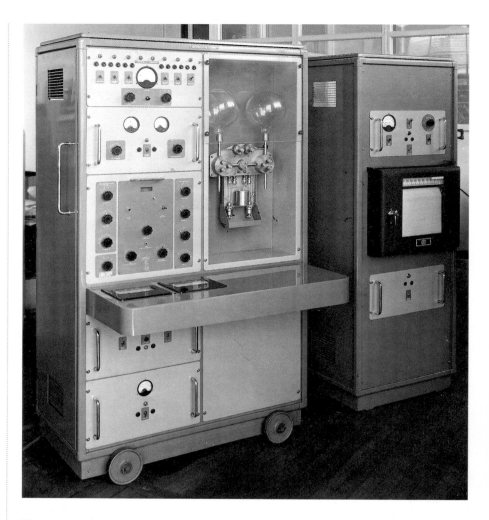

The Metropolitan Vickers MS3 isotope ratio mass spectrometer first manufactured in 1952.

The next product, the MS3, was a scaled down version of the MS2 and built to sell at half its price. The first model was shipped to the University of Aarhus, Denmark, in 1952. The sample inlet system, the four inch radius 90° magnetic sector, the vacuum pumping plant and the electronic control circuits were contained in a single cubicle. It could be fitted with a double collector for accurate isotope ratio measurements, and it was suitable for the routine isotopic analysis of stable gases, such as oxygen and nitrogen, used as isotopic tracers in biochemical studies.

The first three instruments (MS1, MS2 and MS3) had been developed in the Vacuum Physics section of the Research Department. Then, in 1953, the MV Scientific Apparatus Department was created and vacuum-related operations were relocated to new premises in Barton Dock Road on the edge of Trafford Park. Part of the Vacuum Physics group moved to this site with Blears to continue the development and manufacture of the existing mass spectrometer products. The remainder of the group, led by Waldron, remained in the Research Department to continue with research orientated work in the field of mass spectrometry. By now MV was becoming well known as a manufacturer of mass spectrometers and its next instruments (MS4, MS5, MS7 and MS8) resulted from external approaches and collaborations.

The MS4 was designed to provide rapid gas analysis for research into respiratory problems. The instrument, first manufactured in 1959, followed the design of K.T. Fowler of the Medical Research Council at Hammersmith Hospital. The analyser used a small permanent magnet and the source voltage was scanned 25 times per second whilst recording the signal for four masses (*m/z* 28, 32, 40 and 44) which enabled the instrument to produce graphs showing the changes in the lung gas composition during the breathing cycle.

The specification of the MS5 was agreed during a single afternoon conversation with scientists from the UK Atomic Energy Research Establishment (AERE) at Harwell in 1953. The AERE wanted a magnetic sector instrument for analysis of transuranic specimens collected from high levels in the atmosphere after atomic explosions. A new method of thermal ionisation had been developed and this was to be incorporated, as was a sliding bar vacuum lock which allowed the next source filament assembly, carrying the sample for analysis, to be loaded into the lock while the current sample was being analysed. This novel mechanism for rapid specimen changes without closing down the machine enabled the unprecedented throughput of 20 one-microgram samples of uranium to be analysed in one day. The MS5,

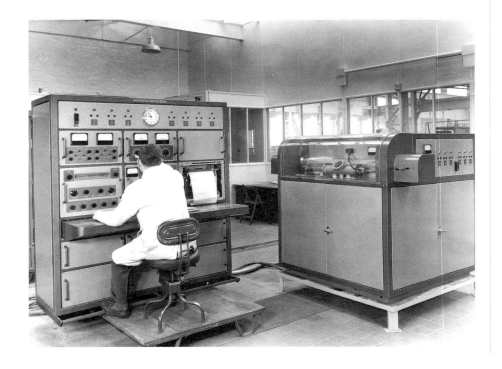

The Metropolitan Vickers MS5 thermal ionisation mass spectrometer, produced from 1955 until 1970. The instrument is being operated by Barry Russell from the test department.

the first of which was delivered in 1955, was a scaled-up version of the MS2, using a 12 inch radius 90° magnetic sector, and had its maximum source voltage increased to 6 kV. It also used, for the first time in a commercial mass spectrometer, an electron multiplier ion detector. The electron multiplier was based on a design from Harwell and its manufacture was set up in the Research Department in Trafford Park. For the first time MV scientists and engineers were able to observe the arrival of individual ions and were confronted by signals exhibiting ion statistical noise, or shot noise, characteristic of the much smaller ion currents that can be recorded by such detectors. The electron multiplier was subsequently fitted to the MS2.

DOUBLE-FOCUSSING MASS SPECTROMETERS

1953 was to be a momentous year for MV mass spectrometry. Blears was invited to give a paper on "The Metropolitan Vickers Mass Spectrometers" at the Pittsburgh Conference by the ASTM Mass Spectrometry Committee. A few days before leaving for the US he gave a paper to the Institute of Electronics in Manchester which was attended by J.H. Beynon from ICI's Dyestuffs Division in Blakeley, Manchester.

At that time Beynon was unknown to Blears. Beynon had joined ICI in 1947 and, with A.E. Williams, had built a mass spectrometer for use in pharmaceutical research at ICI. Beynon had been the first to explore and develop the use of accurate mass measurement of organic molecules in the determination of their elemental composition. Beynon later wrote

> "The different chemical elements have masses in ratios close to whole numbers, so in principle a sizeable ion of given mass could have one of a number of different chemical compositions, each giving the same mass. However, since elemental masses are not in exact integral ratios, if the mass of the ion is known sufficiently accurately, only one or a few combinations of elements can be selected to provide that total mass."

Since the magnetic field could not be varied as accurately as the accelerating voltage, Beynon used the peak matching method to measure the masses of ions. The magnetic field was first scanned in order to find peaks of interest, and was next adjusted to bring a known ion into focus. Then, holding the magnetic field constant, the voltage was varied to bring another ion into focus in its place. The inverse ratio of the voltages for the two ions (given the constant magnetic field) gave directly the ratio of their masses. Using this method Beynon could measure masses up to mass 250 with an accuracy of about 50 parts per million (ppm). This accuracy was sufficient to enable him to identify the chemical composition of an ion sometimes unambiguously, but more commonly to narrow the field to just a few possibilities.

It was apparent to Beynon that improved accuracy could be obtained from a higher resolution mass spectrometer, perhaps a double-focussing instrument: that is, one which includes both a magnetic sector and an electric sector arranged such that the energy dispersion due to one is cancelled out by the energy dispersion due to the other. When this is achieved the final image at the collector slit is not broadened as a result of different ions having different kinetic energies. After Blears' presentation in Manchester, Beynon asked him if MV would make an instrument for ICI which would have high resolution and high abundance sensitivity, possibly a double-focussing instrument. Blears, who had recently become inspired by Nier's latest publication on the double-focussing mass spectrometer, said probably yes, but he would get back with an answer after his month long trip to the USA. Blears calculated the mass differences of a number of mass doublets for himself and convinced himself that a Nier-type double-focussing mass spectrometer would be able to resolve a substantial proportion of them. He also convinced himself that an electric sector could be mounted on top of an existing MS2 to convert it into a Nier-type double-focussing instrument.

During his visit to the USA, Blears visited Bell Laboratories where he saw a Mattauch–Herzog double-focussing mass spectrograph which they had built for determining the quantities of trace elements in solids. It used a spark source to form the ions and a photographic plate to collect them and determine their masses and relative abundances. This instrument did not provide particularly high resolution; it needed to be double-focussing simply to cope with the very large spread of ion energies produced from a spark source. It transpired that Bell had no intention to market this instrument and were even prepared to make available some design information to assist MV with the design of its own instrument.

The two proposed double-focussing mass spectrometers presented a dilemma for Blears and Craig. Which should be built? This led to many searching discussions, and eventually it was decided that both should be built. Blears wrote to Beynon explaining his thoughts and calculations. Beynon accepted Blears' line of thinking and so the double-focussing version of the MS2, to become known as the MS8, was born. The spark source double-focussing Mattauch–Herzog instrument was to become known as the MS7.

The first double-focussing mass spectrometer fitted with a spark source for the analysis of solids, the prototype MS7, was built in the Research Department in 1955. A second prototype was installed in 1956 at BTH in Rugby. Its Mattauch–Hertzog design used a 10 inch photoplate and had an accelerating voltage of 18 kV. Neither had vacuum locks and so it was necessary to let the whole instrument up to atmosphere to change the photoplate. The system used rubber gaskets so the vacuum and elemental detection limits were quite limited. The production units were equipped with vacuum locks and had an accelerating voltage of 20 kV. The all-metal system used gold seal joints and was bakeable to between 200°C and 300°C allowing pressures of 10^{-8} torr to be maintained in the analyser system thus enabling low detection limits (1 part of boron in 10^9 parts of silicon) to be achieved. The first two production units were installed in 1959 at the Mond Nickel Company in Birmingham and at the UKAEA uranium enrichment plant in Capenhurst. An MS7 was shipped to RCA in New Jersey in 1961, Metrovick's first mass spectrometer to be exported to the USA. Electrical detection using an electron multiplier was later added to the instrument, as were thermal ionisation, Knudsen cell and ion microprobe accessories.

The AEI MS7 spark source mass spectrometer installed at RCA in Princeton, New Jersey. The instrument, photographed in 1961, is being operated by J. Rogers-Woolston from RCA. This was AEI's first mass spectrometer to be exported to the USA.

The MS8 double-focussing instrument was designed by adding a seven and a half inch radius 90° electric sector to the MS2's six inch radius 90° magnet sector. The instrument had an EB configuration, meaning that the ions from the source passed first through the electric sector (E) before passing through the magnetic sector (B). The maximum source voltage was increased from 2 kV to 8 kV, although it was rarely used at this voltage. The field strength of the magnet was increased by about 20% to give it a mass range of 240 at 8 kV source voltage, and 480 at 4 kV source voltage. It used the electron multiplier detector that had recently been introduced to the MS2. Its expected resolving power was about 2500 (10% valley definition), enough to split the triplet ($CO/N_2/C_2H_4$) at m/z 28, but a resolution of over 13,000 was soon achieved. Using the peak matching technique a mass could be measured to an accuracy of a few ppm, an accuracy found to be sufficient for reliable identification of the chemical composition of many ions. The instrument was built at MV's Research Department in Trafford Park and completed in 1955. Beynon worked on it in the Research Department for many months before it was eventually installed at ICI in 1957.

In order to suppress the continuing rivalry between Metropolitan Vickers and BTH, the long-established names were eliminated on 1 January 1960, and were replaced by the AEI brand name, a move which was almost universally resented within both companies. At about the same time the mass spectrometry group in the Research Department at Trafford Park moved to Barton Dock Road, now the home of AEI Scientific Apparatus Ltd.

The Metropolitan Vickers MS8 double-focussing mass spectrometer built in 1955 for John Beynon at ICI Dyestuffs Division in Blakeley, Manchester. The instrument is photographed in the MV Research Department in Trafford Park, Manchester.

Although only one MS8 was built, its performance was so impressive that AEI decided to turn it into a new product, but with twice the size of the MS8. Its maximum accelerating voltage was to remain at 8 kV and therefore, with a 15" radius electric sector and 12" radius magnet sector, its mass range at full source voltage would increase by a factor of four to about 960. This was to be the MS9 which was to have such an impact on the development of organic mass spectrometry. Its development was assured by four "drawing board" orders (Shell, BP, University of Glasgow and University College London) and the first of these instruments was delivered to Shell in Amsterdam in 1962. It had a specification resolving power of 10,000 (10% valley definition) and used the peak matching technique for accurate mass measurement to about 1 ppm. Progressive development of the MS9 resulted in a final specification of 100,000 before it was superseded in 1972. This was the highest performance level demonstrated by any commercial instrument at that time and was achieved as a result of the high mechanical precision and high stability of its electric and magnetic fields.

In spite of the introduction of double-focussing instruments into its product range AEI did not immediately abandon single-focussing instrumentation and, in 1961, added the MS10. This employed a 2" radius, 180° magnetic sector and used a permanent magnet, similar to that of the MS4. It had a big dial for adjusting the accelerating voltage and was used for tuning in a mass, rather like the dial common to radios of that time for tuning in a radio station. Mass 2 was tuned in at a source voltage of about 2 kV, mass 44 at about 90 V etc. The instrument was used for residual gas analysis and general gas analysis, and was a useful instrument in teaching laboratories. AEI sold more of these instruments in its 12 year lifetime than any other. Another version of the instrument which used an electromagnet, the MS20, was introduced in 1966. In 1964 AEI introduced its last single-focussing instrument,

The AEI MS9 double-focussing mass spectrometer, produced from 1962 to 1972. The instrument is being tested by Nigel Bean, final inspection test manager.

the MS12, which, with its 12" radius magnetic sector, was essentially a single-focussing version of the MS9. Apart from its applications in organic mass spectrometry a version with a double collector was made available for the isotopic analysis of uranium in UF_6.

One of the characteristics of the MS9 was the copious appearance of "metastable ion" peaks arising from the dissociation of ions in the field free region between the two sectors, referred to as the second field free region. The ΔV control on the MS9 allowed the accelerating voltage (V) to be varied by up to about ±2% from the value required for the main beam to pass through the centre of the energy defining slit. It was discovered that this made it very useful to detect metastable ion transitions that occurred in the first field free region of the MS9 in which either a hydrogen atom or hydrogen molecule was lost. This became known as the Barber–Elliott scan and was first reported at the Montreal ASMS meeting in 1964. It provided, for the first time, a means of directly determining the masses of the precursor ion (m_1) and product ion (m_2) in a metastable ion reaction. Prior to this time the broad "metastable ion" peaks had only been observed for transitions occurring in the field free region immediately before a magnetic sector. These "metastable ion" peaks were observed with apparent mass m^*, where $m^* = (m_2^2/m_1)$, and this does not allow unambiguous calculation of the masses of the precursor and product ions, even though in most cases these masses could easily be assumed from observation of the peaks present in the conventional EI mass spectrum.

K.R. Jennings at the University of Sheffield suggested that it would be interesting if the ΔV control could be made to change the accelerating voltage by up to 100% so that the loss of heavier neutral fragments may be observed. The accelerating voltage control was subsequently arranged to be varied from 4 kV to 8 kV, and later from 2 kV to 8 kV, to allow identification of precursor ions to a pre-defined product ion up to twice, and then four times, its mass. Jennings subsequently carried out a series of experiments to try and discover if specific metastable ion reactions were truly unimolecular or if they were, at least in part, due to collisions with residual gas molecules in the vacuum system. He tried increasing the pressure, first by loosening the flange of the analyser tube ion gauge and later by heating and outgassing the electric sector housing, and was surprised to observe a large number of new decomposition reactions. This work, reporting the observation of Collision Induced Decompositions (CID), was published in 1968. The linked source voltage (V) and electric sector voltage (E) scan, in which the ratio ($V^{\frac{1}{2}}/E$) is held constant and the magnetic field is held constant, was later made available on the MS9. This scan allowed a spectrum of daughter ions from a pre-defined parent ion to be generated, albeit over quite a narrow range of daughter ion masses.

In the early to mid-1960s the main competitor to the AEI MS9 was the CEC (Consolidated Electrodynamics) Model 21-110 mass spectrometer. This was a Mattauch–Hertzog type double-focussing magnetic sector which focussed all masses along a plane and used photoplate detection to record all masses simultaneously. The photoplate detection sensitivity, however, was considerably less than that of electrical detection using an electron multiplier and this disadvantage more or less cancelled out its advantage of parallel detection. Several

Some of AEI's technical and sales staff gathered around the control console of the MS9 in the Consultant Laboratory at AEI's facility in Barton Dock Road, Trafford Park. This photograph is copied from AEI's internal newspaper in 1965 and includes, from left to right, Bob Brown, Eddie Willdig, Patrick Powers, Malcolm Fitches, Brian Green, Alan Errock, John Wilcox and Martin Elliott.

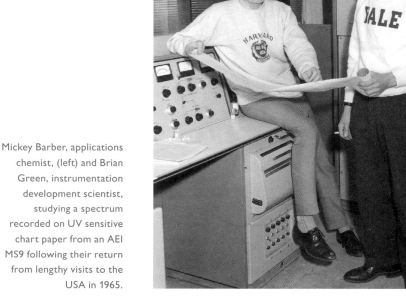

Mickey Barber, applications chemist, (left) and Brian Green, instrumentation development scientist, studying a spectrum recorded on UV sensitive chart paper from an AEI MS9 following their return from lengthy visits to the USA in 1965.

exposures were made of the spectrum across the width of the photoplate and, where accurate measurements were needed, subsequent densitometer scanning was used. This allowed the precise position of each peak along the photoplate to be measured and, by reference to known peaks, the accurate mass of each ion of interest could be calculated. In comparison the accurate mass of ions of interest could be measured, one at a time, by the peak matching technique using the MS9. Each of these approaches had their perceived advantages and disadvantages, but both were time consuming and labour intensive.

In 1964, at the ASTM E-14 meeting in Montreal, J.T. Watson and K. Biemann at MIT first described the direct coupling of gas chromatography (GC) to MS. At the same meeting D. Desiderio and K. Biemann reported the direct interfacing of the output of the densitometer to a computer which calculated the accurate masses and elemental composition of major peaks quickly and automatically. It was immediately clear that this development would provide the CEC 21-110 with its photoplate recording system a major advantage in speed and throughput over the MS9. This was followed later in the same year by the introduction of a digitising system connected to a Varian minicomputer that yielded nominal mass measured spectra from scanning the magnetic field of an Atlas MAT single-focussing instrument. These events led to a feeling of panic at AEI, and triggered a major change of research priorities.

For a high resolution instrument to be useful in GC-MS it was thought it would have to be possible to scan the magnet over a decade in mass (that is, from mass M to mass $0.1M$) in 10 seconds at a resolution of 10,000 (10% valley definition) and achieve mass measurements to an accuracy of 10 ppm. To allow the detector amplifier and digitising system to operate optimally it was desirable to spend equal times scanning through each peak in the spectrum, which could be achieved by the use of an exponential scan. For an exponential scan over a decade in mass in 10 s at a resolution of 10,000 the time/peak is 0.435 ms, and for this it was necessary to increase the amplifier bandwidth of the MS9 to 10 kHz. It was calculated that under these conditions as few as five ions would be needed in a peak to achieve one standard deviation of 10 ppm in its mass measurement. It was later demonstrated that 10 to 15 ions were adequate to achieve mass accuracies of about 10 ppm.

At this time digitisation rates were not fast enough to make sufficient measurements across a peak only 0.434 ms wide. This problem was overcome, at least for a while, by the FM analogue recording of mass spectra onto magnetic tape, a technique that had been developed by S.R. Lipsky and W.J. McMurray at Yale University Medical School. Using a modified MS9 at Yale a mass spectrum was recorded on magnetic tape at 60 inch s^{-1}, played back 16 times more slowly at 3.75 inch s^{-1}, and digitised with an 8 bit analogue-to-digital convertor (ADC) at 1.5 kHz sampling rate. With an internal reference compound and using the department's IBM 1401 computer, mass measurements of between 3 ppm and 10 ppm were obtained for 300 ng of tribenzylamine. These results, demonstrating for the first time automated, accurately mass measured spectra acquired by magnet scanning, were presented at the 1965 meeting of the ASTM E-14 at St Louis, Missouri.

Applied Data Research (ADR), a software company in Princeton, New Jersey, was awarded the contract to develop a minicomputer system that could process single high resolution scans right through from on-line data acquisition to elemental composition. The chosen computer was the Digital Equipment Corporation (DEC) PDP-8 with 4 kbytes of 12 bit computer word main memory, but with no backup storage. The size of the entire computer program exceeded by many times the 4 kbytes of memory of the PDP-8 and so it was decided to break up the complete process into four sub-processes, each executed in sequence. The various programs were held in a single "pack" of folded five punched-hole paper tape which was read in as needed throughout the process. The resulting product was called the AEI DS10, and by the time of its introduction at the IMSC meeting in Berlin in 1967 a 12 bit ADC operating with a sampling frequency of 12.5 kHz had become available and this was sufficient to allow digitisation of the signal from the mass spectrometer directly without the need to record the spectra previously on magnetic tape.

1970s AND NEW ORGANISATIONS

In the late 1960s a small mass spectrometer, with the designated name Minimass, was designed at AEI for residual gas analysis applications. It consisted of a 1 cm radius 180° magnetic sector housed in a glass envelope and used a magnetron permanent magnet. The design and manufacture of the electronics for this instrument was contracted out to Vacuum Generators (VG). VG was founded in 1962 by B. Eastwell and colleagues in

The AEI "Minimass" mass
spectrometer in a glass
vacuum envelope (above),
and the VG "Micromass"
mass spectrometer in a
metal vacuum envelope
(below).

East Grinstead, Sussex, to supply ultra-high vacuum components and systems. In 1966 VG began to supply surface science instrumentation and in 1967 VG Electronics was set up in Hastings to manufacture electronics. At this time VG was a very small company and fear of the possibility that VG may be acquired by one of its competitors led AEI to insist on a clause in the contract which relieved either party of any further interest in the product in the event of that party being acquired by another company. However, in 1967, GEC's Arnold Weinstock made an historic and successful £120 million bid for AEI. Consequently AEI's interest in the product was relinquished and VG found itself with the opportunity to market a small mass spectrometer. This mass spectrometer was re-housed in a metal envelope and was renamed the Micromass 1 (MM1).

In 1968, R.D. Craig, seeing an unsettled future at AEI following the takeover by GEC, joined VG in East Grinstead to manage VG's new MS business. In 1970 the independent VG Micromass company was formed in the small Cheshire town of Winsford, close to Manchester, to supply mass spectrometers. The MM1 was soon joined by the MM6, a 6 cm radius single-focussing magnetic sector for residual and general gas analysis which could be purchased in kit form or as a complete analytical system. Still in 1970 VG Micromass introduced the Q7, a quadrupole mass spectrometer with a mass range of 120, also available in kit form or as a complete analytical system. In 1971 the MM12 single-focussing 12 cm radius magnetic sector and the 300 mass range Q8 quadrupole were added. VG Micromass designed its instruments using common building blocks and electronics housed in industrial standard 19 inch rack-mounted format. Although the instruments did not have the purpose built, cosmetically designed control consoles that had become characteristic of AEI's products this approach offered much greater flexibility and allowed new instruments to be configured and introduced relatively quickly.

VG Micromass started to concentrate on the supply of isotope ratio mass spectrometers, a branch of MS that AEI was beginning to neglect. In 1971 the MM602 dual collector version of the MM6 was introduced for high precision stable gas isotope ratio measurements, an application previously served by AEI's MS3. The following year the MM30 single-focussing 30 cm radius magnetic sector instrument was introduced with EI ionisation for UF_6 analysis. The MM30B with six manually selected thermal ionisation source filaments was introduced for isotope ratio measurements of solid elements, in particular of uranium and plutonium for applications in nuclear chemistry, and of rubidium and strontium for dating of geological samples.

Meanwhile, in 1970, AEI introduced a new double-focussing mass spectrometer, the MS30, the first to incorporate the double beam technique. Its double-focussing optical arrangement consisted of an 8.5" radius, 90° electric sector followed by a 6.5" radius, 90° magnetic sector. It had a maximum source voltage of 4 kV, and was AEI's first instrument to use all solid state electronics. It included two independent ion sources with their respective collectors, the ions from each source travelling side by side through the double-focussing optical arrangement. The second source was used exclusively for the reference compound so that it was no longer necessary to use high resolving power to separate sample ions from reference ions. This in turn allowed faster scanning into the data system, making it particularly well suited to accurate mass GC-MS applications. A second, smaller, double-focussing instrument to use the double beam technique was introduced in 1973. This was named the 1073 (it was named in October 1973) and comprised a 5.2" radius, 90° electric sector followed by a 4" radius, 90° magnetic sector, and also had a maximum source voltage of 4 kV.

The AEI MS9 was replaced in 1972 by the MS50 which used substantially the same ion optical system but with several improvements and innovations. These included the addition of two DC hexapole lenses positioned before and after the magnet which provided means to reduce peak broadening due to mechanical misalignments and to correct for the effect of fringe fields on the ion beam as it entered and exited the magnetic sector. It was initially specified to have a resolution of 100,000 (10% valley), but this was later increased to 150,000 resolution, the highest resolution for any commercial magnetic sector mass spectrometer.

In 1972 J.D. Waldron moved from AEI to become chairman of VG Instruments, and later that year and over the following few years several more staff from AEI moved to VG. These included a group that set up the independent VG Data Systems company at the Winsford factory in Cheshire to provide data systems, including data systems for VG's surface science instruments and mass spectrometers.

The influx of staff from AEI provided VG Micromass with the capability to build its own double-focussing instrument. This comprised a 7.5" radius, 70° electric sector followed by a 5" radius, 70° magnetic sector, and naturally was called the MM 70-70. It had a maximum source voltage of 4 kV. The first of these instruments was sold from the drawing board to Sheffield University's Department of Metallurgy, with financial support from Pilkington Glass, for the thermo-chemical study of glasses at up to 20,000 resolving power. It was built with its flight path in the vertical plane, VG's first and last double-focussing instrument to be built in this orientation, and was fitted with a 1500°C Knudsen Cell.

In 1974 VG Micromass was divided into four separate companies, VG Isotopes, VG Organic, VG Quadrupoles and VG Inorganic. Three of these remained in Winsford whilst VG Organic, along with VG Data Systems, moved to Altrincham, Manchester. The rationale behind the division into smaller companies was B. Eastwell's "Christmas card principle"; most people address Christmas cards to between 50 and 100 people and therefore this represents a natural maximum number of people with whom to associate in a company. Companies with many more staff find a need to build a strongly hierarchical organisation. Furthermore, spinning out new companies to cover particular product areas or applications leads to greater expertise in these areas and encourages these companies to develop and grow within their particular market. In the short term this strategy generally worked well. Small companies have lower overhead costs, are more efficient and are able to react more quickly to customer requirements and to new technology. In the longer term this strategy started to become constrained. The number of companies has a tendency to grow almost exponentially until such time that they find themselves competing against each other.

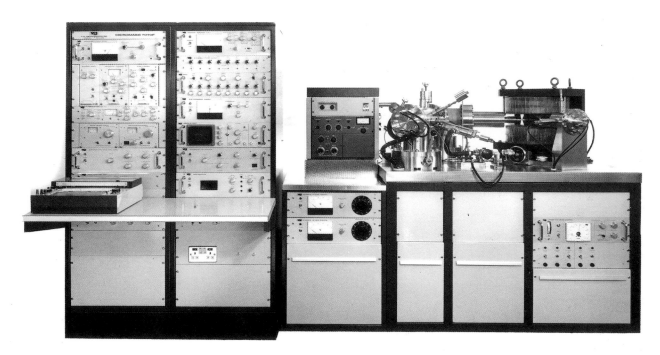

The VG MM 7070F double-focussing mass spectrometer for analysis of organic materials. This instrument went into production in 1975 and, with the aid of several redesigns, continued in production until 1990 over which time more than 500 units were sold.

This strategy did not always go quite to plan. VG Quadrupoles continued to supply the Q7 and Q8, which used 6 mm diameter quadrupole rods, for gas analysis applications, and introduced first the Q50 with 18 mm diameter rods, and later the Q40 with 12 mm diameter rods. In addition to completing development of the MM 70-70 Knudsen Cell instrument VG Inorganic continued to supply the MM6 and MM12 magnetic sector instruments for gas analysis, and introduced the MM5 with multiple Faraday detectors for monitoring of multiple pre-designated gases, such as respiratory gases. However, in 1976 these two companies were combined and renamed VG Gas Analysis.

As AEI ceased production of single-focussing instruments in the early 1970s VG Organic stepped in with the introduction of the MM 12F and MM 30F, fast pumped versions of the MM 12 and MM 30, to accommodate chemical ionisation (CI) and the direct coupling of capillary GC columns to the source. Later in 1974 the MM 12F was superseded by the MM 16F when its 12 cm radius 60° magnet was reconfigured into a 16 cm radius 55° magnet to increase its mass range. VG Organic also re-engineered the MM 70-70 to have a horizontal flight path, and added fast pumping for accurate mass GC-MS applications. The first MM 70-70F was delivered to the Department of Pharmacology in Oxford in 1975 and, following its decommissioning in 1995, was presented to the Museum of Science and Industry in Manchester.

In 1975 VG Organic began work on the MM ZAB-2F, a large double-focussing mass spectrometer built in a reverse geometry configuration to allow acquisition of MIKES (Mass analysed Ion Kinetic Energy Spectrometry) and CID-MIKES spectra. This was designed to meet requirements specified by J. H. Beynon, now at Swansea University. Beynon had previously spent time at Purdue University working on an extensively modified MS9 to allow recording of MIKES spectra. The ZAB's optical arrangement included a 11.75" radius, 55° magnet sector followed by a 15" radius, 81.5° electric sector, an arrangement taken from several published by Hintenberger and König that had zero first and second order aberration terms due to the angular divergence (alpha) and energy divergence (beta) of the ion beam. It was its zero alpha and beta aberration terms that led to the instrument being named ZAB. Its BE configuration meant that ions passed through the magnetic sector (B) first before passing through the electric sector (E), the reverse order to that of previous double-focussing instruments built in Manchester. The instrument had two detectors; the single-focussing detector positioned after the magnetic sector and the double-focussing detector positioned after the electric sector. In the MIKES mode of operation the magnetic sector allowed selection of a precursor ion and the double-focussing detector allowed recording of the product ion spectrum generated by scanning the electric sector. The electric sector is an energy analyser, but here it also becomes a mass analyser since the product ions have kinetic energies in proportion to their mass. A gas collision cell was included at the intermediate image point between the two sectors to allow CID to be performed. Hence the instrument could be operated in single-focussing, double-focussing, MIKES and CID-MIKES modes. It was the first commercial mass spectrometer that included all the key components to allow operation as a true tandem MS/MS instrument with CID of precursor ions. Six instruments were ordered from the drawing board and the first was delivered to the University of Swansea in 1976.

By the late 1960s strategies were under development for the sequencing of any protein, regardless of molecular weight, based upon the mass spectrometric analysis of mixtures of peptides produced from the macromolecule by enzymic digestion with trypsin or chymotrypsin. Theoretical analysis of published protein structures showed that virtually all

Robert Craig photographed in 1978 alongside the gas collision cell housing of a MM ZAB-2F. The MM ZAB-2F double-focussing mass spectrometer was the first commercial instrument to also function as a tandem MS/MS instrument.

The control console of a fully accessorised MM ZAB-2F, photographed in 1978. The industrial rack mounting consoles used by VG could easily be extended to include new accessories, in contrast to the custom designed consoles used by AEI. The instrument is being operated by Bob Bateman from the design and development group.

tryptic peptides from proteins would have a mass of less than 3000 daltons. H.R. Morris at Cambridge University reasoned that the way ahead in biopolymer MS would depend on an instrument with that mass range at full sensitivity. In response to enquiries by Morris, who was setting up a new laboratory at Imperial College in London, VG Organic proposed an enlarged version of the ZAB with a 20" radius magnetic sector to give a mass range of 3000 at a source voltage of 8 kV. However, the Science Research Council, who had at the same time received the application to fund the new ZAB instrument for Swansea University, chose to fund AEI's proposal to build a special high field magnet for the MS50. This magnet had an enlarged core and its pole tips were made of the alloy Permendur, which contains 60% cobalt. Several problems were encountered, in particular the presence of inclusions were discovered when machining the Permendur, and it was found necessary to x-ray sections of the alloy first to avoid those with the troublesome inclusions. The instrument, delivered in 1977, had a maximum field strength of 2.3 tesla and its mass range was 3200 daltons at its full source voltage of 8 kV.

John Beynon photographed
at the control console of a
MM ZAB-2F (c. 1988).

In 1976 a Californian-based company, Kratos, having recently acquired the MS data systems
company Instem based in Stone, Staffordshire, acquired the AEI Scientific Apparatus business from GEC. Waldron subsequently moved from VG Instruments to Kratos to manage
this business.

During the 1970s it became standard practice to use temperature regulated Hall effect
devices to measure and control the magnetic field strength, enabling faster and more
accurate magnet switching and scanning. The use of this device also helped the development of the magnetic and electric sector "linked scanning" techniques for recording product
and precursor ion spectra of transitions occurring in the first field free region of double-
focussing mass spectrometers. These superseded the voltage linked scanning techniques
developed over a decade earlier, thereby avoiding the many problems associated with scanning the accelerating voltage. Kratos and VG Organic introduced these techniques for their
respective double-focussing mass spectrometers almost simultaneously in 1977, perhaps an
indication of the intense competiveness that now existed between the two companies.

The 1970s also saw rapid advances in digitisation rates and data systems. For example,
by 1978, the VG 2035 Data System was available with a 12 bit digitiser with a sampling
frequency of 75 kHz. This system supported the use of a secondary reference, a technique
first proposed by Hadden and Lukens in 1974. Here a "primary reference" for a magnet
scan is generated using a conventional reference mixture such as perfluorokerosene (PFK),
and this is used to generate a "secondary reference" for use with a simpler reference
compound, such as tetraiodoethylene (C_2I_4), the mass spectrum of which contains just a few

strongly mass deficient peaks. This technique, and faster digitisation rates, allowed accurate mass measurement at fast scan rates and medium resolution, for example 1.5 second per mass decade at 1500 resolution, and provided a relative simple and inexpensive means for acquiring accurately mass measured spectra from GC peaks. This and other developments undermined the justification for the relatively complex dual beam mass spectrometers and in 1978 Kratos re-engineered the 1073 into a single beam instrument, the MS25, with improved sensitivity. A similar exercise was carried out on the MS30 and in 1980 this was introduced with a single beam and improved sensitivity as the MS80.

At VG Isotopes development of its MM 30B thermal ionisation instrument continued with the introduction, in 1979, of the MM 54E. In the MM 30B ions entered and exited the 30 cm radius, 90° magnetic sector at the conventional angle normal to the magnet boundaries. In the MM 54E the entry and exit angles to the magnet were adjusted away from normal so as to reduce its focal power. This increased the path length from source to magnet, and magnet to collector, and increased its mass dispersion from 30 cm to 54 cm. This arrangement, based on a geometry proposed by W.G. Cross in 1951, also had the benefit of having stigmatic focussing. Using the same magnet geometry, the VG 5400 mass spectrometer with EI ionisation was introduced for noble gas isotope ratio measurements.

The following year, at the request of the French Nuclear Research Laboratories in Saclay, the MM 54-38 double-focussing geometry was developed. This high resolution, high sensitivity instrument was developed for ultra-high sensitivity abundance measurements using the thermal ionisation source. It used the MM 54E magnetic sector followed by the 38 cm radius electric sector from the ZAB, and the exit angle from the magnet was adjusted such that the combined sectors were both double-focussing and stigmatic focussing, an arrangement sometimes referred to as triple-focussing.

At VG Organic it was becoming recognised that the lower cost, easier to use, quadrupole-based instruments were now seen as adequate for most routine capillary GC-MS applications. The decision was taken to join other quadrupole manufacturers and develop an instrument for organic analysis, a decision that was to prove to be of crucial importance in years to come. Work started in 1976 on an instrument that used the 12 mm rods from the MM Q40, but now with the addition of short RF-only quadrupole rods for use as pre and post filters, an arrangement first described by Brubaker. The first instrument, the MM 12-12F (12 mm diameter rods, 12 kV peak-to-peak RF volts, 1200 mass range) was delivered to CNR Rome in 1978. This was VG's first instrument to be controlled by microprocessors.

Work also continued on the improvement of its sector instruments for capillary column GC-MS applications. One major development led to the introduction of the super-laminated magnet. Its design was based on transformer technology and used 0.3 mm thick grain oriented steel laminations throughout. It was first introduced on the MM 70-70HS in 1980 and this magnet essentially eliminated eddy currents allowing scan speeds down to 0.1 s per decade in mass. Furthermore it had a higher maximum field strength, providing a higher mass range, and its hysteresis and stray fields were significantly reduced. All subsequent magnets for VG's organic instruments used this technology. Many magnets were also offered in a high field version in which the pole tips were made from Permendur alloy, further increasing its mass range by about another 50%. The development of the super-laminated magnet led to the company receiving the Queen's Award for Technological Achievement in 1987.

VG Data Systems had been set up as an independent business to provide data systems to support VG's surface science instrumentation and mass spectrometers, and also to sell directly to its own customers. In fact VG Data Systems sold systems to users of competitor mass spectrometers. Conversely a few of VG Organic's users chose to have the Incos Data System, now supplied by Finnigan Corporation, interfaced to their mass spectrometer. Despite the complications of working with different manufactures these users appeared quite satisfied with the result. It appeared to VG Organic that VG Data Systems did not always give its highest priority to accommodating its growing list of software requests and so, when it was learnt that Finnigan was prepared to supply its Incos system directly to VG for sale with its mass spectrometers, VG Organic proceeded to offer both the Incos and VG 2000 systems. A few users chose the Incos system. This situation was not allowed to continue for long and in 1980 VG Data Systems and VG Organic were combined into a single company, VG Analytical, and the offer to supply the Incos system came to an end. VG Analytical, now spread over three sites in Altrincham, moved in 1983 to a new single site in Wythenshawe, Manchester.

In 1979 Kratos designed and developed a triple-sector version of the MS50, having received a "drawing board" order from the University of Nebraska. This had an additional electric sector (E), similar to the first electric sector, giving the instrument an overall EBE configuration. This allowed the MS50 to record CID-MIKES spectra, but with the benefit of higher precursor ion selection resolution than available on the ZAB. VG proceeded to offer a triple-sector version of the ZAB. This had an additional magnet sector (B) giving the instrument an overall BEB configuration. The additional magnet was similar to the first, and the design was such that the last two sectors also combined to form a double-focussing instrument, now with EB configuration. Gas collision cells were positioned between each pair of sectors, and this allowed tandem MS/MS operation with either high precursor ion resolution or high daughter ion resolution, although not both at the same time. A "drawing board" order was received from Eli Lilly in Indianapolis in 1981 and the first instrument was delivered in 1982.

1980s—THE FAB YEARS

In 1980, M. Barber (1934–1991), R.S. Bordoli (1953–2000), R.D. Sedgwick and A.N. Tyler at the University of Manchester Institute of Science and Technology (UMIST) first demonstrated a new ionisation technique, Fast Atom Bombardment (FAB). Samples were mixed with glycerol, loaded on to a copper electrode on a converted field desorption probe on an old MS9, and bombarded with 4 keV argon atoms. The technique was demonstrated to several visitors to UMIST, and in July of that year VG Analytical provided seven "difficult" samples to test the capability of the new technique. Some samples were attempted in positive ion mode, some in negative mode, some in both modes, and out of ten attempts six

Scientists from UMIST and VG Analytical studying a FAB (Fast Atom Bombardment) mass spectrum recorded on UV sensitive chart paper in 1980. The photograph includes, from left to right, Vic Parr, Bob Bordoli and Andy Tyler (standing), and Mickey Barber, Don Sedgwick and Brian Green (seated).

were successful. This score of "six out of ten" was enough to convince VG Analytical that "the technique has potential for analysing difficult samples and should be added to VG's armoury of sample handling techniques". A prototype system was built to fit to a ZAB-HF, a high mass version of the ZAB fitted with a super-laminated magnet and Permendur pole tips, and within weeks the first spectrum of insulin was obtained. The first of the ZAB-HF instruments was in the process of being installed at Imperial College in London at this time and its specification was promptly revised to be upgraded with the new FAB source.

The invention of FAB proved to be a major advance in the analytical capability and utility of MS. It also became a major stimulus in the development of magnetic sector instrumentation, in particular in a push towards instruments with higher mass range. The mass range of a magnetic sector is proportional to the square of its radius. However, as the radius of the magnet sector is increased the whole instrument must be scaled up in proportion for the instrument to retain its double-focussing characteristics. This soon leads to very large and expensive instruments. The challenge was to find a design of instrument with a high mass range, whilst retaining good sensitivity and resolution, but without becoming too large and expensive.

Kratos first responded to this need by developing a novel design of double-focussing magnetic sector instrument. In this design the magnet sector radius was increased, which normally would proportionally increase its focal length and dispersion, but then the magnet gap was tapered to produce an inhomogeneous field which reduced its focal length and dispersion sufficiently to allow its energy dispersion to remain matched to that of the electric sector. Consequently the resulting instrument had a magnetic sector with a larger radius, and therefore a larger mass range, whilst retaining its double-focussing characteristic and suffering only a small increase in overall size. These inhomogeneous magnets were described as having a "rolling-field" and were given the "RF" designation.

The MS80 was the first instrument to benefit from this innovative new design of magnet. Its 6.5" radius, 90° magnet was replaced with a 12" radius, 90° RF magnet, and the new instrument, the MS80RF, was announced in 1981 with quadrupled mass range. This was followed in 1984 with the introduction of the MS25RF, in which the 4" radius, 90° magnet of the MS25 was replaced with an 8" radius, 60° RF magnet, again quadrupling its mass range. In the same year the MS50RF was introduced in which the 12" radius, 90° magnet of the MS50 was replaced with a 27" radius, 60° RF magnet.

Rumours of a new high mass version of the MS80 filtered through to VG Analytical before it was made public. The rumours were incomplete and muddled, and stories of a new "RF magnet" were quite perplexing. Surely RF here couldn't have its usual meaning of "radio frequency"? Nevertheless the rumours served to instil a sense of urgency at VG Analytical and work immediately started on a response to this expected threat. Investigations were carried out into the effect of rotation of the magnet sector entry and exit angles, in the opposite sense to that applied to the MM 54E magnet sector, for the purpose of reducing its dispersion. It was thought a magnet sector with increased radius, but without the corresponding increase in dispersion, might allow its energy dispersion to remain matched to that of the electric sector.

These investigations were directed at increasing the mass range of the 70-70HS mass spectrometer. It was discovered, somewhat surprisingly, that its 5" radius, 70° magnet could be re-positioned and rotated through 17.5° such that ions traversed an arc with its sector angle halved to 35°, and its radius doubled to 10", and the instrument would retain its double-focussing characteristic. This provided a quick and simple solution to quadrupling its mass range, and the new instrument, the VG 70-E, was announced also in 1981.

New versions of the ZAB, the ZAB-E and the high field ZAB-SE, were subsequently developed using a similar approach and announced in 1984. Here the 11.75" radius magnet of the ZAB was replaced by a new 26" radius magnet. The ZAB-SE had an *m/z* range of 15,000 at a source voltage of 8 kV. The 70-E was itself replaced in 1985 by the 70-S which used a new 12" radius magnet.

Another area of development stimulated by the invention of FAB was the push towards large tandem MS/MS instrumentation. FAB was the first really successful soft ionisation technique to allow analysis of large bio-molecules. However, its success as a soft ionisation technique also meant it produced little fragmentation, and consequently provided little structural information. This led to a rapid growth of interest in the use of tandem MS/MS instrumentation as a tool for determining the structure of large bio-molecules.

The VG ZAB-4F, announced in 1984, was the first commercial "four-sector" MS/MS instrument. It consisted of two complete ZAB-HF mass spectrometers arranged back-to-back in a BEEB configuration. In other words ions traversed the two sectors of the first instrument

A photograph of the test area at VG Analytical's facility in Wythenshawe, Manchester, taken in 1984. The photograph shows the four-sector ZAB-4F in the foreground with development scientist Peter Bott, the three-sector ZAB-3F with development scientist George Lee, and in the background the two-sector ZAB-2F with development scientist David Bell.

in its normal BE sequence and the two sectors of the second instrument in the opposite EB sequence. The collision cell was positioned between the two instruments, allowing both high precursor ion selection resolution and high product ion resolution. This ZAB-SE-4F followed in 1986 and consisted of two ZAB-SE mass spectrometers also arranged back-to-back in a BEEB configuration. Its installation requirements called for a floor space of 9 m × 3.5 m, enough to accommodate five full size billiards tables arranged side by side. Two further "four-sector" MS/MS instruments were built around this time, the 70-SE / 70-SE combination in 1986, and the ZAB-SE / 70-SE combination in 1987.

VG Analytical also introduced the first commercial magnetic sector/quadrupole hybrid MS/MS instrument, the VG 70-EQ. This consisted of the VG 70-E magnetic sector mass spectrometer for precursor ion selection, an RF-only quadrupole gas collision cell and the quadrupole mass filter from the VG 12-12F for daughter ion analysis. A specially modified 12-12 quadrupole and power supply that allowed operation of the quadrupole at 4 kV above ground had previously been supplied to Beynon at Swansea University for use in a tandem electric sector / quadrupole research instrument, and the experience gained here proved to be useful in the design of the 70-EQ where the quadrupole needed to be elevated to 6 kV above ground. The 70-EQ was first announced in June 1982, and was exhibited at the IMSC meeting in Vienna in August 1982. The quadrupole extension, converting a magnetic

sector instrument into a hybrid MS/MS instrument, was subsequently offered on all future magnetic sector instruments from VG. Similar hybrid instruments soon became available from Kratos.

Advances in electronics and data systems during the 1980s allowed progressively more and more computer control and automation of instruments. In the mid-1980s instruments which could only be operated via the data system started to appear, and by the end of the decade instruments were being introduced where essentially all manual analogue controls had disappeared. Also during the 1980s high resolution magnetic sector instruments were increasingly being used in environmental monitoring applications, in particular for the detection and quantification of dioxins and other poly-chlorinated biphenyls. The success of this application was helped by two important developments at VG. First, in 1978, VG Organic had developed a special four channel peak switching unit which allowed voltage switching between three sample mass channels and a fourth "lock-mass" channel, at high resolution. The "lock-mass" could be a separately introduced reference peak and, via means of a feedback mechanism, the instrument could remain locked on to this peak for as long as it existed. This device allowed accurate measurement of peak intensities, at a resolution of 20,000 or higher, throughout the duration of a GC run. The "lock-mass" mechanism was subsequently transferred to the data system when instruments became computer controlled. Second, in 1986, it was discovered that the sensitivity could be increased about five times by operating the EI source at reduced electron energy. Operation with an electron energy of 25–30 eV rather than the traditional 70 eV significantly reduces the ionisation of the helium carrier gas and this in turn allows greater efficiency of ionisation of the sample.

Staff from VG Analytical receiving the Queen's Award for Export Achievement in 1986. The photograph includes, from left to right, Brian Green, Norman Lynaugh, John Race, Bob Bateman, Mr P. Homes from the British Overseas Trade Board, Sir William Downward (the Lord Lieutenant of Manchester), Alf Monks, Barry Mulady (Managing Director of VG Analytical), John Bill, Councillor Kath Robinson (the Lord Mayor of Manchester) and Bob Bordoli.

The first MM ZAB-2F reverse geometry double-focussing mass spectrometer photographed prior to delivery to the University of Swansea in 1976.

Outside the field of organic MS, VG Isotopes, working closely with A.L. Gray and A. Date at Surrey University, was amongst the first to introduce an inductively coupled plasma (ICP) mass spectrometer, the PlasmaQuad. Based on the 12-12 quadrupole mass filter the Plasma-Quad was introduced in 1985. In a separate initiative VG Isotopes developed the VG 9000 for solids analysis using a glow discharge ionisation source on their 54-38 triple-focussing mass spectrometer.

In keeping with VG's "Christmas card principle" its member companies would, from time to time, spin out new companies. In 1982 VG Isotopes had set up VG Isogas to specialise in the supply of its SIRA and 903 small radius instruments for the measurement of stable gas isotope ratios. Now, in 1986, VG Elemental was spun out for the manufacture of the ICP and Glow Discharge instruments. VG Isotopes itself continued to develop the thermal ionisation (TIMS) instrument, now renamed the Sector-54. In 1988 it developed a motorised multiple Faraday detector collector array for the Sector-54 which allowed automated repositioning of the detectors necessary to record the isotopes of different elements.

VG Elemental embarked on the production of a high resolution ICP-MS to address the problem of mass interferences that can exist in ICP mass spectra. The instrument, known as the PlasmaTrace, was based on the VG 70-S mass spectrometer and was introduced in 1989. This was the first commercially available high resolution ICP-MS, and it was used extensively for the analysis of high purity materials for use in the semi-conductor industry. The PlasmaTrace 2, introduced in 1994, saw the development of a completely new double-focussing magnetic sector instrument, purpose designed by VG Elemental to meet the needs of elemental analysis.

At VG Analytical, the quadrupole business had continued to grow steadily since the introduction of the MM 12-12F and in 1984 it was decided to spin out a new company, VG MassLab, to develop the organic quadrupole MS business. MassLab was located back in Altrincham, at the site that VG Analytical had vacated just one year earlier. Over the next three years MassLab introduced the Trio range of fully computerised single and triple quadrupole mass spectrometers, based on the 12-12 quadrupole mass filter.

In 1985 VG Analytical introduced the VG TS250, a novel design of magnetic sector mass spectrometer with an air-cored magnet. The iron-less magnet was essentially free of hysteresis and saturation effects, problems encountered by iron cored magnets which give rise to non-linear responses. It was also essentially free of eddy currents and could be scanned and switched quickly and accurately. However, its maximum field strength was quite weak and a magnet sector with an unusually large radius (1.5 metres) was required. To keep the magnet size manageable it had an unusually small sector angle, just 15°. Two very small electric sectors were added close to the entry and exit to the magnet to provide energy focussing and help keep its path lengths reasonably short. A new company, VG Tritech, was formed in 1987 to supply the TS250. In addition to competing with other manufacturers VG Tritech found itself also competing against the lower cost quadrupoles from VG MassLab and the higher performance VG 70-S from VG Analytical.

In 1987 Kratos introduced the first electrical array detector to be used in commercial mass spectrometers. Ions with a range of masses were focussed onto a 1" long micro-channel plate, the output of which illuminated a phosphor, and the image was recorded with a 1" long, 1024 channel photo-diode array detector. The detector was fitted to an MS50 and could record a 4% mass range in parallel, giving a substantial increase in sensitivity when compared with scanning over the same mass range with a conventional "point" detector.

The benefit to be gained from such a detector, which had fairly low resolution, was quite limited when used with an ionisation technique such as FAB which has substantial chemical background. However, this development stimulated an interest in the use of such detectors in MS/MS instrumentation for recording daughter ion spectra where chemical background is significantly less. VG Analytical built a tandem four-sector MS/MS instrument, the VG ZAB-T, in which the second mass spectrometer was a novel design of double-focussing instrument which allowed a larger mass range to be recorded simultaneously on an array detector. In 1988 a "drawing board" order for the first of these instruments was received from the University of Nebraska. This instrument, delivered in 1990, was able to focus ions with a wide range of masses onto a six inch long micro-channel plate detector, and record the image formed on a phosphor using a combination of photo-diode array detectors with a total of 4096 channels. The detector could be rotated to allow parallel recording over a variable mass range, up to a maximum mass ratio of 1.75:1.

The Kratos magnetic sector instruments all had their layout in a vertical plane. This had presented particular difficulties when constructing the triple-sector version of the MS50 for the University of Nebraska, when the instrument had to be raised onto a specially constructed platform. Ever since that time the company had struggled with the dilemma of whether or not to abandon the vertical configuration in favour of a horizontal layout. The vertical arrangement presented many difficult problems in the design, construction and operation of tandem and hybrid MS/MS instruments and the vertical or horizontal dilemma was the subject of many internal discussions over several years. Eventually, in 1986, the issue was forced when an order was accepted from the University of Warwick to convert their MS50 into a three-sector BEB instrument. Such an instrument would most likely have been difficult to construct and so this order triggered the development of a new instrument, the "Concept". This was introduced in 1988 and had the same ion optical arrangement as the MS50 but, for the first time from the former AEI group, had a horizontal layout. This layout allowed the instrument to be offered in numerous configurations. It was available with the standard mass range or with high mass range using the RF magnet, and was also available in hybrid MS/MS and tandem four-sector MS/MS configurations. The latter were also available with the array detector. In parallel to the development of the "Concept" the MS25RF was re-engineered to be fully computer controlled and the new product was introduced in the following year under the name 'Profile'.

In the same year, VG Analytical introduced the AutoSpec instrument, which was to replace its 70-70 series of magnetic sector instruments, and later the ZAB series of instruments. The 70-70 series of instruments had a "forward" double-focussing geometry (EB configuration), whilst the ZAB instruments had a "reverse" geometry (BE configuration). For many years this had allowed VG to offer a choice of configurations, but this choice also highlighted the fact that each configuration has its own advantages and disadvantages. It was felt the time had come for these ageing instruments to be replaced, ideally with a configuration with all the advantages and none of the disadvantages. Their replacement was the Auto-Spec, having a novel tri-sector double-focussing geometry with EBE configuration. Unlike previous triple-sector instruments in this design all three sectors combine to have the zero energy dispersion necessary for double-focussing. This arrangement benefited from the advantages associated with both forward and reverse geometries in a single instrument.

A special version of this instrument, the AutoSpec Ultima, was developed for CDC in Atlanta, Georgia, in 1991. This had a new magnet with a significantly wider gap, giving improved transmission and stability, albeit at reduced mass range. Nevertheless its mass range was still adequate to allow it to be used for the high resolution analysis, by GC-MS, of environmentally hazardous compounds of interest (e.g. dioxins and other poly-chlorinated biphenyls). In its first 20 years of production more than 700 AutoSpecs and AutoSpec Ultimas were sold, making it the highest selling double-focussing magnetic sector mass spectrometer to be built in Manchester.

The AutoSpec's 15" radius magnet was preceded by a small 2.5" radius electric sector and followed by a larger 5" radius electric sector. A family of instruments soon followed using the same electric sectors. These included the ProSpec in 1992, using two of the smaller electric sectors and a 9" radius magnet, and the ZabSpec in 1993, using two of the larger electric sectors and a 22" radius magnet. The AutoSpec and ZabSpec were also available in hybrid and tandem MS/MS configurations, the latter including the AutoSpec-6F with a record breaking six sectors.

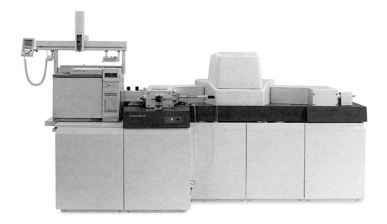

The AutoSpec Ultima double-focussing mass spectrometer with EBE geometry (photographed c. 1998). The Ultima version of the AutoSpec was specially developed for the analysis of environmentally hazardous compounds by high resolution GC-MS.

The end of the 1980s saw yet more changes in ownership of Manchester's MS businesses. In 1989 Kratos was acquired by Shimadzu, the Japanese scientific instrument manufacturer. The following year VG Instruments, which by now had become owned by British American Tobacco (BAT), was sold to Fisons, the British pharmaceutical company. Within the VG organisation, VG Isotech was set up to supply the TIMS, Noble Gas and Stable Gas Isotope products formally supplied by VG Isotopes and VG Isogas.

1990s—THE ARRIVAL OF MALDI AND ELECTROSPRAY

The development of FAB at the beginning of the 1980s had led directly to several major developments in magnetic sector technology, and to significant growth in sales of magnetic sector instruments. The near simultaneous developments of electrospray and matrix-assisted laser desorption/ionisation (MALDI) at the end of the 1980s took MS into a new era where just about all types of organic compounds were now amenable to analysis by mass spectrometry, and their success led to a rapid decline in the use of FAB. However, magnetic sector instruments are not well suited to accommodate either MALDI or electrospray. Furthermore, the tendency for electrospray to produce multiply charged ions allowed the analysis of large bio-molecules to be carried out on analysers with low m/z range such as quadrupoles, and very high mass range magnetic sector instruments were no longer required. These developments led to a decline in the sales of magnetic sector instruments, reversing the increase brought about by the development of FAB at the beginning of the decade.

Electrospray, along with atmospheric pressure chemical ionisation (APCI), also provided the solution to the problem of interfacing liquid chromatography to MS, possibly the most important problem facing mass spectrometry at this time. It soon became clear that quadrupoles with electrospray ionisation would likely supersede magnetic sectors for high mass analysis applications, and would become the preferred technology for interfacing to liquid chromatography. As a consequence the VG Tritech products were moved back into VG

Analytical and a new company, VG Biotech, was set up to develop and supply quadrupole instruments with atmospheric pressure ionisation (API) sources and LC-MS systems.

In 1989 VG Biotech introduced its first electrospray system, the Bio-Q triple quadrupole, using two 12-12 quadrupole mass filters with their *m/z* ranges increased to 4000, and with a hexapole gas collision cell in place of the central quadrupole. This was soon followed by the first of the Quattro series of triple quadrupole instruments. In 1992, in collaboration with J. Skilling at Cambridge University, Biotech introduced the first use of "Maximum Entropy" software for deconvolution of multiply charged electrospray data for complex mixtures. The MaxEnt program repeatedly computes the likely series of multiply charged ions that would be expected from trial components of an unknown mixture when analysed by electrospray and, by comparing the results with the observed data, automatically homes in on the most likely composition of components, their masses and relative abundances, that would give rise to the observed complex electrospray spectrum. This software revolution-ised the interpretation of such data for complex mixtures. In 1993 the Platform-LC single quadrupole instrument was introduced, the first commercial bench-top quadrupole LC-MS system. This was also the first instrument on which the electrospray version of "Open Access" became available. Developed for Burroughs Wellcome, this was a do-it-yourself system enabling non-expert organic chemists to walk up and get their own mass spectra.

Kratos turned its attention to supplying MALDI instrumentation and in 1992 introduced the first of its Kompact series of bench-top MALDI time-of-flight (TOF) instruments. Kratos went on to develop a MALDI-TOF system which used a non-linear reflectron to enable recording of complete post source decay product ion spectra in a single acquisition. In 2002 Kratos launched the Axima, a novel hybrid Quadrupole Ion Trap–TOF mass spectrometer, first with a MALDI source and later with an API source. VG Analytical also ventured into the world of TOF-MS and introduced its own MALDI-TOF instrument, the TofSpec in 1992. This and its successors were floor standing instruments, but in 1999 the company intro-duced a new bench-top instrument, the perplexingly named M@LDI.

The arrival of electrospray and MALDI led to a rapid demise in the use of magnetic sector instruments for general analysis applications and, in 1993, almost half a century after Met-ropolitan Vickers started their production, Kratos stopped production of magnetic sector mass spectrometers. However, at VG Analytical, sales of the AutoSpec Ultima for the quantification of specific environmentally hazardous compounds were not affected and its production continued unabated.

In 1989, J.H.J. Dawson (1948–1991) and M. Guilhaus (1954–2009) at the University of New South Wales, Australia, published a theoretical paper on the orthogonal acceleration time-of-flight (oa-TOF) mass analyser. Guilhaus presented this work at the ASMS meet-ing in Washington in June 1992 and was subsequently invited to visit VG Analytical on his way back to Australia. At this stage he had no means of acquiring data to demonstrate the sensitivity of the oa-TOF, but nevertheless his enthusiasm for this mass analyser was enough to convince VG Analytical to go ahead and build its own prototype. At VG it was seen as a potential second analyser in a tandem MS/MS instrument, in particular as an alternative to the large and complex double-focussing magnetic sector with array detector system used in the AutoSpec-T and ZabSpec-T.

A theoretical analysis of the expected performance of the oa-TOF in an MS/MS configuration looked encouraging and by the end of 1992 VG Analytical had received a "drawing board" order for an instrument, to be known as the AutoSpec-TOF, from Sahlgrenska University Hospital in Gothenburg, Sweden. Early in the following year a second "drawing board" order was received for a ZabSpec-TOF from Proctor and Gamble in Cincinnati, Ohio.

The specification for the data acquisition electronics was right at the cutting edge of fast electronics for that time, and Precision Instruments in Knoxville, Tennessee, were asked to design and supply a time-to-digital convertor (TDC) with a 1 GHz sampling frequency. The first prototype was delivered early in 1994 and at last the true performance of the mass analyser could be measured. The contrast in performance of the new analyser was amply illustrated during its first demonstration a few weeks later to B. Samuelsson visiting from Sahlgrenska Hospital. On previous two-day visits to evaluate first the ZAB-T, and then the AutoSpec-T, the intention had been to analyse six samples, gangliosides, by FAB MS/MS. Each occasion had failed to see the completion of the analysis of all six samples. However, on this occasion, all six samples were completed successfully by mid-morning on the first day. The rest of the morning was taken up with cancelling the hotel booking, rearranging flights and departing for an early and enjoyable lunch.

The AutoSpec-TOF quickly succeeded the tandem sector-sector instruments. However, the euphoria following its first FAB MS/MS demonstration was short lived. At the first electrospray MS/MS demonstration a few weeks later the sensitivity was quite disappointing, struggling to equal that of VG Biotech's new Quattro-2 triple quadrupole. This was assumed to be due in part to poorer source sensitivity, but more importantly due to the relatively poor efficiency of its "box type" gas cell for fragmentation of "cold" electrospray ions compared to that of the RF hexapole gas cell used on the Quattro-2.

It was thought that a hybrid quadrupole orthogonal-TOF instrument might perform better than a hybrid magnetic sector orthogonal-TOF instrument for MS/MS applications with electrospray ions. Such an instrument could be based on the Quattro-2 with the last quadrupole mass filter replaced by an orthogonal-TOF mass analyser. The question arose as to where this development should take place—at VG Analytical which had become the home for TOF instrumentation or at VG Biotech which was the home for API quadrupole instrumentation? Work started at VG Biotech but eventually it was decided the new instrument should be developed at VG Analytical. The Micromass Q-TOF was introduced at the ASMS meeting in Portland, Oregon, in 1996, and the first instruments were delivered later that year. It provided a substantial improvement in sensitivity and speed of acquisition, and was capable of providing accurately mass measured spectra, even on short lived chromatography peaks. It was the first instrument of this type and its development led to the company receiving its second Queen's Award for Technological Achievement in 2000.

The Q-TOF mass spectrometer fitted with the Micromass Z-Spray source (photographed c. 1998). The Micromass Q-TOF was the world's first commercial tandem quadrupole-orthogonal acceleration TOF mass spectrometer, with deliveries commencing in 1996.

In 1995 VG Isotech was relocated to VG Analytical's site in Manchester. Shortly afterwards several of its staff left the company to set up various independent mass spectrometer manufacturing companies specialising in one or more types of isotope ratio MS. Most notable amongst these was Nu-Instruments, which set up production at Wrexham in North Wales, about 45 miles south west of Manchester. Nu-Instruments developed an innovative multiple collector instrument that incorporated a zoom lens that allows the isotopes of different elements to be recorded without the need for mechanical repositioning of the collectors.

In 1995, Thermo Electron Corporation, having previously acquired Finnigan MAT in 1990, made an offer for Fisons Instruments, which included VG Instruments. Because of monopoly considerations it was finally ruled that Fisons should first divest itself of the activities of VG Analytical, VG Biotech, VG Isotech and VG Elemental's PlasmaTrace-2 high resolution ICP mass spectrometer. These were bought by a management team, led by N. Lynaugh, in 1996 and the new company, with factories in the Wythenshawe and Altrincham areas of Manchester, was named Micromass (UK) Ltd. Within months of its formation Micromass was able to introduce two new developments that had been in the pipeline, the Q-TOF and a new API source configuration known as the Z-Spray source. This source included two stages of orthogonal extraction of ions which serve to prevent direct transmission of droplets and particulate matter, thereby reducing noise and reducing contamination of critical optical components. This gave a substantial improvement in reliability, and LC-MS was becoming as routine and robust as GC-MS had become many years earlier.

In 1997, 18 months after its formation, Micromass was acquired by Waters Corporation, based in Massachusetts, a supplier of liquid chromatography equipment. For the chromatographer a mass spectrometer is seen as a useful detector, whereas for the mass spectroscopist chromatography is seen as a useful inlet system. Whatever the point of view, most agree that the combination of LC and MS is worth more than its parts. Waters required a quadrupole mass spectrometer for use as a high-performance liquid chromatography (HPLC) detector and the Micromass Platform-LC, now fitted with the new Z-Spray source, was re-engineered and renamed the ZMD. Although supplied by Micromass, the ZMD was distributed exclusively by Waters as a detector for its Alliance HPLC system. For the next five years all the remaining mass spectrometers continued to be distributed by Micromass, after which all its mass spectrometers were distributed by Waters.

New MS-only instruments using the orthogonal-TOF mass analyser soon followed. The LCT, a bench-top LC-MS instrument using an orthogonal-TOF mass analyser, was introduced in 1997, and 1999 saw the introduction of the GCT, a bench-top GC-MS instrument using the same mass analyser. The LCT with the Z-Spray source allowed acquisition of full spectra quickly and with good sensitivity, and this made possible the development of a multiplexed electrospray sampling system. Developed for SmithKline Beecham (SKB) in 1999, this consisted of a rotatable shutter mechanism for selection of any one of eight inlet sprays allowing acquisition of mass spectra from eight HPLC columns in parallel. The following year a similar mechanism with just two sprays, where one was dedicated to delivery of a mass reference, was also developed for SKB. Termed LockSpray, this became a standard feature on the LCT and Q-TOF for providing accurately mass measured spectra throughout the duration of an HPLC experiment.

The GCT and LCT could also be used to determine the accurate mass of components eluting from GC and LC columns, and usually were easier to use and more sensitive than magnetic sector instruments. The GCT also proved to be particularly well suited for use with Field Ionisation (FI), a technique commonly used in petroleum analysis. The introduction of these instruments served to further curtail the role of magnetic sector instruments and this led, a few years later, to the introduction of the AutoSpec Premier, a simplified version of the AutoSpec Ultima in which all ion sources other than EI and CI were no longer available.

Later generations of the Q-TOF saw the introduction of several new developments. The Q-TOF had proved to be particularly effective for the analysis of macromolecular assemblies for which m/z values could be as high as 30,000 and in 2000, following a development initiated by C.V. Robinson at Oxford University, a 30,000 m/z range quadrupole option was introduced. The same year saw the introduction of the W-Optics. Here the ions either take one flight through the reflectron (V-mode) or are returned by an additional small reflectron to take a second flight through the reflectron (W-mode), doubling the flight path and almost doubling the mass resolution. The following year saw the introduction of a MALDI source for the Q-TOF, and in the same year a smaller bench-top version, the Q-TOF Micro, was introduced.

The isotope and elemental analysis products previously supplied by VG Isotech were now in the hands of Micromass. New developments included the introduction of the IsoPrime stable gas isotope instrument, the development of a multiple ion counting detector for the Sector-54, and the introduction of two new ICP-MS products, the Platform-ICP and the IsoProbe. The Platform-ICP used the 12-12 quadrupole and included a novel RF hexapole gas collision cell for the decomposition of polyatomic ions, and for cooling ions, prior to mass analysis. The same technology was incorporated in the IsoProbe, a version of the Sector-54 in which the thermal ionisation source was replaced by an ICP source.

In 2003 a few former employees of VG Isotopes formed a new company, GV Instruments, to acquire the Micromass isotope and elemental analysis products. In 2006 GV Instruments was itself acquired by Thermo Instruments and, yet again, Thermo were required, on monopoly considerations, to dispose of the stable gas isotope and thermal ionisation products. These disposals were completed in 2008. The stable gas isotope MS, the IsoPrime, was acquired by Elementar and moved to Cheadle in Manchester, whilst a new company, IsotopX, was set up in Middlewich, Cheshire, to supply the Sector-54 TIMS.

After so many years of commercial MS in and around Manchester it is not surprising that there have been, and continue to be, several other enterprises designing, developing and supplying mass spectrometers, and many more providing service and support to users of mass spectrometers. Many of these companies have made their own unique contribution to MS. Of particular interest is HD Technologies, set up in 1993 in Wythenshawe, Manchester, by A. Hoffman and S. Davis, formally with Kratos. HD Technologies specialised in the design and development of TOF instrumentation, but also built the first prototype of the Orbitrap Fourier transform mass spectrometer. Details of the Orbitrap's performance were presented at the ASMS meeting in Dallas in 1999, and the company was acquired by Thermo Instruments a year later.

2000s—THE DEVELOPMENT OF ION MOBILITY

In 1999 Micromass introduced a new higher transmission version of the Quattro that had an additional stage of differential pumping between the atmospheric pressure source and the first quadrupole mass filter, and which used an additional RF hexapole ion guide to transport ions through this chamber. A new RF ion guide was developed in 2001 in which the two hexapole ion guides were replaced by ion guides consisting of a stack of rings, or washers, with the RF voltage applied between neighbouring rings. This configuration allowed different DC voltages to be applied between neighbouring rings and this added significant versatility to the ion guide. Potential gradients could be applied along the length of the ion guide, and if transient DC voltages were applied the potential profile along the ion guide could be programmed to take on almost any static or dynamic form.

A profile of particular interest was the "travelling wave", a periodic wave profile similar to a sine wave distributed along the length of the ion guide and which moved along the ion guide with programmable velocity. The "travelling wave" ion guide (TWIG) was first introduced in the gas cell of the Quattro in 2003. Here ions travel through the gas cell in the wave troughs with the programmed transit time. Previously ions could slow down to a stand still and remain in the gas cell until pushed along by following ions. This could result in memory effects and cross talk problems in multiple reaction monitoring experiments, one of the main applications of the triple quadrupole. The TWIG ion guide successfully overcame this problem.

During the 1990s D.E. Clemmer at the University of Indiana published several papers that showed the combination of ion mobility separation and TOF-MS of peptides could be useful in the study of proteomics. This inspired interest in this technique at several institutions, including Micromass. Experiments at Micromass with the RF ring stack ion guide and superimposed DC potential gradient demonstrated that ions could be transported though this device, and separated according to their mobility, with very low or zero losses. The development of a new Q-TOF instrument incorporating high transmission ion mobility separation was assured by a "drawing board" order received from the University of Warwick in March 2002.

In December 2002 further experiments were carried out using the TWIG gas cell. The pressure in the gas cell was increased to a much higher level than normal, to about 0.05 mbar. This was about as high as the pressure could be raised before the vacuum system could no longer cope with the gas flow. Packets of ions were pulsed into the ion guide and groups of ions were observed to exit the ion guide at different times. Normally the transit time for all ions through the travelling wave ion guide is the same, and is equal to the transit time for a single wave. Now, at this elevated pressure, the viscous drag on ions was sufficient to cause ions to slip from one wave trough to the next, and the less mobile the ion the more it would slip. This discovery led to the development of a new form of ion mobility analyser that was eventually incorporated into the Q-TOF.

The new instrument, the Waters "Synapt", was introduced in 2006, and the first instrument was delivered to J.H. Scrivens at Warwick University later in the year. This had a new double gas cell, taking the form of a gas cell within a gas cell. The differentially pumped double gas cell allowed the inner cell to be operated at pressures of about 0.5 mbar, and up to about 3 mbar in later versions of the instrument, which was adequate for separation of ions according to their mobility, whilst the outer cell operated at the normal pressure required for collision induced decomposition. Ions pass through the first stage of the outer cell, where they may be fragmented, through the inner cell, where they may be separated by mobility, and finally through the second stage of the outer cell, where again they may be fragmented if required, before mass analysis in the orthogonal-TOF. Use of an RF ion guide, together with ion trapping prior to injection into the inner cell, provided ion mobility analysis essentially without loss in transmission. The Synapt was the first commercial mass spectrometer with the ability to separate ions by mobility and provide information on their shape and size, all without loss in sensitivity. This instrument made it possible for the first time to make such measurements practical for large bio-molecules and macromolecular assemblies.

Mass spectrometers have been manufactured in and around Manchester continuously since the end of World War II. Throughout most of this time it has provided employment in the Manchester area to several hundred people who, in return, have made many significant contributions to the technology and practice of MS. As Blears observed when reflecting on the origin of commercial MS in Manchester, "determining events are more often *chance* and *coincidence* rather than logical planning. However, there are preconditions for chance to be taken, notably some *relevant skills* to recognise that a chance exists and that the chance must be taken." The continued presence of a mass spectrometer manufacturing industry in Manchester has ensured that those *relevant skills* continue to exist in Manchester.

FURTHER READING

J.H. Beynon, "Thirty years of mass spectrometry", *Appl. Spectrosc.* **33,** 339–345 (1979).

A. Quayle, "Recollections of mass spectrometry of the fifties in a UK petroleum laboratory", *Org. Mass Spectrom.* **22(9),** 569–585 (1987).

J.R. Chapman, G.A. Errock and J.A. Race, "Science and technology in Manchester: the nurture of mass spectrometry", *Rapid Commun. Mass Spectrom.* **11(14),** 1575–1586 (1997).

J.S. Halliday, "Jack Blears (Obituary)", *IEE News* March (2001).

M. Morris and D. Jones, "Brian N Green OBE", *Mass Matters* Edition 55, 7 (2008).

A.G. Brenton, "John Beynon", *Mass Matters* Edition 56, 9 (2008).

A.G. Brenton, J.J. Monaghan, R.W. Munn and J.M. Thomas, "Professor Michael Barber FRS (Obituary)", *Rapid Commun. Mass Spectrom.* **5(7),** 340–342 (1991).

J.J. Monaghan, "Dr Robert S. Bordoli (Obituary)", *BMSS Newsletter* Edition 39, 3–4 (2000).

Mass spectrometry in Bremen, a tribute to Dr Ludolf Jenckel

Jochen Franzen

Bruker Daltonik GmbH, Bremen, Germany

BREMEN: TODAY A CAPITAL OF MASS SPECTROMETRY

Almost unnoticed by the public of Bremen, and known only to a few insiders, a small but remarkable industrial sector has developed in Bremen and the surrounding region. Employing some 800 highly qualified personnel, this highly specialised industry has made Bremen a familiar name amongst experts in mass spectrometry worldwide. Founded in 1947 through a private initiative by Dr Ludolf Jenckel, who was then employed at the shipbuilding company Atlas-Werke, the sector today encompasses two major firms and a dozen smaller businesses, each of which belong to the world elite in their respective specialties. Mass spectrometry in Bremen generates an estimated annual turnover of around a quarter of a billion Euros and such is the rate of growth that, in spite of worldwide competition in England, Japan and North America, one may fairly describe Bremen as a "capital of mass spectrometry".

Mass spectrometers are scientific instruments used to perform a range of different investigative measures on matter, and they are principally employed in world-class chemical, pharmaceutical, biological and medical research. That is why the industry is always positioned at the leading edge of technology and has to employ highly qualified scientists in its development departments. In most cases, the capabilities of mass spectrometers for solving a wide range of analytical problems can be illustrated effectively only by demonstrating measurements on samples from customers. Consequently, Bremen is host to a constant stream of scientific visitors from all corners of the world. Bremen's reputation in expert circles also makes it possible to attract scientific conferences to the Hanseatic city: the "International Mass Spectrometry Foundation" held its triennial conference at Bremen Congress Centre in 2009, receiving over 2600 visitors. In 2006, the "German Mass Spectrometry Society" (DGMS) also chose Bremen as the venue for its 40th symposium.

In the first half of the last century, mass spectrometry was restricted to "home-made" devices built at university laboratories and research institutes by enthusiastic scientists, aiming at isotope detection, isotope ratio measurements, precise mass measurement of atomic nuclei for the investigation of atomic binding energies etc. Industrially manufactured devices had yet to make an appearance. All the development work on the various mass spectrometric principles was based almost exclusively on magnetic sector instruments and carried out at university institutes. For example, Alfred Otto Nier, at Harvard, developed the "Nier geometry" of deflection in a magnetic sector of exactly 60° for so-called single-focussing mass spectrometers. In this arrangement, the ion source, the ion detector and the tip of the 60° sector are aligned. In 1934, Josef Mattauch and Richard Herzog, in Vienna, developed the double-focussing mass spectrograph which could be used for ion detection with photographic plates over a wide range of the mass spectrum. Other famous names are Arthur Jeffrey Dempster (University of Chicago) and Kenneth Tompkins Bainbridge (Harvard). In nuclear technology circles, mass spectrometry became widely known when the "Manhattan Project" at Oak Ridge used huge magnetic mass spectrometers for large-scale separation of weighable quantities of the isotopes of uranium. The uranium 235 isotope formed the explosive for the first atomic bomb.

Dr Ludolf Jenckel

Opposite: Jenckel's first mass spectrometer.

A further demand in the use of mass spectrometry only began during and after the Second World War, when it was realised that not only the atoms of elements but also complex organic molecules could be ionised and investigated by mass spectrometry. This was useful in various branches of chemistry, such as the petrochemical industry, and in 1942 the first commercially manufactured mass spectrometers (the "21-101") were duly launched on the market by Consolidated Engineering Corporation (CEC) in Pasadena, California, USA. In 1948, Metropolitan Vickers Electric Company (MetroVick) in Manchester, UK, launched the first commercial European mass spectrometer. It was now possible to determine the elementary composition, structure and identity of molecules very quickly and relatively simply. Mixtures of different types of substances could also be analysed. This marked the dawn of the era of "organic mass spectrometry" of vaporisable organic molecules. Today several thousand mass spectrometers are in use around the world.

Thus, physical atomic mass spectrometry was very quickly overtaken by chemical molecular mass spectrometry. Today we are going a step further. We are now in the age of molecular biology and molecular medicine, dealing with the basic building blocks of the human body and, indeed, of human life: the millions of proteins which make our bodies function, or malfunction, are today investigated by biochemical mass spectrometry.

THE BEGINNING OF MASS SPECTROMETRY IN BREMEN

In 1997, the 50th anniversary of the MAT company, a commemorative publication entitled "50 years of MAT in Bremen" appeared, first privately in the German language,[1] later as a publication in English.[2] Its author, Dr Curt Brunnée, was a colleague of Dr Ludolf Jenckel, with whom he worked for many years as chief developer. "MAT" stands for "Mess- und Analysen-Technik" (Measurement and Analysis Technology). The following is a translated extract from the introduction of the German version:

"In 1947, Dr Ludolf Jenckel, a young physicist working at the Atlas-Werke in Bremen, had an idea: he rented a cellar in a hospital and in his spare time there attempted to construct a mass spectrometer. Once he had completed a primitive prototype, Dr Jenckel persuaded the Atlas management to set up a small department—MAT—to build commercial mass spectrometers for sale. The prototype was modified, and in 1950 the first production model, the CH3, was launched on the market. During MAT's early years, sales were rather modest, but Dr Jenckel refused to give up. He began developing a successor model, the 60° sector device CH4, which was launched in 1958. In the following years, MAT's position was strengthened by sales of more than 400 of these devices. In 1967, MAT was taken over by Varian Associates (Palo Alto, California) and the business continued to expand. New technologies were introduced, and new mass spectrometers were developed for different applications. MAT became one of the leading mass spectrometer manufacturers in the world. By 1976, sales broke through the 1000 barrier. In 1981, Finnigan (San Jose, California) took over MAT, marking the start of a fruitful cooperation between Bremen and San Jose. This year, MAT celebrates its 50th birthday. It is one of the few firms in the field of mass spectrometry to have been a market leader throughout all these years."

What this introduction does not make clear, however, is the pioneering spirit, determination, optimism and powers of persuasion required to found such a business and to make it a success. The industrial environment in Bremen at that time was anything but favourable for the development of complex scientific instruments: shipbuilding and automobile manufacture were dominant; there was also a residual aircraft industry (from which Bremen's aerospace activities would later develop), but there was no precision engineering, no ultra-high vacuum technology, no electronic measuring technology for minuscule ion currents far below a billionth of an ampere, no knowledge base for the production of high-stability electromagnets, no glassblowers and no university to provide scientific support. In fact, Bremen was something of a technological wilderness; in addition to which, there were psychological barriers to be surmounted. If one disregards ship's instruments, Bremen was certainly not known as a production location for high-quality scientific measuring instruments as was, for example, Göttingen or Jena. All this forms the background to the rather dry statement in Dr Brunnée's introduction: "but Dr Jenckel refused to give up".

LUDOLF JENCKEL, THE PERSON

Ludolf Hans Franz Jenckel was born in Hassendorf (District of Rotenburg near Bremen) on 4 December 1912, the son of a chemist. His father, Dr Ludolf Jenckel, had a small chemical factory in Hassendorf producing hydrofluoric acid. After elementary school in Hassendorf, Ludolf Jenckel attended the Neues Gymnasium, a high school in Bremen. During this period he lived with a family by the name of Maass, who were later to play a decisive role in his life. Following his high-school graduation in 1931, he spent six months as a student trainee with a railway repair shop in Bremen before going on to study physics, mathematics and chemistry in Göttingen for two years, with a half-year break during which he attempted, without success, to save his father's business after his death.

Following six months of "labour service", he resumed his studies, this time at Munich Technical University, where he took his intermediate exam in engineering physics after a further year. At the Technical University in Berlin-Charlottenburg he graduated with a diploma in physics in 1937. This was followed by four months of military service. In Berlin he must have met his later teacher and PhD supervisor, Hans Kopfermann, and also Kopfermann's assistant, Wilhelm Walcher, who later became a close friend of his. In 1937, Kopfermann was appointed to the "Grenzlanduniversität Kiel" and, therefore, Ludolf Jenckel began his doctoral thesis on "A method of observing very small Stark effects" in Kiel. At the outbreak of war in 1939, he was drafted, but was able to complete his doctorate in Berlin-Charlottenburg during a period of special leave in 1940. His thesis was published in 1941, in Volume 117 of the famous *Zeitschrift für Physik* with Hans Kopfermann as co-author. In the publication, Ludolf Jenckel's address is given as "in the field", meaning that he was serving in the armed forces. The method for measuring very small Stark effects has become known as the "Jenckel–Kopfermann method".

At the Kopfermann Institute there were two teaching assistants who would later become very famous, and who both remained lifelong friends of Ludolf Jenckel: Wilhelm Walcher and Wolfgang Paul. Wilhelm Walcher had been assistant to Gustav Hertz in Berlin since 1933, then assistant to Geiger (the inventor of the Geiger counter). Following the period spent working with Kopfermann, he was appointed Professor of Experimental Physics in Marburg, where he became famous for his exciting lectures on experimental physics, which his students affectionately, and admiringly, dubbed the "Walcher Circus". Walcher also held the office of president of the German Physical Society (DPG) and was, for a long time, vice-president of the German Research Foundation (DFG). He died in Marburg in 2005 at the age of 95. Wolfgang Paul became Professor of Experimental Physics in Bonn, where he invented quadrupole mass spectrometry and mass spectrometric ion traps in the early 1950s, an achievement for which he was awarded the Nobel Prize almost forty years later in 1989. Wolfgang Paul was also director of CERN, chairman of the directorate at the DESY (German Electron Synchroton) and long-standing president of the Alexander von Humboldt Foundation; he was awarded numerous honorary doctorates, medals of honour and scientific awards.

The projects of the Institute of Experimental Physics at the "Grenzlanduniversität Kiel", to which Kopfermann had been appointed, focussed almost entirely on measuring the properties of minute particles. Wilhelm Walcher had already turned his attention to mass spectrometry during his time at this institute, and his interest in this field probably "rubbed off" on Ludolf Jenckel, even at this stage.

It is said that all Hans Kopfermann's students went on to have successful careers. In a tribute at the time of his death, Wolfgang Paul emphasised that 16 of Kopfermann's students had become university professors of wide repute. This formative influence was also enjoyed by Ludolf Jenckel who, in contrast, pursued a career in industry.

Prior to this, however, he was called upon to do his military service. In various theatres of war, on the Western and Eastern Fronts, he held a range of positions, from bombardier to ordnance officer, from private to lieutenant, winning various medals for bravery along the way. In 1943, he was suddenly exempted from military service and took up a position as physicist and group leader at the then Atlas-Werke in Bremen, where he worked on the development of sonar and medical electrical equipment. Sonar had become extremely important for locating ships, especially submarines. For this surprising new departure in his life he was indebted to Dr Heinz Maass, in whose home and family he had lived during his high-school days, and who held an important position at Atlas-Werke. After the end of the war, Ludolf Jenckel stayed at Atlas-Werke and continued his work on the development of sonar and medical equipment. Atlas-Werke, at that time an eclectic mixture of shipyard and manufacturer of all sorts of accessory equipment for shipping, was largely in the hands of Hugo Stinnes junior, son of the finance and business magnate Hugo Stinnes, who had died in 1923. Hugo Stinnes junior held a majority shareholding and chaired the Supervisory Committee. As can be seen from his later correspondence with Ludolf Jenckel, Hugo Stinnes took a lively interest in his career and in his company, MAT.

JENCKEL'S PATH TO SUCCESS

Ludolf Jenckel's path to success was by no means an easy one. In 1947, he asked the Atlas management whether he could develop a commercially viable mass spectrometer from within the company. But his request was turned down. Thereafter, he worked half-days and rented a cellar at the Sankt-Jürgen-Strasse Hospital, where he set about building the prototype "MS1" mass spectrometer, for which his friend, Wilhelm Walcher, provided the electro-magnet. A year later, he demonstrated this instrument to the Atlas management and was given permission to set up a small department for "Measurement and Analysis Technology" (MAT) and to develop a commercial mass spectrometer. It was a sector instrument called CH3, with a vertical, curved vacuum tube with 60° deflection in the magnetic field (Nier geometry). This was concealed behind what resembled an old-fashioned telephone switchboard, with its array of rotary potentiometers, switches and measuring instruments on the front and a desk-like shelf for the laboratory journal, in which all the measurements had to be recorded manually.

Jenckel's first mass spectrometer, put together in a rented cellar room in the hospital "Sankt-Jürgensstraße", with wooden frame, vacuum system made from glass and a 60° magnetic separator with metal tube.

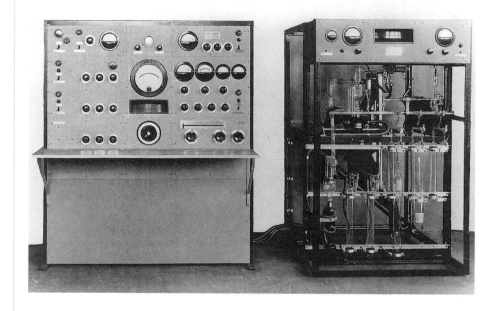

Laboratory prototype of the first mass spectrometer of MAT on the market, the "CH3", with electronic console and spectrometer console. The vacuum system was still made from glass.

Mass spectrometry is always a combination of various technologies, and demands top performance in every respect. For example, ions to be analysed can only fly in an ultra-high vacuum, which in turn requires ultra-high-vacuum pumps. At the time, only so-called mercury diffusion pumps were available, and they required traps cooled with liquid nitrogen to prevent the mercury from entering the mass spectrometry apparatus. Diffusion pumps and cooling traps were made of glass. Every morning and evening, including Saturdays and Sundays, these cooling traps had to be topped up. Sound knowledge and skill in vacuum-tight welding and sealing were also essential. Electrical bushings were usually made of glass, which had to be fused onto tubes made of a suitable metal. For many years, Dr Jenckel undertook all the glassblowing work himself as there were no glassblowers to be found in Bremen. Later, after the development of suitable high-vacuum pump oils, the mercury diffusion pumps were replaced with oil diffusion pumps and, for a long time, these too were manufactured from glass and required appropriate cooling traps. Other skills were demanded for the development of the electronics: extremely stable high voltages for accelerating the ions, highly stable electrical generators to create the magnetic field and highly sensitive amplifiers for the minute ion currents.

Jenckel launched the CH3 mass spectrometer in 1950, but had only modest success initially in the face of competition from American and British devices, which had already been on the market for at least two years. The word "market" is, in fact, rather a misnomer because general ignorance about mass spectrometry and its applications meant that no demand really existed. The market first had to be created by tireless work to inform scientific institutes, the petrochemical and pharmaceutical industries and many other sectors of its capabilities. The CH3, like its rival products, was developed principally for analysing volatile organic substances with ionisation by electron impact. As the organic substances had to be vaporised and bombarded by electrons, the analyses were limited to relatively small molecules with masses up to about 400 daltons. Many hundreds of thousands of substances fall into this category, however, including many previously unknown substances in petrochemistry, derived from crude oil, especially from distillation residues in which many pharmacologically useful substances are found, and also many naturally-occurring substances obtained, predominantly from plants.

In the USA, the company CEC dominated the still tiny and underdeveloped market with a magnetic sector mass spectrometer for this type of analysis; in Great Britain, Metropolitan Vickers Electrical Company Ltd. (MetroVick) produced a similar instrument. These firms were able to rely on the basic research done by the likes of Thomson, Aston, Bainbridge, Dempster, Nier and many other scientists living in the USA, Canada and the UK. In this respect, too, Germany was something of a wilderness; only Wilhelm Walcher, now at Marburg, and researchers at the Max-Planck-Institute for Chemistry in Mainz were actually working in the field of mass spectrometry. The Max-Planck-Institute was founded in 1946 as successor to the Kaiser-Wilhelm-Institute for Chemistry in Berlin and headed by Josef Mattauch, the co-inventor of the famous Mattauch–Herzog geometry for mass spectrometers. His co-workers Heinz Ewald and Heinrich Hintenberger designed a variety of mass spectrometers for use in cosmology and determination of nuclear structures of the elements, including spark source mass spectrometers, huge thermionic magnetic sector instruments for precise isotope mass measurements, or ^{3}He/^{4}He mass spectrometers for cosmological age determinations. These very special developments were far removed from laboratory mass spectrometers which could form the basis for a commercial mass spectrometer.

The MAT department at Atlas-Werke experienced a financial rollercoaster ride. Faced with a desperate financial situation, the ever-optimistic Dr Ludolf Jenckel organised a mass spectrometry conference in Bremen, about which Dr Curt Brunnée writes as follows in the 50th anniversary commemorative publication (translated from his German version):

"Annual turnover rose to around $100,000 in 1954, not enough to pay the department's twenty employees. So a decision had to be made either to throw in the towel or to stake everything on one chance. Dr Jenckel organised a "mass spectrometry conference" in Bremen to arouse the attention of scientists and the chemical industry. During the conference, Dr Jenckel gave guided tours of his plant and painted a glowing, optimistic picture of the future of mass spectrometry in Bremen. In the evening, a sumptuous buffet was served up in one of Bremen's best-known and most expensive restaurants [the name, "Goldener Saal" (Golden Chamber), certainly did not reflect

MAT's financial situation at that time]. The author, who attended the conference, was so impressed that he decided to join MAT: a company that could afford to put on such a lavish event evidently had plentiful funds for interesting projects, he assumed. Although this turned out to be a misconception, the author nevertheless stayed at MAT for 35 years."

Dr Curt Brunnée, who had just completed his doctorate under Wilhelm Walcher in Marburg, was to prove a godsend for MAT and for Dr Jenckel. The life of Dr Curt Brunnée, not only a scientist, but also a magician and cartoonist, earns a wonderful article by itself: his friend Michael C. ten Noever de Brauw took over this task and published *A Short Story About the Life of Curt Brunnée*.[3] (This article is reprinted in the next chapter.)

Dr Brunnée largely took over the development of the next-generation mass spectrometer, the CH4. He succeeded in designing a much improved instrument. As many mass spectrometers at that time were used for quantitative analyses of mixtures of substances, it was important that the ion source, based on electron impact in those days, should produce ions in a quantity proportional to the concentration of the substances in the mixture; otherwise accurate quantitative measurement of the substances was not possible. The greatest shortcoming of the electron impact ion source of the old CH3 was that it did not deliver quantitatively accurate ion currents. Nobody could explain why this should be the case; but

The highly successful mass spectrometer "MAT CH4", with heatable ion source made from metal, 400 were built between 1958 and 1967, coupled to a gas chromatograph at the right-hand side. Design and presentation are typical for the 1960s.

it was known that the CEC instrument did not have this drawback; its ion currents were far more proportional to the varying substance concentrations.

In spite of much hard work, intensive deliberation and numerous experiments, the cause of this disproportionality remained a mystery until, by chance, an operating error led to significantly better results. Although the reason was still not understood, the system was further optimised until an ion source was achieved which was ideal for quantitative work, better even than the ion sources used by the competitors. At the same time, a new, all-metal heatable inlet system for the substances was introduced—at that time still in gaseous form—permitting clean working almost completely free of chemical background. The new CH4 was born and was rolled out in 1958. This marked an upturn in MAT's fortunes. Over four hundred CH4s had been sold by 1967. Multiple applications were possible, such as headspace analyses of coffee aromas, identification of carcinogenic constituents in cigarette smoke, or analysis of perfume mixtures. Numerous add-ons were developed for the CH4, including a certain type of coupling with a gas chromatograph to enable better analysis of mixtures. The CH4 thus became a platform for many applications.

Under Jenckel's management, a variety of further mass spectrometers were developed: CH5 (an improved single-focussing magnetic sector instrument with horizontal reflection), CH6 (small magnetic field sector radius, allowed to be exported into eastern countries), CH7 (simplified version of the CH5), SM1 (a double-focussing Mattauch–Herzog instrument), MAT 711 (improved SM1 for electric scanning), MAT 731 (improved SM1 for photographic detection) and many more. Some of them won awards for best industrial products, for example the "Gnome" (a small lab mass spectrometer) received the famous IR-100 award. The history of MAT's instruments is marvellously outlined in the famous article by Curt Brunnée,[2] together with deep and wise insight into the driving forces behind progress: not the ever changing management paroles invented by super-wise advisors, but the enthusiastic creativity of devoted and excited single individuals guides companies to success which, at least in this branch of the economy, is still true today. In this way, about 50% of the instrumental developments may become flops, sometimes because problems could not be solved adequately, sometimes because the instruments were too progressive or innovative for the market, but the remaining 50% could keep the company in the favour of the customers.

Dr Jenckel was what the ladies in Bremen called a real gentleman—charming, a good conversationalist and a good dancer. Tall, with an upright posture, and elegantly dressed, he was astutely and appositely described as an "admiral" by one female customer, albeit not in his presence. His colleagues at MAT had an affectionate, and especially respectful, nickname for him: "lieber Jott" (The Lord, from his initial "J", pronounced "Jot" in Germany). But they also found that he never wore his heart on his sleeve. You could not tell what went on inside his head. Dr Jenckel always kept a low profile, never trying to be too chummy with his colleagues, nor overly jovial. He maintained a certain Hanseatic aloofness, but once a colleague had won his confidence, he would open up and would support that person through thick and thin.

THE FATE OF MAT UNDER JENCKEL: VIA KRUPP TO VARIAN

The success of the MAT department within Atlas-Werke led to its transition to an independent company, "Atlas MAT GmbH", in 1962. It remained in the Atlas-Werke group, with Dr Jenckel acting as sole managing director. In the maelstrom of conflicts surrounding the Stinnes family inheritance, Atlas-Werke, including Atlas MAT GmbH, was sold to Fried. Krupp AG in Essen for almost DM 60 million at the end of 1965, as the newspaper *Die Welt* reported in a lengthy article on 11 March 1966, under the title "The wasted inheritance" (of business magnate Hugo Stinnes, who died in 1923). A reorganisation in January 1966 led to the electronics business of Atlas-Werke being hived off as an operating division (later to become Bremen's well-known company Atlas-Elektronik, focussing by then on sonar technology); Atlas MAT was also converted into an operating division of Fried. Krupp AG, under the name Fried. Krupp MAT. Dr Jenckel remained its sole managing director. Krupp described the acquisition with the management catchword of the day, "diversification", which was supposed to free companies from the ups and downs of the various markets. The diversification was followed, two years later, by the next corporate trend "return to core business". On 7 September 1967, MAT was sold to the California-based Varian Associates, and renamed Varian MAT GmbH. Still, Dr Jenckel remained the sole managing director. Hugo Stinnes junior, formerly chairman of the Supervisory Board at Atlas-Werke, wrote in a letter to Dr Jenckel dated 9 September 1967 (translated):[4]

"In yesterday's "Die Welt", I read a report that saddened me greatly. My fears are now indeed becoming reality, and Krupp is progressively selling off Atlas-Werke. Achgelis has been stripped of its assets, old Atlas more or less shut down, Süd-Atlas sold, and now it's your turn.

You will recall the conversation we had shortly before the sale of my Atlas shares. It was my intention to avoid this happening and to find a constructive solution with you; I sincerely regret that it has turned out so differently.

Varian Associates, Palo Alto, California, are, if my memory serves me correctly, the people with whom the two of us once negotiated, but on an equal footing. I am not happy about the sell-off; it is down to the bankers, who always stand to gain from every transaction.

It is, furthermore, symptomatic that, in this context, things once again have to be jumbled up and, worse still, the term "Stinnes bankruptcy settlement" is being used, although no such thing ever existed.

I hope that you have at least been able to retain your own position for the future so that you can continue in the field of work to which you are so devoted and in which you have been so successful and demonstrated such ability…"

In his reply, Dr Jenckel wrote:[5]

"…It is, of course, regrettable that more and more German companies are passing into foreign ownership. On the other hand, the world is becoming a much smaller place, specialisation is intensifying, and the consolidation of companies with complementary operations is becoming increasingly unavoidable. But I hardly need to tell you that! Undoubtedly, in terms of our field of work, we fit more comfortably with Varian—they are indeed the people with whom we once negotiated—than with Krupp. It is questionable whether one should, or can, therefore criticize Krupp or Beitz. The price obtained was considerable, and both parties were satisfied with the transaction. It remains to be seen whether MAT, and I personally, can be satisfied. The honeymoon period has got off to a good start, but the marriage may, of course, prove to be quite a different matter. A lot will depend on us."

Dr Jenckel at his 60th birthday party.

We learn more about the marriage in the handwritten text of a talk given by Dr Jenckel to the Rotary Club of Bremen-Vegesack in 1972, entitled "My American friends". It is a very personal account, which does not attempt to make any generalisations. It does, however, give an insight into Jenckel's relationship with his American bosses and colleagues. What is also interesting is how he characterises the Varian corporation and its CEO:[6]

"…Here in Germany, the Americans are often accused of being ruthless in business life. That has not been my experience to-date in our company; and if this company is different than, and better than, the average American business in this respect, the credit certainly belongs in large part to its long-standing president, who is now Chairman of the Board and, as such, participates in the running of the company. In an American corporation, there is not the clear-cut distinction between the Supervisory Board, as controlling body, and the executive. The chairman, whose name is Ed, was professor of physics at nearby Stanford University before going into industry and reaching the top of our corporate group; a highly qualified scientist, and a man endowed with great good sense. I do not wish to go into too much detail here, but I shall mention one of his grandfathers, who left school and emigrated to America as a stowaway. That he so disdainfully turned his back on his native town will naturally surprise some of you, for he came from Vegesack. But now back to the grandson and chairman, who has philanthropic and social inclinations in addition to his scientific interests. He strives to endow the company with a greater meaning than simply the primitive objective of earning money, and seeks to develop and maintain professional ideals, which can, of course, easily conflict with harsh reality in difficult economic times…"

Jenckel then gives a quite affectionate account of his colleagues' unusual hobbies, which range from restoring old automobiles to operating railway engines from old rail company stocks; and he expresses admiration for his colleagues' wives, who were, on the one hand, cool and aloof but, on the other hand, were not only excellent housewives (looking after large houses without any home help), but also found the time and energy to engage in many voluntary activities in the local parish or charitable organisations. Jenckel's talk displays a considerable fondness for his colleagues.

On 28 February 1974, the philanthropic chief executive Ed (whose full name was Edward Leonard Ginzton) fired Dr Jenckel as managing director of MAT and forbade him to enter the company premises. The reasons for this have never became entirely clear. Dr Jenckel was at least offered a "gilded cage" by Varian (he was, after all, 61 years old), a sort of retirement on full pay tied to an undertaking no longer to work in his field of expertise. Dr Jenckel was too proud to accept this offer. He once indicated to me privately that he had made efforts to bring about the sale of MAT to Siemens, but without success. He explained that there was a change in the Siemens board at the critical moment.

In his book about Atlas-Werke, Dr Heinrich Maass writes the following on this matter (we recall that Ludolf Jenckel lived with the Maass family during his schooldays in Bremen, and Dr Maass brought him to Atlas-Werke from the Eastern Front):

"It is not certain whether Dr Jenckel was familiar with Bismarck's definition of politics as "the art of the possible". What is certain, however, is that he applied this maxim brilliantly when he implemented the measures he considered necessary to expand the company in carefully calculated stages so as to overcome the resistance of the Board of Directors or the delaying tactics of the management board."

Elsewhere he writes:

"…Jenckel left his post as company director in mid-1975 (on this point, Maass was mistaken; it was in fact at the beginning of 1974) as a result of disagreement over management policy; he was then appointed commercial director by the management board of C. Plath GmbH for the period from fall 1975 until the beginning of 1978 in order to give Dr Wächtler's son time to take over this function and, in particular, to streamline the internal organisation of this company."

This marked the end of the Dr Jenckel era in mass spectrometry.

MAT IN THE POST-JENCKEL ERA

A few years later, MAT was sold by Varian Associates to the California-based Finnigan Corporation and seems to have been run more cooperatively than under Varian. The new company, Finnigan MAT GmbH, certainly experienced both good and less good times, but it was stable enough—not least thanks to its past history and the reputation it enjoyed with scientific customers—to survive with its own range of high-quality products, to which it constantly added. Finnigan was then taken over in the USA by the Thermo Electron Corporation and the Bremen-based company was duly renamed Thermo Electron Bremen GmbH. The merger of Thermo Electron and Fisher Scientific toward the end of 2007 brought the current company name of Thermo Fisher Scientific (Bremen) GmbH.

The original instrumental focus of MAT had been on low-resolution and (somewhat later) high-resolution magnetic sector mass spectrometers for volatile and non-volatile organic compounds. "Non-volatile" compounds were understood as thermally vaporisable without degradation, i.e. substances with molecular weights far below 1000 Dalton, well suited to magnetic sector instruments. CH4 and its successor CH5 became platforms for many special analytical tasks by numerous special add-ons. An electrical sector behind the 90° CH5 magnetic sector lead to the MAT 311, a high-resolution instrument, also capable of measuring "metastable ion kinetic energies" (MIKE), the energy released by decay of excited molecular ions. Analysis of the fragment ions by the electric sector lead to one of the first tandem mass spectrometers. Magnetic sector mass spectrometers are also well suited to the precise measurement of isotope ratios, used for age determinations in geology and cosmology, for analysing the origin of substances such as sugar from different varieties of plants and many other interesting investigations. As an example, adding beet-sugar to wines could be detected with these instruments. For precise isotope measurements, general mass spectrometers were used initially but later, slightly modified instruments like the TH5 was used for solids and the UF5 and the MAT 311 for gases. In the mid-seventies, however, a completely new generation of highly specialised instruments such as the MAT 260 for thermionic ionisation and the MAT 250 for gaseous substances were developed; the successors of these instruments are still predominant on the isotope measuring scene. In the mid-nineties, a new product line for elemental analysis with inductively coupled plasma (ICP), still on the base of magnetic sector instruments, was launched: the "MAT Element".

Just three decades ago, the prevailing opinion was that it would never be possible to examine large biomolecules using mass spectrometry because it was assumed that the molecules first had to be vaporised and then ionised in order to perform spectrometry. But large biomolecules decompose long before they vaporise. Even normal sugar cannot be vaporised because it decomposes immediately (and turns into caramel candy). Proteins are even more unstable: they decompose at the temperature of boiling water (meat becomes cooked, eggs turn from liquid to solid). Furthermore, mass spectrometers were designed for a maximum molecular weight of around 1000 daltons, allowing sufficient reserves for all sizes of molecule to be investigated in the future, or so it was thought.

Then, towards the end of the 1980s, two new ionisation methods were discovered which were also suitable for ionising biomolecules: electrospraying of solutions containing bio-molecules (ESI), developed by John Bennet Fenn (USA) and ionising matrix-assisted laser desorption (MALDI) of solid analyte samples, independently developed by Michael Karas and Franz Hillenkamp (Germany) for solids in a crystalline environment and Koichi Tanaka (Japan) in liquid solutions. These two techniques, ESI and MALDI, for which J.B. Fenn and K. Tanaka were awarded the Nobel Prize in 2002, suddenly extended the applications of mass spectrometry to questions of molecular biology and molecular medicine. A new era of "bio-organic mass spectrometry" dawned, requiring new types of mass spectrometers.

At that time, MAT was badly equipped for these new ion sources. They decided, with the help of Karas and Hillenkamp, to develop a MALDI time-of-flight mass spectrometer, but the "Vision 2000" did not really meet the requirements. After Finnigan bought Nicolet, an ion-cyclotron resonance (ICR) company, MAT grasped the opportunity to develop, inside the Thermo-Finnigan family, a new ICR mass spectrometer in Bremen and did a marvel-lous job by combining this instrument with the highly successful linear quadrupole ion trap of Finnigan. A still more exciting development began with Thermo's acquisition of HD Technologies Ltd in Manchester, where Dr Alexander Alexeyevich Makarov had initiated a completely new type of mass spectrometer, the Orbitrap, an electrostatic ion trap based on the Kingdon principle for trapping ions. Makarov was transferred to Bremen, and an excited team began to solve the many problems connected with such a new development. The invention of the C-curved storage quadrupole for ion injection and the hybridisation with the LTQ linear ion trap made the Orbitrap an outstanding success.

HOW A NEW COMPANY CAME TO BE ESTABLISHED

I first met Dr Jenckel and his wife in 1969, when I was a young scientist travelling to a scien-tific conference in Kyoto, Japan. The journey to the "International Mass Spectrometry Con-ference" was organised and funded by the German Research Foundation (DFG). Dr Jenckel was the only participating industrialist on this journey, which he paid for himself. He always remained somewhat aloof, so I never came into close personal contact with him. However, somehow he must have noticed me, because two years later, at the beginning of 1973, he brought me to Bremen as the new head of development. It was only with some hesita-tion that I accepted the appointment because, at that time in Germany, moving from an academic career to a job in industry was regarded as more or less an act of betrayal. They were two completely different worlds and you did not simply move from one to the other as in the USA, where even multiple moves between academia and industry were quick and easy. At that time I was head of the mass spectrometry department at the "Institute of Spectrochemistry and Applied Spectroscopy" in Dortmund. The department had a staff of nine and heading up the team was easy. It happened quite naturally according to the work in hand at any particular time.

I took the position of head of the development department at Varian MAT GmbH, with responsibility for a team of 128 staff, only on condition that I was given an introduction into industrial practices. The Institute of Spectrochemistry in Dortmund had stood in the assets column of the budget of the Federal State of North Rhine-Westphalia and was, therefore, obliged to operate a special public system of financial management and bookkeeping. Industrial bookkeeping was completely new for me, as was the job of managing around 20 development projects such as spectrometer developments, electronics developments to achieve greater constancy of voltages and currents even at fluctuating room temperatures, or software development for controlling processes and investigations into corona discharges for chemical ionisation. I was promised the introduction into industrial practices that I had requested, but amidst the hurly-burly of daily business, it simply got forgotten.

The first year flew by. At the start of my second year, at the end of February 1974, I attended the world's largest conference on analytical instruments, the Pittsburgh Conference, which was being held outside Pittsburgh for the first time, in Cleveland. I was summoned by the Varian boss, Ed Ginzton. In his hotel suite he informed me that, at the same time, Dr Jenckel was leaving his office and would never return there. He wanted to know whether I was prepared to continue working for Varian under these circumstances. I was shocked. However, I could not return to the academic circles whence I had come because I was tarred a "traitor". So I had little choice but to agree to stay, provided that Dr Jenckel's promise of an introduction into industrial practices was realised.

Of course I was naïve. In industry, it is a question of sink of swim. I never did receive an active and helpful introduction into industrial practices, but I'm not sure that Dr Jenckel would have given me one either. You have to learn to grow and act for yourself. The story of every company is a story of people who take action.

Dr Jenckel was replaced in the Varian management by an American, Andy Steinherz, an exceptional astute analyst and a fast decision-maker. I admired his abilities. It took a long time before I came to realise that quick decisions are not always good decisions. Moreover, he was a devotee of the management philosophy that says one should never step back from a decision once taken. In the summer of 1976, he came to the conclusion that development costs were far too high in relation to turnover, compared to other companies. This resulted specifically in a dispute about whether or not Varian MAT should continue to implement customer-specific modifications to its instruments. Andy Steinherz wanted me to immediately cut the workforce of the development department by 40. I countered this demand with the argument that these customisations, which affected some 70% of the mass spectrometers we supplied, were in fact MAT's strong point; if we were to limit ourselves to standard catalogue instruments, we would be at a competitive disadvantage to the British firms, which operated at very low cost levels. British wages were only half those in Germany at that time. The customer-specific modifications were designed and implemented in the development department and it was only this arrangement that drove up the development costs. The assignment of these costs was largely discretionary; a different assignment would have halved our development costs at a stroke in accounting terms. Following our argument, I believed that the matter was settled, and left with my family for our long-planned holiday in Spain.

When I returned, I found that my deputy was in hospital after suffering a heart attack. He had been forced to dismiss forty members of staff. I felt that I had been deliberately hoodwinked, and I resigned without having a clue as to what my future would be. However, I had to serve a relatively long period of notice of six months. Andy Steinherz relieved me of my position as head of development, moved me to a windowless workroom (something which is not permitted under German labour law, but was common practice in the USA) and gave me all kinds of statistical jobs to do. He also required me to draw up a study that had been requested by the German Armed Forces to assess the potential for rapid, on-the-spot detection of chemical warfare agents using mass spectrometry. The study was one of 12 similar ones, each of which was to employ different techniques for analysing the chemical agents: infrared spectroscopy, fluorescence spectrometry, microwave spectrometry, nuclear magnetic resonance spectrometry and several others. In the course of writing the study, I became convinced in my own mind that mass spectrometry was the only technology capable of providing the answer to the task of performing on-the-spot analysis of warfare agents in a matter of seconds.

One day, Andy Steinherz came to my small room, sat down on the edge of my cramped desk (there was nowhere else to sit), and asked me about my future. I told him that I was going to start up my own company to manufacture mass spectrometers. That shocked him; he said that it was something he could not do; he always needed a large team which he could direct like an orchestra, and could not conceive of starting from nothing. I suspected that he did not think I was capable of doing it either. In any event, he thought over the situation, immediately suspended me and forbade me to enter the company premises.

On 1 April (April fools day), 1977 I started up with a team of seven (including myself) in a "Schnaps Fabrik" (a distillery). In two rooms rented from Güldenhaus, in Bremen's Hohentorstrasse, which were already equipped with two rather ancient lathes and an even older milling machine, I launched "Dr Franzen Analysentechnik GmbH & Co, KG". The limited partners had provided me with a capital of DM 4 million, in return for which they expected loss allocations, which they could write off at far above 100% under the tax laws of those days, thus enabling them to make a small profit at top income rates. (This tax model was later restricted to the financing of shipbuilding and house building; and today it has disappeared altogether). In a glass cubicle I worked with a secretary, who doubled up as head of human resources and bookkeeper, to set up a suitable industrial system of accounts. I had a tremendous amount to learn. It was my tax consultant and solicitor at the time, Dr Kessler, who found the limited partners, so I only had to convince them with my scientific knowledge (in which I succeeded). Dr Kessler then explained to me that as managing director I was, for the purpose of company law, a professional businessman, with all the statutory obligations that entails (although I had no commercial training as such). Back then, there was no outside assistance of the kind enjoyed by start-up companies today, such as a complete infrastructure with heated rooms or technology centres to which the accounting could be outsourced. Even organising a telephone line without committing oneself to a ten-year contract at extortionate tariffs was a nerve-racking feat.

In my private thoughts I had concentrated purely on the task of developing a "sniffer" mass spectrometer for the armed forces because I was convinced that this was the only device that could do the job. However, all existing mass spectrometers were regarded, first, as highly touchy and unreliable and, second, at least the size of a grand piano. A mass spectrometer no larger than a small refrigerator installed in a rocking and rattling NBC reconnaissance vehicle was surely out of the question. So I set about building a compact and robust desktop device, an integral GC-MS instrument for medical analysis in a single housing. GC-MS means coupling together gas chromatography and mass spectrometry. The central component, a single-block quadrupole filter, with a quickly patented method of manufacture, was already in the back of my mind as the basis for meeting the demands of the sniffer mass spectrometers for military use. The complete digital control system, which no mass spectrometer in the world could boast, except for the brand-new MAT 44, was developed with the same purpose in mind. The electronics developer behind the MAT 44 had followed me to the newly established company and we worked together as a successful team.

In the spring of 1980, the device was ready. The first two instruments had been sold, but the contract from the armed forces, which I had silently and naively expected would follow, had not materialised. Before the military placed an order, three feasibility studies were to be conducted, and the results of these would be some time in coming. Although I was still convinced that mass spectrometry would come out on top in the feasibility studies, I first had to approach my limited partners for additional capital in order to set up production. I could not tell them about the secretly expected military contract, as they would have thought I was crazy (which I was). Instead I told them that I had nearly reached breakeven point; and further investment was urgent because I had a liquidity problem. But operating at a profit was of no interest to them for their tax purposes, so they decreed that the business had to be restructured and sold. My stomach hit the ground.

CONTINUATION BY BRUKER

It was at this point that the Bruker Corporation entered the frame, again through the intermediacy of Dr Kessler. The Karlsruhe-based company had been established in the early 1950s by Professor Günther Laukien for the development and marketing of nuclear magnetic resonance spectrometry. Professor Laukien bought the firm from the restructuring plan, converted it into "Bruker-Franzen Analytik GmbH", invested DM 5 million of new capital, and installed Dr Koch, from Karlsruhe, as joint director. From that point on, everything happened very quickly. The German Armed Forces opted for mass spectrometry and invited tenders for development of the sniffer device. We tendered alongside three other well-known manufacturers and won the contract because we were able to offer the best technologies. We also beat the competition on price because we were still a very small company with the lowest overheads. The contract required us to deliver the first proto-types in the time frame of just nine months.

We dropped all other projects and devoted ourselves fully to the new task. I myself had to develop the control software at breakneck speed because my software engineer was incapacitated by a spinal operation. To this day I am proud that my program, written mainly in assembly language for an 8-bit Zilog Z80 processor with 2 MHz clock rate, has never suffered any outages to this day. Nor has the integrated computer itself ever crashed, as is commonplace nowadays. I first had to learn the assembly language. It must be remembered that the program does a lot more than just control the actual measuring operations and perform calculations in specially developed, and very economical, floating point math-ematics. It also has to supply fast screen graphics for warning displays, mass spectra and chromatograms, drive a printer introduced in the military, handle vehicle coordinates and much more besides. (Today's 32-bit and 64-bit processors are more than 2000 times faster, but today the far higher capacity is usually nullified by cumbersome and faulty multi-layer software.)

Delivery of the prototypes was followed by a lean time for us because testing of the four prototypes took almost two years: logistical testing, physicochemical testing of sensitivity for detection of warfare agents, ergonomic testing in the field and testing of resistance to external influences, including a nuclear flash outside the Earth's atmosphere, which causes a huge voltage pulse capable of damaging all ground-based electronic equipment. We utilised this waiting period to carry out further enhancements at our own expense. Then, after a further phase of post-development, for which we did receive payment, our device finally entered NATO-wide service, exactly four years and one day after the first development contract was signed. In fact, this set a record in terms of speed of development for an item of technical equipment of this complexity.

We also won the follow-on tender for the production of the devices, thus laying the founda-tion stone for the company to enjoy a healthy future and also for mass spectrometers used in civil applications. It was never my intention to compete with Varian MAT in the produc-tion of magnetic mass spectrometers. There are several other principles for separating ions by mass. In the military device, the MM1, we use the principle of trajectory instability in linear RF quadrupole mass filters, which was discovered by Wolfgang Paul. Although MAT many years ago had also built devices of this type as residual gas analysers (AMP series), they soon discontinued production because the high-vacuum industry brought less expen-sive devices utilising different basic principles onto the market. In the USA, the companies Uthe, Extrel and especially Finnigan focussed on building these quadrupole filters for analyti-cal purposes in organic chemistry, with the company founded by Bob Finnigan pushing out its rivals. In contrast to the quadrupole mass filters from these companies, our devices had a hyperbolic shape, which made them around ten times better. These shapes were, however, very difficult to manufacture with the necessary precision unless one employed a great deal of innovativeness in developing completely new production processes, as we did for our mass spectrometer.

We were also interested in time-of-flight mass spectrometers, which were originally marketed back in 1950 by the American firm, Bendix, although their technology finally failed due to the difficulty of achieving rapid detection of the ion currents. The principle is simple: if one suddenly accelerates a bunch of ions of different types using the same acceleration voltage, the light ions fly very fast, while the heavy ions are really slow. So one only needs to measure the arrival time of the ions after a flight path of one or two metres. A spectrum, which essentially consists of many thousands of such measurements, had to be recorded in less than 100 microseconds. This was not possible in the days of the Bendix spectrometer. My chief electronics developer informed me that transient recorders had, by then, been invented, which were capable of solving this problem. Today, these devices are able to take between two and eight single ion current measurements per nanosecond, permanently ongoing for more than 200 microseconds. Furthermore, Boris A. Mamyrin, in Russia, discovered that slight velocity differences in a time-of-flight mass spectrometer could be refocused by means of an ion reflector. We began developing high-resolution time-of-flight mass spectrometers, which today are one of the foundation stones of our success. It is a characteristic of time-of-flight mass spectrometers that they are also able to measure much heavier ions than is possible with magnetic sector field mass spectrometry.

Not only the German Armed Forces adopted the sniffer mass spectrometer MM1, but also other armies. The American army, however, upon introduction of the MM1 made the serious mistake of calling the device not MM1 (Mobile Mass Spectrometer No. 1), but GEMS: "German Mass Spectrometer". That wounded the pride of every patriotic GI, so an American mass spectrometer had to be developed. Of course, the military budget would only permit such a development if it produced a device with much greater capabilities. Consequently, in 1984, the specialists at Edgewood Proving Ground, the American military scientific centre, came up with the idea that the new mass spectrometer should also be capable of measuring biological threats from bacteria, viruses and toxins. This meant it would have to detect the structures of suspicious ions by means of tandem mass spectrometry. A tandem mass spectrometer basically consists of two mass spectrometers, the first of which filters out the suspicious ions, which are then fragmented by hard impacts with a collision gas in a collision chamber. The fragment ions, which have a characteristic pattern rather like a fingerprint for a particular ionic species, are then measured in a second mass spectrometer. Whereas both mass spectrometers have to be operated at ultra-high vacuum, the collision chamber has to maintain a fairly high pressure of collision gas: huge pumps have to be installed to maintain the right vacuum pressures, representing a big problem for a fieldable instrument.

We had the idea that tandem mass spectrometry could take place sequentially in a single fist-sized ion trap like that designed by Wolfgang Paul. Although such an ion trap had just been launched on the market by Finnigan Corp. in 1984 (coincidentally in the same month as we submitted our proposal to the American army), the Finnigan instrument did not incorporate the principle of tandem mass spectrometry which we proposed. As an ion trap only

Remark: For the American mass spectrometer CBMS, we only developed the "concept", but we lost out to another consortium in the bid to develop the system through to production. The military acceptance for this final instrument has still not been granted even today, in spite of the fact that our concept model already was hardened for military use. However, the American army had an urgent requirement and therefore commissioned us to produce a large number of concept models. These concept models belong to a different program within the American army, and are not a substitute for the sniffer vehicles equipped with the MM1 device, which are still in service after more than twenty-five years.

functions as an effective mass spectrometer when it contains collision gases, it can, at first, be used to select the suspicious ions by ejecting all other ions. Then the suspicious ions can be fragmented by forced collisions with the gas molecules and, finally, the resulting fragment ions measured as a mass spectrum. As a result of our proposal, we eventually (after numerous intermediate stages and delays) received the development contract for this CBMS (Chemical Biological Mass Spectrometer). It was signed on 24 December 1986, and gave the American army the home-grown mass spectrometer they desired, while giving us a fully developed ion trap technology, which we later implemented in a civil mass spectrometer, in collaboration with Hewlett-Packard. When Hewlett-Packard was split up, its mass spectrometry arm was continued by Agilent.

Bruker also brought another type of mass spectrometry to our company, namely ICR mass spectrometry. As a result, the mass spectrometry arm of Bruker soon had a wider range of technologies for analysing organic materials than any other mass spectrometer manufacturer. This diversity became important when mass spectrometry set its sights on a completely new area of application, the investigation of the building blocks of life itself: bio-organic mass spectrometry.

When, two decades ago, the new ionisation procedures for bio-organic molecules came to light, Bruker-Franzen Analytik in Bremen was luckily well equipped with suitable mass spectrometers: highly sensitive Paul quadrupole ion traps with a mass range of up to 3000 daltons, easily adaptable to electrospray ionisation for molecular ion and fragment ion mass spectrometry by tandem-in-time; ultra-high mass precision and mass resolution by ICR mass spectrometry of electrospray ions; and time-of-flight mass spectrometers for ultra-high mass ranges, quickly adapted to ionisation by matrix-assisted laser desorption (MALDI). Somewhat later, the time-of-flight mass spectrometers were also adapted to electrospray ionisation, using the principle of orthogonal ion injection. The present demand for a moderately-priced mass spectrometer for super-high mass resolution and mass accuracy was answered by the development of the "Bruker maXis", an orthogonal injection time-of-flight spectrometer with extra long flight path. This instrument offers a fairly constant high mass resolution in excess of $R = 40,000$ over a wide mass range up to about 4000 daltons, with high speed data acquisition of 20 mass spectra per second without loss in resolution; quite in contrast to ICR mass spectrometers or the Orbitrap, the mass resolution of which diminishes towards higher masses and shorter acquisition times,

I have to confess that not all of the instruments we developed were really successful. Because, 20 years ago, the pollution of our environment was a subject of much discussion, we designed a special light-weight mass spectrometer which could be operated by the 24 V battery of a normal truck; it detected pollutants in the field down to below allowable concentration limits, each in three minute GC-MS runs. Add-ons allowed for analyses of poisons in the ground, in water and even in air. A database with more than 200,000 mass spectra completed the ruggedised instrument. We offered the instrument to many offices in communities and states responsible for environmental problems, but (almost) no one wanted to buy the device. It was much better to shut one's eyes instead of knowing. A detected pollution problem immediately created the next problem: how to clean the ground, the lake or the river without having a budget? The highly specialised mass spectrometer EM 460 became a flop; only a mere hundred instruments were sold over the years instead of the thousand we had expected.

Professor Günther Laukien's death in 1998 led to a restructuring and unification of all the wide network of Bruker companies into four sectors: nuclear magnetic resonance spectrometry, optical spectrometry, x-ray spectrometry and mass spectrometry. The mass spectrometry companies were united under the name Bruker Daltonik in Germany (Bruker Daltonics in the USA and UK; Bruker Daltonique in France), in honour of John Dalton. The Bremen-based Bruker-Franzen Analytik GmbH was merged with its subsidiary Bruker Saxonia Analytik GmbH in Leipzig and renamed Bruker Daltonik GmbH. It has its headquarters in Bremen. In the meantime, this company has become one of the world's largest production and development centres for bio-organic mass spectrometers.

HOW BIO-ORGANIC MASS SPECTROMETRY INFLUENCED THE TECHNICAL DESIGN

Mass spectrometry remains extremely important in nuclear engineering, materials research, archaeological dating, food control, doping tests, production control and many other fields. In addition, a new branch of application has developed over the last 15 years or so: "bio-organic mass spectrometry".

This term describes mass spectrometry as applied to biochemical, biological and medical problems. It demands different types of mass spectrometers and different ionisation methods, and entails not only measuring the mass of large biomolecules, but also determining their structure, for example analysing amino acid sequences in a protein. Modifications of such proteins, which constantly occur in humans, animals and plants due to the effect of active proteins, can also be determined. (Approximately a third of all protein types, called enzymes, are like miniature chemical factories contained in a single molecule, chemically modifying other molecules). Other objectives include measurements of specific foldings of long protein chains and their association with other proteins. Abnormalities in proteins are indicators of diseases, for many of which no other diagnostic technique is available. Imaging mass spectrometry shows the distribution of proteins or pharmacological substances in tissue sections so that diseased tissue can be distinguished from healthy tissue. Another application of particular interest is the fast identification of entire microorganisms, such as bacteria or single-cell fungi, by means of mass spectrometry, for example to defend against biological weapons, but also to ensure the targeted use of antibiotics.

The human body and animal body function on the basis of these proteins. We humans have several hundred thousands different types of proteins, derived from around some 20,300 genes. Each type of protein performs a specific function: the "craftsmen" carry out repairs, the "soldiers" defend our body against intruders, the "builders" construct other proteins, the "messengers" transport messages, the "refuse collectors" cut up and take away used proteins, the "administrators" control everything, the "workers" keep us mobile etc. All

Opposite, clockwise from top-left

A MALDI time-of-flight mass spectrometer of the 1980s: Bruker's "Reflex", still proudly showing a great part of technical details.

Bruker's "Autoflex" MALDI time-of-flight mass spectrometer in upright position; launched in 2001. The instrument received the prestigious "iF Design Award" of the International Forum for Design.

A top of the line electrospray ionisation (ESI) mass spectrometer: Bruker's maxis with 40,000 mass resolution.

Thermo Fisher Scientific's LTQ-Orbitrap, a combination of a linear Paul ion trap with a Kingdon-type electrostatic ion trap for high precision mass measurements.

Thermo Fisher Scientific LTQ-FT-Ultra, an ion cyclotron resonance mass spectrometer in modern design in combination with a linear Paul ion trap.

A small table-top mass spectrometer with an ion trap according to Wolfgang Paul: Bruker's "Amazon".

these tasks, all these functions need to be researched. Many diseases are caused by malfunctioning proteins.

The new mass spectrometers for these biochemical and biological tasks bear no resemblance to the earlier devices, which proudly displayed their components for all to see: high-vacuum pumps (the old mercury diffusion pumps were long ago replaced by gently humming turbomolecular pumps), gleaming stainless-steel flight tubes with flanges, secured vacuum-tight by dozens of stainless-steel screws, visible measuring tubes, high-voltage feedthroughs and vacuum locks. Today's mass spectrometers are completely enclosed for different reasons: today's safety requirements are much more stringent; and second, biologists and medical doctors are more fond of neat designs. An instrument must have a nice cover (like an automobile) and should not show the machinery inside. Access prohibited. This creates opportunities for new designs; and prestigious design awards, such as the "German Industrial Design Award", or the "Red Dot", have come the way of the mass spectrometers made in Bremen.

Bio-organic mass spectrometry, equipped with the new ion sources ESI and MALDI, experienced an unexpected surge in popularity. Whereas, in the 1980s, the largest mass spectrometry conference, the annual "ASMS Conference on Mass Spectrometry and Allied Topics" in the USA, used to attract only a few hundred participants, today that number has risen to more than 6000. Over half of the presentations and poster sessions deal with bio-organic subjects.

Bremen's mass spectrometer makers have succeeded in maintaining their market position, even though the market for mass spectrometers in Germany and other European countries has not grown at the same rate as that of the United States. Strong growth is also evident in the countries of eastern Asia, where, interestingly, European and American companies (including those based in Bremen) have often been successful, even in the face of competition from their Japanese counterparts. Some 80% to 85% of the mass spectrometers manufactured in Bremen are exported, thereby contributing to the balance of trade.

OUTLOOK

Thanks to Dr Jenckel's initiative, energy and stamina, a mass spectrometry industry was established in Bremen. His company, Atlas MAT, gave rise to today's company, Thermo Fisher Scientific (Bremen) GmbH and, through a start-up by a member of staff, the current Bruker Daltonik GmbH. Both of these companies are amongst the world leaders in their field. Spin-offs, outsourcing of critical production processes and further business start-ups mean that there are now about a dozen mass spectrometry-related companies in and around Bremen. All of them compete on the world stage. Thus, Bremen has become a capital of mass spectrometry: no other city can boast such a concentration of companies, such a wealth of research and development activity or such manufacturing capacity in the field of mass spectrometry.

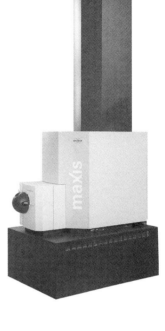

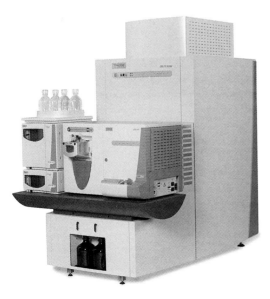

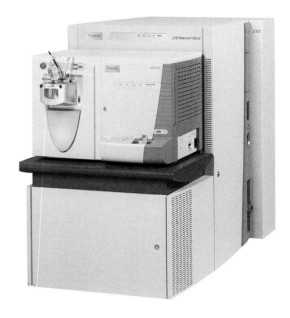

I, personally, am very grateful to Dr Jenckel for giving me my start in this industry. I have sought to repay him by continuing the job to which he was so devoted, namely the creation and implementation of a mass spectrometry industry, by myself founding another mass spectrometry firm that is prospering today.

ACKNOWLEDGEMENTS

I thank Dr Karleugen Habfast and Dr Curt Brunnée for providing so many personal details about Dr Jenckel and the establishment of MAT. They both held the post of head of development at the company for a long period. Dr Brunnée, who enjoys a worldwide reputation as a mass spectrometry specialist, and after whom an award of the International Mass Spectrometry Foundation is named, is the author of the commemorative publication to mark the 50th anniversary of the founding of MAT, from which I have quoted. Special thanks go to Peter Jenckel, Dr Ludolf Jenckel's son, for providing me with numerous documents and giving me his personal insight into his father.

REFERENCES

1. Curt Brunnée, private communication

2. Curt Brunnée, "50 years of MAT in Bremen", *Rapid Commun. Mass Spectrom.* **2,** 694–707 (1997).

3. M.C. ten Noever de Brauw "A short story about the life of Curt Brunnée", *Rapid Commun. Mass Spectrom.* **11,** 708–713 (1997). Now reprinted in this book starting on page 162.

4. Peter Jenckel, private communication

5. Peter Jenckel, private communication

6. Peter Jenckel, private communication

A short story about the life of Curt Brunnée

Michael C. ten Noever de Brauw

(Old Friend, Adviser and Customer of MAT)

TNO Nutrition and Food Research Institute,

PO Box 360, 3700, AJ Zeist, The Netherlands

EARLY YEARS

Dr Curt Brunnée was born on 24 May 1928 in Rostock (Mecklenburg) in the former East Germany, where he spent his childhood. At the age of 12 he had an experience that had a crucial influence on the rest of his life with respect to the choice of his profession.

His father showed him a small glass plate, carved with very thin lines, hardly visible with the naked eye (1000 lines per millimeter). This small piece of glass, known as the famous Rowland grating, was handmade by Curt's grandfather in his optical factory located in Göttingen. In this factory, grandfather built microscopes and other optical instruments.

Grandfather's Rowland gratings were among the best available at the time, on the world market. The young Curt Brunnée was immensely intrigued and impressed by this piece of craftsmanship and decided that when he grew up he would like to be involved in this type of work. From that time on his father, who was a dentist, strongly supported this tendency of his son's and never even tried to persuade Curt to become a dentist as well.

There was another small event which pre-programmed the young Curt's brain. One day his father performed a magic trick for his son, making cigarettes appear and disappear in his hands. Several weeks later his father gave his son a magician's kit and Curt started studying and diligently practising all the available tricks while his mother functioned as a patient and enthusiastic spectator. Typical of Curt's character is that as a teenager he had already started to build his own magic apparatus which is still operational today, just like Curt himself! He always has a stack of cards or a napkin within reach so he can demonstrate magic

This chapter was originally published as Rapid. Commun. Mass Spectrom. **11,** *708–713 (1997). It is Copyright ©1997, John Wiley and Sons. It is reproduced here with the kind permission of John Wiley and Sons.*

Figure 1. Dr Curt Brunnée, Director of R&D, Finnigan MAT.

Figure 2. Curt the magician.

Opposite: Part of Curt Brunnée's "treasure islands". See Figure 6 for the full story.

Figure 3. Curt the circus artist.

tricks whenever he is in the mood for it. This is perfectly demonstrated in Figure 2, showing Curt in action with one of his disappearing tricks. Curt has many different interests and one of his favorite occupations was and still is, visiting a circus or variety theatre.

As a teenager he studied all the literature about famous artists like Houdini, who always succeeded in freeing himself from all kinds of chains, and the great juggler, Rastelli, keeping 8 balls or clubs in the air at the same time. Ten years ago Curt told his two sons (27 and 30 years old at that time) about the famous Rastelli. The sons gave their father a set of clubs for his next birthday, and it goes without saying that Curt Brunnée started exercising diligently. After three months he was able to give a demonstration with three clubs in his garden recorded for the family photo album (see Figure 3).

From time to time the young Curt dreamed of becoming a circus artist or animal tamer, travelling around the world.

In spite of these dreams, physics started to become his main interest. At school it was subject number one and at home he started to experiment with electric arcs, stroboscopes and other home-made devices. In this period he also experienced some disappointment, which occurred when he used the power switch of his first self-made radio. There was no music but only a short fierce light coming from the irreplaceable radio tube. Curt had transformed the radio tube into an ordinary light bulb by exchanging cathode and anode voltage. Curt also invented the first primitive disco light machine. In the attic of his parents' house he found an old human skull. The young inventor placed small light bulbs in the eye-sockets of the skull. Then he put the skull on the piano in his room. From his bed, Curt, using a self made voltage divider, was able to slowly fluctuate the light in the skull's eyes, frightening nightly visitors.

The world of his childhood was shattered when the family home was destroyed during a bombing raid in 1942. The family was very lucky because they had left the town a few days before the bombardment. Two years later the family had a very narrow escape when a bomb exploded in the back yard of the house where they were living in 1944. The heavy explosion severely damaged the house and part of the cellar, where the family was sheltering. By a miracle the family were not hurt and were saved from the debris.

After the end of the war in 1945, schools started to function again. Curt went back to school and graduated after one year. In 1946 he began to study physics and philosophy at the university in Rostock. Rostock was located in the Soviet occupation zone. The pressure of the political system became more and more unbearable day by day. Because of these problems Curt's parents suggested he should interrupt his studies in Rostock and try to go to the West. In the severe winter of 1947–1948 Curt Brunnée packed his belongings and started heading west. In a dark night he tried to cross, illegally, a frozen boundary river near Lübeck. That night luck was not with him. The ice was not strong enough to carry Curt, so he was almost drowned but managed to get out of the icy water. Completely soaking wet, walking around for an hour, at a temperature of –20°C he was almost frozen to death. Finally he found shelter with a friendly farmer, where he could dry and get warm after his dangerous adventure.

The next day he succeeded in passing the heavily guarded border as a stowaway hiding between crates on a small truck. The guards did not find him while searching the truck and Curt arrived unharmed in the West.

Later, when he wanted to visit his parents, who still stayed on the other side, Curt was caught crossing the frontier in the opposite direction. After one week in jail, his parents managed to get him out and Curt reentered West Germany via Berlin, which was easier at the time. In 1948 Curt restarted his study at the university of Marburg, obtaining his degree in 1952 as a "Diplom Physiker". His teacher was Professor Wilhelm Walcher, one of the German pioneers in mass spectrometry. Immediately Curt began his Ph.D. work, studying ion reflection and secondary electron emission from clean molybdenum surfaces. The available mass spectrometer was a home made 60° sector instrument. One of the main obstacles was to obtain very clean surfaces. Ultra high vacuum technology was not available at the time. The molybdenum targets were cleaned by glowing them in vacuum, giving Curt only one minute to do his measurement, yielding only one data point. After one minute a new gas layer was formed and the target had to be cleaned again. It took Curt more than one year of laborious work to acquire all the necessary data.

For Curt, life was not too bad because he had the help of a female assistant named Curta. Curta is not a female German name, but her father apparently liked the name and she had no say in it. During the experiments, Curt was turning all available potentiometers while Curta was making notes of the data points indicated by a galvanometer spot on a scale fixed to the wall. These measurements could only be done during the night because in the day time the mains voltage fluctuated too much and passing trucks caused too many vibrations. These common experiences were probably the basis for the later marriage of Curt and Curta! (1953). Instrumentation in this period was very primitive and somewhat dangerous and almost responsible for the early death of the young investigator.

One day Curt was proudly demonstrating the experimental set-up, explaining to a visitor the working of his mass spectrometer, pointing enthusiastically with a metal pointer at the 10 kV capacitor. To the visitor's horror, Curt got a severe electric shock and was thrown to the floor where he stayed for some time. Curt survived his first electro-shock therapy and no harm was done. It was not the last shock in his life.

WORKING AND LIVING IN BREMEN

After he finished his Ph.D., Curt was attracted by the shining prospects of a small company in Bremen, led by its founder, Dr Ludolf Jenckel. In 1956 Curt joined this small group of enthusiastic scientists who kept themselves busy, constructing a very complicated analytical instrument called a mass spectrometer. The name of this famous company was ATLAS MAT. Curt did not realize at the beginning of his career that he would stay for the next 35 years. Also he did not know that this company would change its name and management style so often. Only the characters MAT and Curt Brunnée remained the same during all the transformations (Atlas, Krupp, Varian, Finnigan, Thermo). Due to his strong character and great many-sided qualities, Curt survived this turmoil like a rock in bad weather and high seas.

Curt started his work developing, constructing, testing and installing mass spectrometers suitable for analytical tasks, in a broad field of applications, used in chemistry, medicine, physics and geology. His first job was the installation of a CH3 mass spectrometer at the University of Osaka (Japan). This job turned out to be a nightmare and after six weeks of stress and frustration, Curt had lost 10 kg of weight as well as all his appetite for mass spectrometry. However the first impressions from a completely new and strange culture put all the other bad technical experiences to the background. It was not the last time he went to Japan where he made many friends.

The CH3 was not competitive with the mass spectrometers from Metrovick and CEC. For the survival of ATLAS MAT it was necessary to develop a much more sophisticated instrument. In 1958 the first CH4 mass spectrometer was born, equipped with a new heatable, all metal inlet system. This system could be heated, together with the ion source housing up to 180°C. For that time this feature was unique and reduced the memory effects. In the following years, Curt and his coworkers improved the already successful CH4 mass spectrometer, making a wide spectrum of applications possible. This mass spectrometer was ahead of its time. It was a very flexible, sensitive and reliable instrument, capable of doing positive and negative electron ionization, thermal ionization, isotope ratio measurements. The system was also capable of scanning a GC/MS spectrum in 0.5 sec. per mass decade (exp. scan). The sensitivity was high and made it possible to detect, in selected ion detection (SID) mode, one picogram of benzene, eluating from a vacuum coupled GC capillary column. This was possible because the CH4 was equipped with a sophisticated and powerful differential pumping system that could handle 0.6 mL He carrier gas per minute.

The most advanced feature, however, was a motor-driven vacuum-lock inlet system. This device made it possible to insert an interchangeable ionization chamber directly into the ionizing electron beam (TO4 ion source). Using this technique made it possible to introduce thermally unstable, high-boiling or solid organic compounds.

The other benefit was that ion source contamination was restricted to the removable ion volume. Dr G. Spiteller was one of the first customers who successfully analyzed unstable alkaloids. One day Curt was shocked, hearing that a CH4 customer, from CIVO TNO in the Netherlands, had put a complete raw egg in the vacuum lock system, trying to identify a compound causing a musty taste in eggs at very low concentrations. This attempt was also successful and proved the great versatility of this mass spectrometer.

For some obscure reason this removable ion volume disappeared in the successors of the CH4 (CH5, CH7, MAT 8200) and reappeared much later in the MAT 90 series.

Curt and his team had to solve many problems in malfunctioning spectrometers. From time to time they had to deal with charge effects in the analyser tubes, causing peaks to vary in size and shape and destroying the resolution. One exceptional problem occurred at the university in Amsterdam (Prof. Nico Nibbering's lab.). They were not able to obtain accurate mass measurements, caused by irregular peak shifting, visible on the matching screen. After some time the colleagues from the electronics lab. discovered that this magnetic effect was caused by the strong electro-magnetic field originating from a tramway power cable, located near the lab. The problem was finally solved by installing a big copper coil above the MAT 711, compensating the fluctuating electro-magnetic field from the power cable.

Such unpredictable problems, a disaster for any timetable, sometimes made Curt sad and angry. Some people have to write down their frustrations, in order to get rid of them. The many-sided Curt Brunnée, who is also a talented cartoonist, used this gift to digest his moods making drawings, reflecting his feelings perfectly well. These are illustrated in the next two cartoons made by Curt (Figure 4).

Curt did almost everything imaginable in order to provide the exacting customers with powerful and reliable instruments. Curt was a real perfectionist and could not stand failures. Once he presented some magic at a conference dinner in Japan and failed with the

Figure 4. The cartoonist Curt, self-portraying two different stages of his mood during development of the MAT 8200.

last trick. In an effort to console him, Prof. H. Matsuda spoke the wise words 'On occasion monkeys fall down the tree'. Curt did not like to be the monkey. To achieve his goal he learned the hard way to overcome the depth of failures and disappointments but he also enjoyed the flavor of success. When Curt set out on a certain line in order to achieve his aim, he consequently followed the road to the end. His friend and colleague Dr Karleugen Habfast, whilst achieving his goals also, was quite an opposite character. He came from the Munich MAT facilities and led the MS development department in Bremen for some time. Dr Habfast had a poster behind his desk reflecting an important part of his character. It showed a prayer, written in big Gothic characters: 'Oh Lord please give us our daily inspiration and forgive us what we planned yesterday'. This poster was not favoured by the general management. Dr Habfast did not really need this prayer because he usually had more than one inspiration a day, causing the management some headaches. However these two complementary characters formed an interesting and powerful team. They had a very important impact and contributed much to the success story of MAT.

After working in the field of development, design and construction for 14 years, Curt Brunnée became head of the manufacturing facility in Bremen during the period 1970–1975. This was a complete new challenge for Curt, leading a production group of 280 people. In this period he had to modernize the production and introduce new computer controlled manufacturing methods.

One of Curt's philosophies was: when you want to command and get people to do certain things, you have to experience and do them yourself first. Thus he learned drilling and cutting and became a very acceptable turner and milling machine operator. He manufactured ion source parts designed by himself. Curt was also responsible for the implementation of high precision manufacturing techniques, indispensable for the production of hyperbolic quadrupole rods. These 6 years of leading a high technology production unit, of having not only to introduce new production methods, but also achieving at the same time a strong reduction in the manufacturing costs, were not easy. This was a never ending competition battle and many of his colleagues wondered why he took this job and if he was happy with it. One thing is certain: Curt learned many things which he could use in his hobby, as a very skilled, almost professional modeller.

One of his masterpieces, built together with his wife, is a dolls' house having eleven completely furnished rooms. Everything is worked out in the greatest detail. These pieces of furniture (scale 1:12) are exact replicas of antique historic models. This project took almost 10 years to accomplish. Figure 5 is a picture showing a close up from the music room in this house.

This dolls' house has now a prominent place in the family living room, to the great joy of his five grandchildren.

Curt also constructed boat models and, to make it more difficult, these boats had to be built in a bottle. This bizarre habit probably originates from the construction department

Figure 5. Christmas party
1996 in Curt and Curta's
dolls' house.

where the designers always succeed in placing mass spectrometry parts at places almost
unreachable for the customer and even for their own service engineers.

In 1976 Curt made his comeback in the R&D department where he led the construction
department and experimental machine shop. He was again heavily involved in the development of new series of mass spectrometers. One of his tasks was the transformation of a
small magnetic sector GC/MS mass spectrometer MAT 111 into a compact high-resolution
instrument, the MAT 112, which was upgraded later to a good working instrument known
as the MAT 112 S; at the same time another family of double focussing instruments, MAT
311/312, were developed. The successor MAT 8200 was a powerful high resolution magnetic sector instrument. The many attachments like field desorption, chemical ionization,
direct chemical ionization, fast-atom bombardment (FAB), continuous-flow FAB, automated
direct insertion, liquid chromatography/mass spectrometry moving belt etc., made this instrument suitable for a broad spectrum of applications. The most complex attachment was
a quadrupole system which turned the instrument into a hybrid tandem mass spectrometer
(MS/MS) (MAT HSQ 30). At this time Varian MAT had already been taken over by Finnigan,
and bore the name: 'Finnigan MAT' from then on. Again Curt had to adapt himself to a new
management style. He was quite successful in doing so and made many friends. Mike Story
(from Finnigan, San José) and Curt Brunnée had developed a kind of a competition by send-
ing back and forth a bottle housing a model boat, which had to be furnished with new parts
(mast gear, lifeboats etc.) by the receiver. By this means they could test and develop their
skills on both sides of the ocean.

In 1981 Curt became head of the total R&D department where his last job was the development of the first completely computer controlled high resolution magnetic sector mass
spectrometer. The MAT 90 family was born and became a worldwide success.

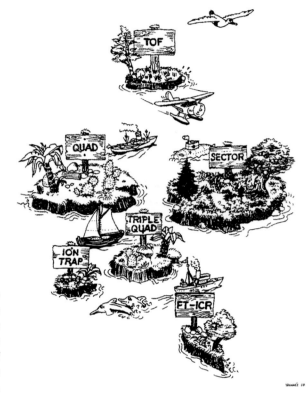

Figure 6. Curt's treasure islands. These islands are the result of a multi-variant analysis concerning the different properties of different types of mass analysers.

In 1988 Curt Brunnée was promoted to Director of Research for Finnigan worldwide. In this period Curt put in a great effort in creating a close, open and effective cooperation between the different R&D groups, and their different cultures [San José (USA), Hemel Hempstead (GB) and Bremen (FRG)]. He also evaluated the possibility for the Finnigan Corporation of entering new fields of application like trace analysis by inductively coupled plasma mass spectrometry (ICP/ MS) and high molecular compound analysis using the (MALDI) technique. (In 1970 there had already been experiments, in close cooperation with CIVO TNO in the Netherlands, using a laser ionization source, mounted on the ATLAS MAT SM1 with photoplate detection. This project was not continued because the available technology was not advanced enough at the time.)

Curt visited many laboratories around the world and had discussions with many scientists of different disciplines, exploring new fields where mass spectrometry could play an important supporting role. Some impressions from his journeys were put down in one of Curt's cartoons used in the famous lecture entitled 'The Ideal Mass Analyser: Fact or Fiction' (Figure 6).

In 1991 Curt Brunnée retired after a fruitful life of working hard. Some of his colleagues thought that he was able to get more than twenty-four hours out of a day, considering his

Figure 7. The car Curt
always wanted.

high productivity in his work at MAT and his hobbies and cultural life at home. The versatile
Curt also constructed, in a long term project with his wife, a church organ, and even
learned to play it. After his retirement Curt bought a commercial organ and studied every
day, playing music from Bach and for a change sometimes evergreens, youthful memories,
like the 'Moonlight Serenade' and the 'St Louis Blues'.

Curt is now devoting all his time to his many hobbies. One year ago he built a new magic
apparatus (Card Rise) of which nobody has been able to discover the working mechanism.
Probably Curt's pension was not sufficient to afford his dream automobile, a Rolls Royce
Phantom II, year 1934. He solved the problem by building, also with his wife Curta, an
exact replica (scale 1:8). This magnificent model was finished a short time ago complete
with license plate number: CCB-96. (Curt and Curta Brunnée 1996) and is seen in Figure 7
together with a small matchbox model.

Typical for Curt is that even after his retirement he is still planning projects. For 1997 Curt
announced the construction of a Mississippi steamer (model!).

During his numerous trips, visiting foreign countries, Curt came into contact with many
different cultures. He was most attracted by the Far East with its cultures and philosophies.
He made a profound study of them and presented some lectures on these highly spiritual
subjects. Since he is now at home, Curt has now found more time to study philosophy again
attending seminars at the University of Bremen, concerning questions about epistemol-
ogy, and philosophical problems related to physics and mathematics. Also he is interested
in consciousness research, investigating the secrets of the human brain: questions about
our conscience, where does it come from, where do we differ from animals (and why do
we build mass spectrometers) etc. One may say that Curt is genuinely interested in all the
questions arising from the mysteries in human life and its place in the cosmos.

CONCLUSION

Summarizing, one can say that Curt has a very rich life behind him and that it is still getting richer. During his 35 years at MAT Curt Brunnée designed and developed more than 20 different mass spectrometers including a variety of different attachments like a dual GC/MS ion source, combined EI/FID source, GC/MS interfaces, molecular beams systems etc. He also did theoretical work on ion optics, together with Prof. H. Wollnik and had many co-operations with scientists all over the world. Together with Dr H. Voshage, he wrote a well known book about mass spectrometry (1963). Curt has more than 40 publications bearing his name as author or co-author. He was an editorial board member of several scientific journals and has presented numerous papers at national and international conferences.

His most famous lectures were the plenary lecture at the International Mass Spectrometry Conference (IMSC) in Vienna 1982 entitled 'New Instrumentation in Mass Spectrometry'[1] and the 5th Asomilar Conference 1986, CA, USA,[2] 'The Ideal Mass Analyser: Fact or Fiction?'. On these occasions he presented lectures on new developments in mass spectrometry in a perfect synthesis between culture historical views and scientific developments.

From 1989 to 1991 Curt was president of the German Society For Mass Spectrometry (AGMS).

In 1991 Finnigan founded a prize bearing the name of Curt Brunnée, which is given to young promising scientists, who made an essential contribution to the development in experimental and theoretical mass spectrometry. The Curt Brunnée prize was awarded for the first time at the IMSC meeting in Budapest (1994). It was given to Prof. G. Brenton for his outstanding contribution to experimental and theoretical mass spectrometry. At the same conference, the International Committee of the IMSC, honored Curt Brunnée with the Thomson medal gold which can be considered as the crown on Curt Brunnée's career. This appreciation reveals only some aspects of Curt's interesting personality, a man that so many colleagues of the mass spectrometry family have been grateful to work and discuss science with.

REFERENCES

1. *Int. J. Mass Spectrom. Ion Phys.* **45,** 81–86 (1982).
2. *Int. J. Mass Spectrom. Ion Phys.* **76,** 125–237 (1987).

The European history of peptide and protein mass spectrometry

Peter Roepstorff
University of Southern Denmark, Odense, Denmark

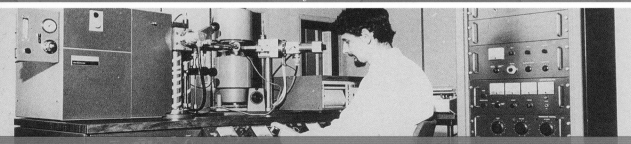

THE BEGINNING, THE 1960S

In the 1960s, almost all mass spectrometric analysis was based on electron ionisation which required that the samples were in the gas phase and that they could be evaporated into the ion source. The mass range of the mass spectrometers was also limited to a maximum of around m/z 1000 or somewhat higher if one worked at a reduced accelerating voltage. Peptides and proteins were not volatile due to their zwitterionic character and analysis of proteins could not even be considered due to their size. The introduction of the direct heated inlet probe opened up the possibility of analyses of compounds with low volatility provided that sufficient vapour pressure could be obtained before the compounds thermally degraded.

Sequence determination of proteins was a hot topic at that time and British biochemist Frederick Sanger had been awarded the 1958 Nobel Prize in chemistry for his method of determining the sequence of proteins. This was based on the generation of overlapping small peptides by partial acid hydrolysis followed by amino acid analysis of the peptides and the solving of a complicated puzzle to assign the sequence. It would be a great improvement to the method if such small peptides could be sequenced by mass spectrometry. To my knowledge, the first mass spectra of peptides were published by Einar Stenhagen in Sweden in 1960 and by Klaus Biemann in the USA in 1959. Stenhagen derivatised the peptides by N-trifluoroacetylation and methyl esterification. Biemann N-acylated the peptides, reduced them to amino alcohols and later separated mixtures of such derivatised peptides by gas chromatography (GC) coupled to mass spectrometry (MS).

A number of mass spectrometry groups, most of them European, took up the challenge in the following years. These included the Russian group headed by Shemyakin from the Shemyakin Institute of Bioorganic Chemistry in Moscow, Heyns and Grützmacher from the University of Hamburg, Weigand and Prox from the Technical University in Munich, König from the University of Tübingen and in England, Agarwal and collaborators in Liverpool, Aplin and Jones from Oxford University and at AEI in Manchester by Barber and Wolstenholme. Almost all these studies were made on small synthetic di- to tetrapeptides in order to establish the fragmentation pattern produced by EI and the effect of different amino acid residues on the fragmentation. European scientists were main players in this field and demonstrated that it was possible to sequence peptides using mass spectrometry, but none of these studies involved natural peptides.

A paper published in 1965 by Michael (Mickey) Barber, in collaboration with the French group of Edgar Lederer from Institut de Chimie des Substances Naturelles, on the structure determination of a natural peptidolipid called Fortuitine opened my eyes to the potential mass spectrometry offered for the analysis of peptides. The spectra were obtained by Mickey by electron ionisation on an AEI MS9 mass spectrometer at AEI in Manchester. Due to the heterogeneity of an N-terminal acyl group, the molecular weights of this peptidolipid were 1331 and 1359, far larger than any peptide previously analysed by MS. Fortuitine was a very fortuitous compound because it was naturally derivatised, N-terminally acylated, C-terminally esterified, threonine residues were acetylated and a number of the amino acid residues were N-methylated. In the following years, the French group followed this success by determining

Opposite: the author at his
first mass spectrometer.

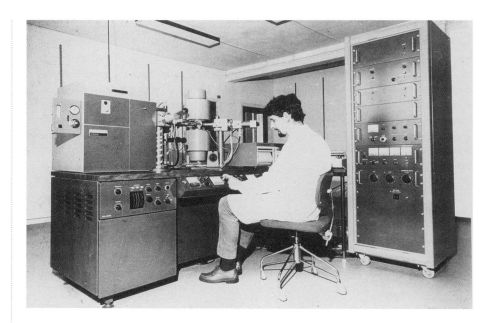

Figure 1. The author at his first mass spectrometer, a Perkin Elmer 270.

the structures of a number of other peptidolipids and other natural peptides. These studies led J. van Heijenoort from the French group to suggest that N-methylation of peptides would generate more volatile derivatives by eliminating the possibility of hydrogen bonding occurring. Bhupesh Das adapted the Hakamori method, well known from carbohydrate chemistry, for permethylation and later, in collaboration with David Thomas, refined the method further. The spectra obtained after permethylation were surprisingly simple, dominated by N-terminal sequence ions, nowadays called *a*- and *b*-ions. Now the perspectives for mass spectrometric peptide sequencing seemed much more promising.

I was working as a young research associate in a protein research institute in Copenhagen where we had the first commercial Edman protein sequencer in Europe. We had encountered its limitations for the sequencing of N-terminally blocked proteins and for solving this problem, mass spectrometry seemed to be the obvious solution. I went to AEI to carry out some tests with Mickey Barber and we installed our first mass spectrometer, a Perkin Elmer 270 double focussing low-resolution instrument in our laboratory in 1968 (Figure 1). My first attempts to permethylate failed and I therefore arranged to visit Bhupesh Das for two months to learn how to permethylate. I was not the only one being taught there. Next to me was a young British scientist, Howard Morris, who was there with the same purpose. At the end of the day, we would leave our small test tubes with our attempts to permethylate peptides on Bupesh Das's desk. He would then analyse the samples during the night on their newly installed MS9 instrument and, the next morning, we could pick up the spectra recorded on UV-photographic paper with his mass assignments, interpretation and comments marked with a pencil.

I quickly realised that if I wanted to learn something about mass spectrometry, I should adapt to Bhupesh's working rhythm and be in the laboratory between 2 am and 4 am, at which time he would run the samples and also share his knowledge with us. The funding for consumables was very limited in the French institute and on our arrival, we were given two small test tubes and two Pasteur pipettes for our stay. This also meant that each morning we cleaned the glassware before we could make two attempts to permethylate during the day. So, after a weekend back in Denmark, I brought back two boxes with 200 test tubes and two boxes with 200 Pasteur pipettes for general use in the laboratory. That made me a very popular guest.

THE 1970s: THE FIGHT TO BE ACCEPTED BY THE BIOLOGISTS

I returned to Copenhagen and Howard to the University of Leeds, both of us now convinced that mass spectrometry had a future in protein studies and that permethylation was the magic trick for sequencing proteins by mass spectrometry. In the 1970s, several groups, among them the above mentioned groups in England and France, continued to develop peptide sequencing by mass spectrometry. There were still a number of problems to solve. Certain amino acid residues were problematic upon permethylation due to the formation of quaternary ions making the resulting derivatised peptides involatile and several attempts to solve these problems were published by, among others, Howard and me. Howard Morris moved to Dudley Williams' laboratory in Cambridge and a number of excellent papers investigating the possibility for protein sequencing were published from there. This work was continued and even strengthened after Howard Morris moved to Imperial College in London. Other groups in England, among them John Priddle at Oxford University, also took up peptide mass spectrometry. The French group concentrated their efforts on natural peptides which could not be sequenced by Edman degradation because they were N-terminally blocked. The German groups focussed on analyses of peptide conjugates and did not adopt permethylation. I concentrated on identifying novel post translational modifications (PTMs) by MS, the most successful being the discovery, using a combination of MS and NMR, of γ-carboxyglutamic acid in the blood clotting proteins in collaboration with Johan Stenflo's group at the University of Lund. Shortly afterwards, Howard Morris published the same results paradoxically in collaboration with a Danish group from the University of Aarhus. Unfortunately, some of the most important PTMs, namely phosphorylation and glycosylation, could not be analysed by EI-MS.

The methods for separation of the peptides resulting from enzymatic digestions met with only limited success since they were not sufficiently sensitive to meet the requirements of the biochemists, and the size of peptides which could be analysed was limited to rather small peptides containing up to ten amino acid residues. Several of us tried to sequence the peptides in mixtures without prior separation. The problem to be solved in direct mixture analysis was that during interpretation of the spectra from the mixtures, it was possible to jump from the sequence of one peptide to another when certain sequences were present in the mixture. Attempts to overcome these problems were made by slowly heating the direct inlet probe which partially separated the peptides by fractional vaporisation or by comparing the results obtained with different derivatives, including the use of deuterated derivatives, of the peptide mixture. I presented this concept on peptide mixture analysis at the 6th International Mass Spectrometry Conference in Edinburgh in 1973. It was only my second presentation at international meetings and I was very nervous. Shortly after my lecture, however, Fred McLafferty came up to me and commented favourably on my ideas. For me, it was like a revelation. I had started mass spectrometry all on my own, based on reading the literature, and Fred's book on interpretation of mass spectra was my bible. Our first contact there developed into a lifelong friendship.

Shortly after the Edinburgh meeting, I moved to a new university in Odense (now named University of Southern Denmark), the birth place of the Danish story teller Hans Christian Andersen. There, I tried to implement peptide and protein mass spectrometry in a molecular biology department. In that decade, a number of other new methods made their appearance. Dai Games from the University of Cardiff, who I first met at a meeting in Alghero, Sardinia, in 1975, organised by Alberto Frigerio, had one of the first moving belt interfaces that allowed coupling of liquid chromatography (LC) with EI-MS. I went there and, in collaboration with Dai and one of his graduate students, Mark McDowall, tried to see if that would provide the solution but, unfortunately, the method was not suitable for practical work. In Bonn, Beckey had developed field desorption (FD) mass spectrometry and he and Hans Ulrich Winter had shown that it was possible to analyse underivatised peptides by this method. I went there to see if this was a new opening for peptide mass spectrometry. FD generated mainly molecular ions and, since these were often absent in the spectra of permethylated peptides, it would be a very valuable supplement and might also solve the mixture problem. Unfortunately, the spectra were very transient and we used almost an entire day and numerous loadings on the field emitters to obtain just one spectrum. So FD also did not seem to be a viable solution for peptide analyses.

Although several of us felt that mass spectrometry had a future in protein studies, it was very difficult to convince the biologists. We needed rather large quantities of sample and could not promise results. Consequently, they were very reluctant to share their valuable samples with us. A number of results such as those of Howard Morris, who sequenced the two isoforms of the natural opiate, Enkephalin, for which the traditional wet Dansyl–Edman procedure had failed, and the discovery of γ-carboxyglutamic acid opened the eyes of at least some biologists to the potential of mass spectrometry in protein studies. Each time we, the mass spectrometrists, made a little progress, however, other techniques advanced more rapidly and, at the end of the 1970s, the field was stagnating. The advent of the new genetic techniques such as DNA sequencing and recombinant technology seemed to render protein sequencing superfluous and most of the scientists involved in protein sequencing by classical or mass spectrometric methods changed fields. At that time, I was participating in a Linderstroem Lang conference on protein structure determination. During the conference, I was approached by a Swedish accelerator physicist, Bo Sundqvist, who asked me if I believed that it would be possible to place an intact protein on a solid surface and bombard it with 100 MeV particles to gener-ate the protein in the gas phase and analyse it by mass spectrometry. I did not believe it and explained that if we bombarded carefully derivatised peptides with 70 eV electrons they fell apart. The next question was: "*If it works, then would it be of any use*". My answer was "*Yes, it would revolutionise protein analysis*". He thanked me and left.

thunderstorm. The lecturer was very scared, whereas the three of us conceived a new conference concept—sailing conferences. This was effected a few years later when we collected a multi-disciplinary group of 12 scientists involved in desorption phenomena on two sailboats in the French Mediterranean. Ebs was the captain on one and Yvon on the other boat. Lectures were in the morning on the bigger boat. In the afternoon, we would sail to a new mooring and, in the evening, enjoy good French wines. No AV media were available on the boats, our thoughts and ideas were explained in words and drawn on a flip chart. All in all, this was one of the most inspiring scientific meetings I have ever attended and some scientists showed unexpected talents. For example, one of the accelerator physicists, Yvon LeBeyec, was an excellent cook whereas the other, Karl Wien, demonstrated a very good talent for dish washing (Figure 5).

In the 1980s, many of the ideas leading to proteomics were developed. The concept of peptide mass mapping was described by Howard Morris using FAB and by us using PDMS. Mass spectrometric molecular weight information as a supplement to traditional protein sequencing and

Figure 5. The crew on the sailing conference on desorption phenomena. The crew members are: Front row from the left: Bo Sundqvist, Wilfried Tyszynski, Ebs Hilf, Ute Bahr, Yannik Hoppilliard, Matthias Mann, Peter Roepstorff and in the back row: Michael Karas, Werner Ens, Doug Barofsky, Yvon LeBeyec, Karl Wien, Serge Della-Negra and Brian Chait.

for the characterisation of recombinantly produced and engineered proteins became generally accepted. Numerous post-translational modifications in proteins, including the hitherto inaccessible glycosylations and phosphorylations could now be characterised by mass spectrometry. Several biotech and pharma companies introduced the new methodologies in their research and development laboratories. FAB became installed in many laboratories, industrial as well as academic. PDMS was somewhat slower to be accepted due to national regulations and restrictions for using the highly radioactive ^{252}Cf-source and probably also due to the unconventional design of the Biolon instrument, which did not look like a real mass spectrometer. However, the two Danish insulin manufacturers Novo and Nordisk Gentofte and Willi Richter at Ciba–Geigy in Basel were the first to see the perspectives and to install PDMS instruments in companies. Michael Przybylski in Konstanz and Günter Allmaier in Vienna also took up PDMS for the analysis of biological samples. The now widespread use of peptide mass data for identification of proteins and their modifications in proteomics was initiated by matching peptide and protein molecular weight information obtained by FAB and PDMS with DNA sequence data. In a NATO-funded collaboration with Kim Faull at Stanford University and Doug Barofsky at Oregon State University, we developed a concept termed peptide charting to analyse all the processing products of the neuropeptide precursors. This, in my opinion, was the first attempt to make high through-put large-scale analysis of proteins and peptides and it inspired us to the later use of peptide mass fingerprinting for protein identification.

Although FAB and PDMS changed the perspectives for mass spectrometric analyses in protein studies, there were still limitations. Analysis of proteins was limited to rather small proteins, 20 kDa and 30 kDa, respectively, for the two techniques, most likely because the physical dimensions of larger molecules prevented their desorption. In addition, although the two methods were much more sensitive than previous methods for peptide and protein analysis, there was a need for better sensitivity to cope with the challenges in biological research. In 1988, the picture changed entirely. At the ASMS Conference in San Francisco, John Fenn presented the first electrospray ionisation (ESI) spectra of large proteins and a few months later, at the International Mass Spectrometry Conference in Bordeaux, Hillenkamp and Karas presented MALDI spectra of even larger proteins. The potential use of ESI had been described almost two decades earlier by Dole, but had never been used in practice as an ionisation method for mass spectrometry. Fenn at Yale University and a group of Russian scientists at the Institute of Analytical Instrumentation of the Soviet Academy of Sciences in Leningrad had independently investigated its potential use, the Russians for analysis of rather small peptides in combination with liquid chromatography and Fenn for the analysis of intact proteins. The Nobel Prize in chemistry was awarded in 1988 to John Fenn (USA) and Koichi Tanaka (Japan) for obtaining mass spectra of proteins by electrospray and laser desorption, respectively. It was, as was seen with the later impact of mass spectrometry in protein studies, highly justified to give the Nobel Prize to the development of protein mass spectrometry. In my opinion, however, based on the same arguments as the Nobel Committee, I believe it should have been given to Bo Sundqvist for the first demonstration of the mass spectrometry of proteins or to Hillenkamp and Karas for MALDI, which was described prior to Tanaka's work and is the method used in practice. The award for ESI to Fenn must be considered justified because he, and not the Russian group, demonstrated its use for proteins.

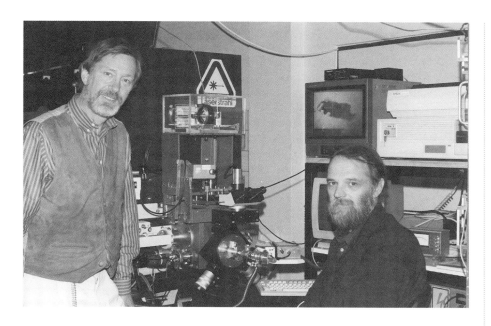

Figure 6. Franz Hillenkamp and Michael Karas in front of the LAMA instrument on which MALDI was developed.

The advent of MALDI and ESI also gave me a number of memorable experiences (Figure 6). Franz Hillenkamp had called me several times before the Bordeaux conference to tell me that they had beaten us by obtaining molecular ions of a 172 kDa tetrameric protein complex by MALDI (Figure 7). Immediately after the conference I went to Münster to try out this new

Figure 7. Dai Games, Kate Rafn (technician at the Odense group), Peter Roepstorff and Bo Sundqvist at the IMSC in Bordeaux, 1988, discussing the MALDI results presented by Franz Hillenkamp.

technique on other proteins and protein complexes including haemoglobin. I worked with Michael Karas in the laboratory and to dry the matrix sample he just used his cigarette lighter to heat the sample plate. Smoking was not banned in the laboratory at that time. We succeeded in obtaining spectra of many proteins but, unfortunately, not of the intact haemoglobin complex. This was the initiation of a long term collaboration and friendship, however. The only other instrument to perform MALDI was in the laboratory of Brian Chait at the Rockefeller University. Brian and I were long time friends from working on PDMS and he had built a combined secondary ion mass spectrometry (SIMS) and PD instrument which could easily be modified for MALDI by using an extra port for the laser.

When I arrived at his laboratory on a Saturday afternoon, he had just recorded a MALDI spectrum of milk (from the local supermarket). The spectrum was in perfect accordance with the signals for the proteins expected to be dominant in bovine milk. A little later in the afternoon, we went for a walk in Central Park. There, a lady was giving breast milk to her baby, and immediately a thought emerged, could we distinguish human and bovine milk by a simple MALDI spectrum. The lady volunteered to give us a little of her milk which we collected in a cup we got from a Coca-Cola sales stand. We ran back to the laboratory and made the analysis and effectively the mass spectra of the human milk revealed the expected differences in composition compared to those of bovine milk.

Now we were caught by comparative MALDI analyses of different beverages and ran to the local supermarket to buy a number of different beer brands. One microlitre from each can was used for MALDI which effectively showed that differences between the different brands could be detected. Almost all the beer was still available, however, so in order not to waste it, we decided to make an international tasting panel representing four continents to assess the beer quality by "organoleptic analysis". By slight manipulation of the MALDI data, we could make a correlation between the spectra and the quality based on the very objective taste panel. Later the same year, we were all going to a NATO meeting in Minaki Lodge in Canada organised by Ken Standing. With these exciting results in hand we called him and suggested that we should give a lecture during the dinner about beer quality testing by MALDI. He accepted the idea and I gave the lecture where the "revolutionising results" leading to a very important application of mass spectrometry were shown and the worldwide consequences of such quality testing outlined (Figure 8). The Minaki meeting in 1990 was one of the first meetings where there was an equal representation of the "old techniques", PD, FAB and SIMS, and the new techniques, MALDI and ESI. The relative potential of the two generations of techniques was assessed by a canoe race in traditional Indian canoes—the old timers against the new comers. The result was not in accordance with the future because the old timers won the race (Figure 9)!

Figure 8. The author outlining the consequences of beer quality testing by MALDI MS during dinner at the Minaki Lodge Conference.

THE 1990s: MASS SPECTROMETRY CONQUERS PROTEIN STUDIES, PROTEOMICS EMERGES

ESI and MALDI, within a few years, made FAB and PDMS redundant for peptide and protein analysis. The strength of ESI was that, as with FAB, it could be implemented directly onto existing mass spectrometers and it was also compatible with liquid chromatography, whereas

Figure 9. The winning "old timer" canoe racing team at the Minaki Conference. From aft, left to right: Peter Roepstorff, Gottfried Feistner, Doug Barofsky, Gunnar Brinkmalm, Bo Sundqvist, Werner Ens, Günter Allmaier and three unknown persons.

MALDI required development of new instrumentation. We, in our laboratory in Odense, modified a linear TOF PDMS instrument for MALDI and also, with generous support from Marvin Vestal, acquired a Vestec single quadrupole thermospray instrument modified for ESI. This allowed us to compare the four techniques for protein analysis which clearly demonstrated the superiority of the two new ionisation techniques, even though we were limited for MALDI performance by the use of the linear modified PDMS instrument. A few years later, Bruker and Finnigan MAT in Bremen and Vestec in Houston were among the first to commercialise high-performance reflecting MALDI-TOF instruments for protein analysis (Figure 10).

After his PhD study with John Fenn, Matthias Mann had joined our group in Odense in 1989 as a postdoctoral research worker. There, he got involved in our first attempts to do what later was termed proteomics. Based on the previous concept of peptide charting, the potential for using mass spectrometry to identify proteins by comparison with DNA sequences was obvious. A number of groups took up this challenge and, within one month in the spring 1993, four papers were published demonstrating that proteins could be identified based on what today is termed peptide mass fingerprinting. Three of the papers were from Europe, two involving our group, one from ETH in Zürich and one from John Stults in California, who also demonstrated the use of in-gel digestion for identification of proteins from 2D-gels. Matthias Mann later joined EMBL in Heidelberg. There, together with Matthias Wilm, he developed nano-ESI, which now dominates all protein ESI-MS, and also the concept of sequence tags for protein identification based on a combination of molecular mass determination and partial sequencing by MS/MS. The potential of mass spectrometry for protein analysis and proteomics now became clear and the instrument manufacturers began to develop high-performance, automated, user-friendly instruments dedicated to use in biological laboratories. Again, European manufacturers

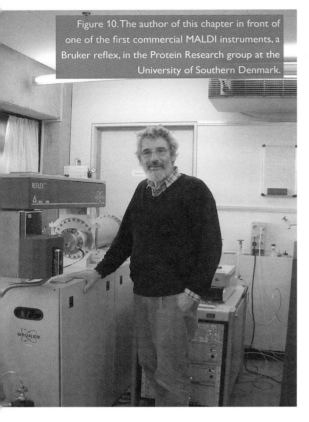

Figure 10. The author of this chapter in front of one of the first commercial MALDI instruments, a Bruker reflex, in the Protein Research group at the University of Southern Denmark.

were leading. VG-Micromass developed the first quadrupole time-of-flight (Q-TOF) instruments, followed shortly afterwards by the Canadian company, Sciex. Bruker adapted ion traps to protein analysis and, as mentioned above, also became one of the leading manufacturers of instruments for MALDI-MS.

The biological community quickly realised the potential of proteomics and, in the following period, protein mass spectrometry was implemented in numerous laboratories worldwide. In the early proteomics period, Europeans with a strong background in protein chemistry and mass spectrometry were among the leaders, both in bringing mass spectrometry into the biological laboratory and also in developing methods for sample preparation for proteomics compatible with subsequent mass spectrometric analysis. Although proteomics now dominated the use of protein mass spectrometry, a number of new, fascinating concepts were developed. In Chris Dobson's group at the University of Oxford, Carol Robinson transferred the experience gained there in the use of deuterium exchange in combination with studies by nuclear magnetic resonance (NMR) to its use in mass spectrometry to monitor deuterium exchange. This led to a number of studies of protein folding using hydrogen/deuterium (H/D) exchange in solution combined with MS. Eric Forest at CEA in Grenoble took up the idea and Albert Heck at the University of Warwick some years later performed H/D exchange in the gas phase in a high field Fourier transform ion cyclotron resonance (FT-ICR) instrument to assess protein interaction in the gas phase. H/D exchange studies were also taken up by Thomas Jorgensen at the University of Southern Denmark with the aim of determining the sites of protein interaction with drugs or other proteins as well as allosteric conformational changes caused by protein interactions. Later, in conflict with papers from the US, he demonstrated that complete scrambling upon collision-induced decomposition (CID) did not allow assignment of the precise location of the deuterium atoms in the analysed peptides, whereas assignment was possible using in-source decay in MALDI or fragmentation by electron capture dissociation or electron transfer dissociation.

Analysis of intact non-covalent protein complexes in the gas phase in a mass spectrometer had, for some time, been a challenge. Carol Robinson took up this challenge and, within a short time, demonstrated that it was possible to bring even very large protein complexes into the gas phase using ESI-MS by carefully controlling the experimental conditions. This resulted in mass spectra being obtained of a number of complexes including that of the intact ribosome, a protein complex containing two sub-units with a total mass of 2.5 MDa containing 54 proteins, many of which are post-translationally modified and three large RNA molecules (also post-transcriptionally modified). I consider these studies, and her following studies that demonstrate that it is possible by CID to peel-off the proteins gradually from the surface of protein complexes, to be amongst the most spectacular demonstrations of the capabilities of mass spectrometry.

OTHER LARGE BIOMOLECULES, NUCLEIC ACIDS AND CARBOHYDRATES

Nucleic acids and carbohydrates had, for many years, been considered out of reach for mass spectrometric analysis. European scientists have also pioneered mass spectrometric analysis of these classes of molecules. Prior to the advent of MALDI and ESI, Anne Dell at Imperial College in London in the early 1980s had already successfully investigated the glycans liberated from glycoproteins by FAB-MS using permethylation of the glycans and, over the years, she has pioneered glycan characterisation. Her method is now adapted to MALDI and is considered to be a standard method for structure determination of glycans. Large carbohydrate polymers such as pectins, arabinoxylans and cellulose are of considerable industrial interest as food additives or for biofuel production. Mass spectrometry has been essential in characterising enzymatic or chemical degradation products of these large polymers. In a project funded by the European Union (EU), the group at the University of Southern Denmark demonstrated that MALDI as well as ESI-MS in a method similar in concept to peptide mapping is highly efficient for the characterisation of degradation products and also that ESI-MS/MS allowed assignment of the linkage positions. Mass spectrometry presently has replaced NMR for the assignment of carbohydrate structures.

Lutz Grotjahn at GBF in Braunschweig demonstrated that it was possible to analyse small oligonucleotides by negative ion FAB-MS. MALDI and ESI opened up new possibilities for the analysis of these types of molecules. Franz Hillenkamp called me just after their discovery of MALDI and told me that we together should apply for an EU grant for the analysis of DNA and RNA. I was very sceptical but Franz was very persistent, so we applied and were awarded a grant. This resulted in a very fruitful collaboration where Edi Nordhoff from the German side and Finn Kirpekar from the Danish side formed a perfect team to develop the analysis of DNA and RNA. In Franz Hillenkamp's laboratory in Münster there was access to infrared (IR) as well as ultraviolet (UV) lasers for MALDI. IR MALDI was shown to be most successful for large DNA molecules whereas UV MALDI also worked well for smaller DNAs and for RNA.

The analytical methods for DNA analysis developed through this collaboration were used by a German/American company, Sequenom, for high throughput mass spectrometry-based analyses of single-nucleotide polymorphisms (SNPs) whereas the method for RNA analysis was further developed by Finn Kirpekar for the analysis of modified RNAs, first in archaea and later in other organisms using a concept very similar to that used for assignment of post-translational modifications in proteins. ESI-MS of oligonucleotides was investigated in Alain van Dorsselaer's group in Strasbourg. They obtained spectra of rather large oligonucleotides (up to a 132-mer) using negative ion ESI-MS. Wolter and Engels from the University in Frankfurt demonstrated that it was possible to sequence small oligonucleotides by negative ion ESI-MS/MS. There is no doubt that European scientists have been pioneers in mass spectrometric analysis of oligonucleotides. However, mass spectrometry has not had an impact similar to that of proteins except for some special purposes, most likely due to the very fast development of wet methods for DNA sequencing.

PRESENT SITUATION AND CONCLUDING REMARKS

By the end of the past millennium, the role of mass spectrometry in protein studies and proteomics had gained worldwide acceptance. Proteomics is a key element in contemporary studies of biological phenomena as well as in studying the causes of diseases. Protein mass spectrometry is the essential analytical technique in proteomics and from being a marginal, almost exotic, subject both at mass spectrometry conferences and also in mass spectrometry sessions at biological conferences, it is now a dominating subject in both types of meetings. Thus, for example, three out of 141 presentations were related to proteins and nucleic acids in the first international meeting I attended, the 5th IMSC meeting in Brussels in 1970, whereas they comprised more than half of the presentations at the latest IMSC 2009 meeting in Bremen. European scientists and companies clearly have played an essential role in the development of protein mass spectrometry for more than three decades, and it has been characterised by a strong and open interaction between the scientists and the companies. Only a few American players, such as Klaus Biemann at MIT, Al Burlingame at UCSF and Dominic Desiderio at the University of Tenneesee in Memphis, have been continuously in the field. Unfortunately, almost all the European mass spectrometer manufacturers have now been acquired by companies from elsewhere, for example MAT by Thermo, VG-Micromass by Waters and Kratos by Shimadzu; only Bruker is still a true European company among the major players.

Has Europe lost its momentum in protein mass spectrometry? Fortunately, the answer is no. European scientists are still essential players in the further development and use of protein mass spectrometry. Now proteomics and protein mass spectrometry are used in almost all European countries and the European presence at scientific conferences in the field is very strong. Some of the most spectacular protein mass spectrometry studies, those dealing with the analysis of large protein complexes, are still dominated by European scientists such as Carol Robinson, now after a period at Cambridge University back in Oxford, and Albert Heck at the University of Utrecht. The most recent development in instrumentation, the Orbitrap mass spectrometer, which is now playing a dominating role in protein mass spectrometry and has been acquired in numerous proteomics laboratories, was invented by the Russian Alexander Makarov and is now produced by Thermo in Bremen. So Europe has not lost its momentum for new development. There are just many more players worldwide and in the words of Hans Christian Andersen: *"The ugly duckling has turned into a swan"*. This has been possible because mass spectrometry of large biomolecules, especially in the 1980s, was dominated by a rather small multi-disciplinary group of scientists who shared information, played together and generated strong friendships.

LITERATURE FOR FURTHER READING

E. Lederer, *Pure Appl. Chem.* **17,** 489 (1968).

H.R. Morris, *Soft Ionization Biological Mass Spectrometry.* Heyden & Sons, London, UK (1981).

B. Sundqvist and R.D. Macfarlane, *Mass Spectrom. Rev.* **4,** 42 (1985).

A. Benninghoven, *Ion Formation from Organic Solids (IFOS IV).* John Wiley & Sons Ltd, Chichester, UK (1989).

A. Hedin, B.U.R. Sundqvist and A. Benninghoven, *Ion Formation from Organic Solids (IFOS V)*. John Wiley & Sons Ltd, Chichester, UK (1990).

F. Hillenkamp and M. Karas, *Int. J. Mass Spectrom.* **200,** 71 (2000).

Applications to small biomolecules and developments in Central and Eastern Europe

Károly Vékey
Hungarian Academy of Sciences, Budapest, Hungary

This chapter covers a very broad field which may loosely be defined as all applications which involve biological matrices (for example, tissue, blood or fruit juice) and analyses of direct relevance to medicinal or pharmaceutical chemistry, biochemistry or biology. There is a large overlap with organic applications (structure elucidation) and with analytical chemistry (identification/quantitation of impurities and/or trace level compounds) as well as with various other fields. Peptide and protein analysis is so widespread that these are discussed in a separate chapter. Full coverage of the field is not feasible in a relatively short chapter but this account aims to describe some of the major contributions made by a number of European mass spectroscopists in these areas, illustrated with a few interesting examples.

In the mid to late 1950s, McLafferty and Sharkey in the United States and Stenhagen and Ryhage in Sweden were among the first to begin systematic structural studies by means of electron ionisation mass spectrometry. Stenhagen and Ryhage later went on to contribute to Samuelsson's work on the oxidation of arachidonic acid to prostaglandins, one of the first examples of the use of mass spectrometry in the elucidation of the structure of a natural product. These developments stimulated a rapid growth in the application of mass spectrometry to structural problems and many European chemists went to the United States, either temporarily or permanently, to participate in this. Klaus Biemann, originally working in Innsbruck, Austria, formed a group at MIT, Boston and carried out some of the earliest studies on the mass spectra of alkaloids. He was soon joined by Josef Seibl who later formed a group at ETH, Zurich, Walter Vetter who later headed a group at Roche in Basel, Hartmut Richter who later headed the group at Ciba in Basel and Gerhard Spiteller who first returned to Vienna and later moved to Bayreuth, all of whom made major contributions to the mass spectrometry of natural products. About the same time, Carl Djerassi, who was born in Austria, attracted Herbert Budzikiewicz who later returned to Braunschweig before moving to Cologne and Dudley Williams who later returned to Cambridge, to work on the mass spectra of alkaloids and steroids at Stanford University. It was during this period that two now classic books on the mass spectra of organic compounds were produced, in 1962 by Biemann and in 1964 by Budzikiewicz, Djerassi and Williams.

During the early 1960s, similar developments took place all over Europe. Although chemists had been quick to recognise the value of infrared (IR) and nuclear magnetic resonance (NMR) spectroscopy in revolutionising the determination of molecular structure, particularly in identifying the presence of particular functional groups, they were slower to appreciate the information that mass spectrometry could provide. Although it gave less accurate structural detail than NMR, it was possible in most cases to determine the molecular mass and various functional units in a molecule could be identified. Comparison with homologues and analogues often allowed the complete structure to be identified. Furthermore, high-resolution mass spectra and isotope peaks could often provide information on the elemental composition of a sample.

In the field of natural compounds, mass spectrometry had two further, very important, advantages:

Opposite: An expedition during the 26th IMMS meeting, Fiera di Primiero, Italy, in 2008, led by Pietro Traldi.

(1) It has high sensitivity, so that very small amounts of natural isolates could be studied. A few µg were sufficient for structure elucidation which was thought to be an unimaginably small amount of material in the early 1960s.

(2) It is also better equipped than either IR or NMR spectroscopy to study impure compounds or mixtures since, in many cases, it is possible to interpret the mass spectra of mixtures to some degree. More importantly, fractional sublimation could readily be performed in a simple electron impact ion source so that it was possible to separate, at least in part, various components of a mixture.

Because of the diversity of the applications covered, some scientists have made significant contributions in more than one of the above areas concerned with small biomolecules. For example, Herbert Budzikiewicz (Austria) not only carried out outstanding studies of both steroids and alkaloids, but also contributed to our understanding of the processes involved in photosynthesis. Pietro Traldi (Italy) pioneered mass spectrometric analysis of unsaturated fatty acids but also made outstanding contributions in various other analytical aspects and clinical applications of mass spectrometry. Similarly, D.E. (Dai) Games (UK) and E. Gelpí (Spain) advanced the use of chromatographic methods in combination with mass spectrometry but their applications in drug analysis and clinical chemistry are of equal importance.

Capabilities and applications of mass spectrometry are closely related; both depending heavily on instrument development. Especially in the early decades of mass spectrometry, instrumentation was often home-built for particular applications. Improvements in sample introduction and ionisation methods have played an important role in determining the type of application that can be undertaken and in the present chapter, somewhat arbitrarily, the discovery and identification of natural compounds together with pharmaceutical and clinical applications have been selected to illustrate developments in a historical perspective.

Pietro Traldi

NATURAL COMPOUNDS

Perhaps the first demonstration of the potential of mass spectrometry in the biochemical field comes from structure analysis of natural compounds. Initial discoveries were described in the two excellent books already referred to earlier. With the use of mass spectrometry, it became possible to identify biologically-active ingredients in a few µg of natural isolates which did not even have to be very pure. Identification may, typically, have taken a few days, mostly spent in elucidating the spectra. This may be compared to a decade of work in the 1920s and 1930s leading to the isolation and identification of Vitamin C (A. Szent-Gyorgyi, Nobel prize in 1937). This work required *ca* 20 kg of raw material (paprika, luckily easily available), yielding *ca* 10 g pure product, which was needed for structure identification. For most natural compounds, this amount of raw material is simply not available. High sensitivity and the possibility for fractionation inside the mass spectrometer opened up new possibilities and initiated a huge advance in the chemistry of natural products, in particular alkaloids, steroids and terpenes, among other types of compound.

The reasoning behind the early success of mass spectrometry in the field of natural products is mirrored in various other areas: high sensitivity coupled with the possibility of mixture analysis—this is a sure recipe for success in many fields. In these respects, mass spectrometry is unequalled by any other method used in structure analysis. Technical developments have improved both aspects since the 1950s but, essentially, these are still the main reasons for its widespread use.

While detailing achievements of even the most important people in this field would be exhausting, some at least should be mentioned. The work of Klaus Biemann (US/Austria) at the MIT on the structure elucidation of alkaloids as early as 1958 has already been referred to. At that time, mass spectrometers were used mainly to analyse the composition of volatile products obtained in the oil industry such as gases consisting of low molecular weight hydrocarbons. Biemann volatised nearly non-volatile indole alkaloids by connecting the inlet line to a tube in which the sample was placed and heating it by means of a Bunsen burner, often until the glass just became red. The ion currents were registered on a film which was removed in a black sack and carried to a darkroom to be developed, after which the peaks had to be counted. The counting was a difficult job, often requiring over two hours, since there were frequently sections showing no peaks which had to be overbridged. This not infrequently meant that the mass determined was incorrect so that the counting had to be repeated.

J. Chmelik

There was considerable activity on the investigation of the mass spectrometry of natural products in many European laboratories. H. Budzikiewicz carried out work on a variety of classes of compounds, including steroids, terpenoids, alkaloids, porphyrins and carotenoids and on photosynthesis. He was also active in the investigation of deuterium labelling and chemical ionisation of natural products. E. Stenhagen, R. Ryhage and P. Traldi were working mainly on fatty acids and long chain aliphatic compounds whereas K. Heyns (Germany), B. Domon (Switzerland), O.S. Chizhov (Russia) and D. Garozzo (Italy), J. Chmelik (Czech Republic) worked mainly on carbohydrates. S.J. Gaskell (UK) investigated sterols (although his main contribution was in the area of peptide and protein analysis). G. Spiteller (Austria) initially worked on steroids and alkaloids, but later his main contributions were to show that mass spectrometry is very useful in the investigation of drug metabolites and pesticides, especially when GC and MS are combined, and to demonstrate the value of MS in the investigation of oxidised unsaturated fatty acids in the elucidation of their connection with aging and age related diseases. H.-F. Grützmacher (Germany) was among the first mass spectrometrists in the 1960s to work on simple saccharides and peptides, amino acid and sugar derivatives, and hydroxylated cyclo-alkanes. Among others, M. Claeys (Belgium) has made significant contributions on flavonoids and organic constituents of aerosols, J.-C. Tabet (France) and K. Pihlaja (Finland) have carried out important work on stereoselectivity and D.H. (Dudley) Williams (UK), G. Allmaier (Austria), A. Selva (Italy) and G. Moneti (Italy) have investigated various other classes of natural compounds.

Hans-Friedrich
Grützmacher

PHARMACEUTICAL APPLICATIONS

As soon as it was realised that mass spectrometry could be used to elucidate the structure of molecules, mass spectrometers became commonplace in pharmaceutical companies and these are now among the mainstream users of mass spectrometry. Whereas analysis of natural compounds was a great innovation and sudden success, pharmaceutical applications started more slowly, but they continue to grow, even today.

Compared to most other industries, pharmaceutical companies were among the first to identify key technologies and have sufficient influence to persuade instrument manufacturers to produce technical improvements. For example, early mass spectrometers were notoriously unreliable. To keep them operational required large technical expertise; breakdowns were frequent, which made it difficult to carry out a series of experiments. What pharmaceutical companies required, on the other hand, were fully operational instruments, capable of carrying out long series of measurements (for example, hundreds of HPLC-MS runs) without breaks or technical changes. This became particularly stringent with the widespread application of GLP (good laboratory practice). This need forced manufacturers to develop fully-automated instruments which work reliably over long periods without a break. Innovations in analytical chemistry usually spread very rapidly among pharmaceutical companies which often adopt the "best" available methodologies. Legislative bodies also keep the pressure on, forcing the adoption of technical improvements and every five years there is an increase in quality requirements which have to be fulfilled. This is a major difference from the situation in other industries in which the cost of analysis is usually the major concern. For example, what may be considered to be a "simple" HPLC-MS analysis is often regarded as too expensive in the food industry, whereas it is not sufficiently sensitive and selective in the pharmaceutical field.

There are many diverse applications of mass spectrometry in the pharmaceutical field. For example, it is used in drug development, both in quality control and in the drug approval process. In a different context, it is used for structure identification or elucidation; to identify/characterise impurities or minor components; or to determine drug metabolism and pharmacokinetic behaviour. Some of these require qualitative analysis, some quantitative analysis and often both are required. Innovations in mass spectrometry in the last 50 years steadily increased the applications of mass spectrometry in this field. Major breakthroughs in instrumentation have had significant impacts on (a) sensitivity; (b) selectivity, (c) productivity of analysis and (d) in the range of substances available for study. These aspects are discussed here with respect to pharmaceutical applications, but are equally important in clinical analysis and studying complex mixtures such as foodstuffs or natural compounds.

With respect to *sensitivity*, there has always been, and there continues to be, a strong desire for improvement. Drugs developed in the 50s were typically applied in $mg\,kg^{-1}$ body weight amount whereas today, these are in the $ng\,kg^{-1}$ range. This corresponds to a decrease in drug concentration by a factor of two for every two to three years and this, in turn, requires a corresponding increase in the sensitivity of analysis. Luckily, mass spectrometry was able to cope with this challenge: its sensitivity in the same period doubled on average every two years. (This is well documented in the case of VG sector instruments from 1977 to 1992; during which time absolute sensitivity increased from $6 \times 10^{-10}\,\mathrm{Cb}\,\mu\mathrm{g}^{-1}$ to $5 \times 10^{-7}\,\mathrm{Cb}\,\mu\mathrm{g}^{-1}$; (i.e. 1000 times increase of sensitivity in 15 years; private correspondence from Bob Bateman). This fast increase in instrumental capabilities can be compared only to the increase in the performance of computers and is one of the prime reasons why mass spectrometry is so common in pharmaceutical companies.

Selectivity is another main issue when dealing with complex mixtures, such as drugs in body fluids. The main breakthrough in this respect is the coupling of chromatographs to mass spectrometers. GC-MS became available in the 1960s and common in the 1970s; while HPLC-MS became available in the 1970s and widespread in the 1990s. The advent of these techniques made it possible to study minor components in body fluids; and these are widely used both in the pharmaceutical industry and in clinical applications. A detailed discussion of these is given elsewhere in this volume.

There are two other factors, mass resolution and tandem mass spectrometry, each of which has had a significant impact on the selectivity of analysis. Both started (and are still widely used) as structure elucidation tools but they are also excellent analytical options to improve selectivity. High-resolution instruments became available in the 1950s and this was one of the prime advantages in using sector instruments up to the early 1990s. Resolving powers of other instruments did not increase spectacularly until the late 1980s [with the exception of Fourier transform ion cyclotron resonance (FT-ICR) which has just started to appear in the pharmaceutical industry] when improvements, especially in time-of-flight (TOF) technology made it much simpler to use routinely, especially when coupled to a chromatograph. Tandem mass spectrometry (MS/MS) made it possible to use the first stage as a mass filter (with or without chromatography) and the second mass filter to get structural information or a specific signal for identification and or quantitation.

Productivity of analysis is becoming more and more important. Computer control was first introduced in the 1970s and automatic operation became common in the 1990s. Both are becoming integrated with mass spectrometry analysis and help in fulfilling legal requirements and assisting in data evaluation. The use of advanced statistical methodologies (for example, chemometrics, bioinformatics) has become widespread with the use of computers and these are widely used both in pharmaceutical and clinical applications.

The range of *compounds available for analysis* is crucial both for pharmaceutical, clinical and biological applications. It is directly related to breakthroughs in ionisation techniques. Fast atom bombardment (FAB) made it possible to study samples of molecular weight in excess of *ca* 800 Da mass and made polar, thermally-labile compounds available for analysis. (Note, many, if not most, drug substances belong to this category.) Electrospray ionisation (ESI) facilitated the analysis of polar compounds [especially using high-performance liquid chromatography mass spectrometry (HPLC-MS)] and made the study of biopharmaceuticals (usually macromolecules) possible. Matrix-assisted laser desorption/ionisation (MALDI) is used less often in the pharmaceutical field, as it is not very suitable for quantitation and cannot easily be connected to a chromatograph. On the other hand, MALDI imaging [for

Ron Heeren (left) and
Laszlo Drahos at the 19th
IMMS meeting, Noszvaj,
Hungary, in 2001.

example, pioneered by R.M.A. (Ron) Heeren (The Netherlands) in Europe] is a promising
new tool for pharmaceutical and clinical applications. Developments in ionisation methods
are considered elsewhere in this volume.

A different type of historical perspective can be seen by considering the type of problems
that could be solved by MS. The "golden age" for structure elucidation using mass spectrometry was late 1960s. Starting from the 1980s, this faded significantly, as developments
in NMR spectroscopy permitted better structure analysis for most pharmaceutically-active
compounds. From the 1970s, the emphasis in mass spectrometry switched to mixture and
trace analysis—a trend that is still very much in evidence today. With continual improvements in technical capabilities, the study and characterisation of mixtures has become
increasingly important as information on decreasing amounts of trace components has been
required. An added trend in the last one or two decades is the use of computers both for
instrument control and automation, and for data evaluation using bioinformatics.

Structure identification of minor components (for example, drug metabolites) in mixtures
(for example, from blood) is still preferentially performed by mass spectrometry—as often
there is not enough material available, even for HPLC-NMR. Typically, the first tentative
structure identification of trace components comes from mass spectrometry. Accurate
mass measurement during HPLC-MS runs has improved considerably and now this can
often provide unequivocal elemental composition of samples of up to 500 Da molecular
mass. When the problem becomes very important (publication of a novel structure, legislation of a new drug) the selected compounds are isolated in larger quantities and purified.
This latter process is, however, very time consuming and, in consequence, NMR is seldom
used for trace component analysis.

There are a large number of leading mass spectrometrists working in pharmaceutical applications. Willi Richter at Ciba–Geigy (Switzerland) was interested in natural compounds and
their metabolites, oligosaccharides, ring closure reactions (which are important in understanding fragmentation and elucidating structure of metabolites) and the use of isotope
labelling. He was a prime leader in the use of mass spectrometry in the pharmaceutical
industry; and motivated the use of advanced methodologies and instrumentation throughout the industry. N.J. (Nev) Haskins (UK) had a similarly important role in the UK, working
in several companies. He advocated using stable isotope labels for accurate quantitation,
which has become a common procedure. Together with Dai Games (UK), he carried out
some of the first assays for drugs in biofluids using LC/MS. Others working in this field
include G. Tarzia (Italy, antibiotics and statistical analysis); G. Moneti (quantitation and
GC-MS); M. Ryska (Czech Republic, various bioessays).

To illustrate the application and significance of mass spectrometry in the pharmaceutical
field, two specific examples are described below. The first of these is by Mirek Ryska, who
has been working in the pharmaceutical industry for four decades, mainly concerned with
applications of mass spectrometry. After the fall of communism in Central and Eastern
Europe (1990), many pharmaceutical companies in this region closed. Ryska decided to form
his own analytical company (Quinta Analytica); his personal account is presented below.

Another personal account is presented by the author of this chapter, and describes the use of mass spectrometry to identify a new antibiotic.

PERSONAL ACCOUNT: FOUNDING A PRIVATE COMPANY FOR DRUG ANALYSIS

Contribution by Mirek Ryska, CZ

Pharmaceuticals represents a field of chemistry with the highest involvement of analytical methods, in comparison with all other branches of chemistry. It is also a field where Contract Research Organisations (CROs) as small or larger private enterprises may develop their own activities. Today, outsourcing of analyses has become the most convenient and economical way widely used by many pharmaceutical companies, especially in the drug development process.

Mass spectrometry is being applied by CROs in many stages of the drug development process. In the synthesis of new drug entities, it is the method of choice for the structure determination of impurities. Similarly, mass spectrometry as a qualitative method is widely used in both preclinical and clinical research, namely for metabolomics in animals and humans. In Phase I and Phase II clinical trials, quantitative LC-MS-MS is a dominating method

1: Annamari Jakab, 2: Kornel Nagy, 3: Marina Kosevich, 4: Magda Claeys, 5: Maciej Jarosz, 6: Vladimir Kovacik, 7: Rod Mason, 8: H-F Grützmacher, 9: Evan Williams, 10: Zoltan Dinya, 11: Peter Juhasz, 12: Pietro Traldi, 13: Krisztina Ludanyi, 14: Jozsef Jeko, 15: Gabriella Pocsfalvi, 16: Gyorgy Vas, 17: John Roboz, 18: Leopoldo Ceraulo, 19: Peter Vegh, 20: Peter Armentrout, 21: Bela Paizs, 22: Karoly Vekey. At the 19th IMMS meeting, Noszvaj, Hungary, 2001.

Mirek Ryska

now for the determination of pharmacokinetic parameters thanks to its high sensitivity and high selectivity. Radioimmunoassay and other immunoassays are competitive with respect to sensitivity, but selectivity of these methods is not high enough. On the other hand, mass spectrometry is rarely used for testing the release of the active compound from a drug formulation. This does not require high specificity, so due to its better reproducibility and lower cost, simple HPLC is usually used.

In 1996, before establishing the private analytical pharmaceutical CRO, a careful economic analysis had to be performed in order to choose the most promising area for work in this field. Our CRO started its activity in quantitative determination of drugs and their metabolites in biological fluids (mostly in human plasma), which were obtained in the course of so-called "bioequivalence" studies. Bioequivalence studies in men provide statistical data for the assessment of two different drug formulations on the bases of their pharmacokinetic parameters. High numbers of plasma samples must be analysed, and this is a good proposition for a positive economic outcome. At that time, however, such bioassays were still mainly performed using HPLC with UV detection, or more sensitive fluorescence detection. GC/MS methods were used mostly only in special cases. The main drawback of the GC/MS method was the laboured sample processing necessary, especially the final volume reduction and sample adjustment. Only non-aqueous solutions are suitable for GC. The application of LC/MS was still not widespread and because of the low reproducibility of the MS detector response in comparison with physical detectors such as UV, it was considered to be inferior. Therefore, our lab had three HPLC systems and one GC/MS/MS system at our disposal when we began.

Thanks to the development, improvement and stability of LC/MS and LC/MS/MS methods, they are now the dominating methods in this field. LC/MS/MS using triple quadrupoles is the method of choice for the quantitative determination of drugs and their metabolites in biological fluids. Today our lab has six LC/MS/MS instruments at our disposal and no single HPLC. Sample processing is very simple, and in many cases the precipitation and separation of proteins without any additional purification may be used. Supernatant liquids may often be used without any dilution and sample adjustment. In cases where a very low quantification limit is required, the solid phase extraction method is normally used in the purification process.

Some special features of LC/MS, however, make this method very different from HPLC/UV or HPLC/field desorption (FD) in many respects and these must be considered. While UV and FD are physical detectors not influenced by chemical processes, the mass spectrometer detector is (in principle) a chemical reactor. The reproducibility of chemical reactions in the ion source is always more problematic than the reproducibility of the physical process in physical detectors such as UV. This problem in bioanalytics, known today as the "matrix effect", should always be taken into consideration. Due to this "matrix effect", internal standards must be used in quantitative LC/MS/MS. The relative matrix effect of the analyte versus internal standard may be minimalised by using analytes labelled with stable isotopes as internal standards. ^{2}H, ^{13}C and ^{15}N are used most frequently. In our laboratory, the Isotopic Dilution Technique with isotopically-labelled internal standards is used as a rule.

Another drawback of LC/MS/MS is the low sensitivity in cases where the analyte is a weak Brønsted base or acid (depending on the ionisation mode used). This drawback may be overcome by using strong bases or acids as additives in the mobile phase.

Remarkable success has been achieved in our laboratory using additives which create an abundant cluster ion with the molecule of the analyte. Very low limits of quantification have been achieved in the analyses of such drugs as Simvastatin, Lacidipin etc., using the cluster ions $[M+H+CH_3NH_2]^+$.

Great productivity and output have been achieved using LC/MS/MS. One assay takes less than five minutes (three minutes as a rule), so the output is approximately three times higher than that of HPLC. The economic impact is high, and fully compensates the cost difference of these two instruments. Quinta–Analytica is therefore able to assay more than 900 plasma samples a day.

For quantitative analyses of pharmaceuticals (active substance or the final product), mass spectrometry is not needed. A remarkable and irreplaceable role is, however, to be noted in cases of the quantitative determination of extremely toxic impurities at ppb levels present from different synthetic routes. Determination of a few nanograms of paroxol in the injection of several milligrams of paroxetine provides a nice example.

In the qualitative structure determination of impurities, mass spectrometry often plays a unique role. Examples include cases in which the structures of several impurities present in active substances were originally erroneously ascribed in pharmacopoeias (for example, in the European Pharmacopeia). Thanks to the introduction of mass spectrometry, their structures were corrected. Interpretation of their fragmentation patterns, based on the known spectra of the parent drugs and on the knowledge of the synthetic route, is very easy and unambiguous as a rule.

PERSONAL ACCOUNT: ROLE OF MASS SPECTROMETRY IDENTIFYING A NATURAL ANTIBIOTIC IN THE LATE 1980s

The example described here is the personal experience of the author from the late 1980s. It relates to antibiotic research in an excellent Italian company (Lepetit Research Centre) specialising in natural antibiotics; where a novel antibiotic (GE2270) was identified. This shows the philosophy and strategy of pharmaceutical research and the role of mass spectrometry not only in structure analysis, but also in strategic decisions. Although the techniques used are now mostly obsolete, similar strategies are typical throughout the industry. Analogous compromises and the complementary nature of analytical methodologies can be considered typical even now.

Finding natural antibiotics is a long, interdisciplinary process. The object is to find an antibiotic, which is novel and not toxic to humans. One way to do this efficiently is to target a biochemical process which is present in bacteria (prokaryotes), but is not present in humans (i.e. inhibition of a non-existent process in humans is unlikely to be toxic). Such a possibility

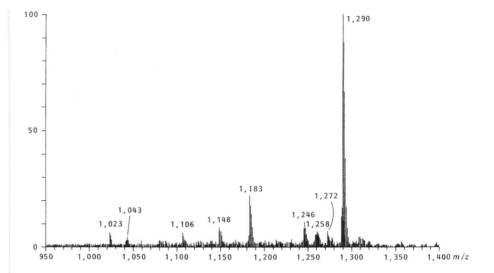

Figure 1. FAB mass
spectrum of antibiotic
GE 2270. Reproduced
from Kettenring et al., J.
Antibiotics **44,** 702–715
(1991).

is to inhibit the prokaryotic elongation factor (EF-Tu), which is not present in eukaryotes. Accordingly, the first step in the research was screening to identify and isolate microbial cultures (from soil samples), which produce antibiotics acting on the EF-Tu. After screening millions of bacterial strains using this relatively simple approach, one was found which both produced antibiotics and also inhibited the prokaryotic EF-Tu. Biological and biochemical tests suggested that the antibiotic found may be a novel compound. The next phase in the research was to isolate this antibiotic from cell culture. Obviously, the first extracts contained only small amounts of the active compound.

The first analytical experiments were used to confirm that it indeed had a novel structure. Possibly the most important test was based on mass spectrometry. The compound was non-volatile (no EI spectra), so was studied by FAB ionisation (the only method at the time for non-volatiles; now HPLC-ESI-MS would be the logical choice). The mass spectrum is shown in Figure 1, indicating that the molecular mass (for the lowest isotope) is 1289 Da. In addition to the molecular mass several fragment ions are also observed. These do give some information on the structure, but this is not sufficient for structure elucidation. The isotope peaks were of much higher intensity than could be accounted for by the presence of C, H, O or N elements alone. It was not possible to determine what other element was present, but the results suggested either one chlorine atom or several sulphur atoms. While these results were far from giving a structural assignment, when combined with results of biochemical tests, they were sufficient to confirm that a novel compound had been found. This observation allowed the project to progress—fermentation and isolation of larger quantities of sample (which is very expensive) to permit structure identification. Similar decision points often occur in pharmaceutical research and mass spectrometry often proves to be the prime tool for decision making. It provides essential structural information from very low amounts of crude sample which can be made in the early phases of a project.

In the next phase, a larger amount of sample was available. This permitted proton and ^{13}C-NMR spectroscopy to be performed on the sample—and it was hoped that this would allow unequivocal structure identification. Unfortunately, this was not the case: partly because the molecule was too large (at that time, now it would be less difficult); partly it was "unfriendly" towards NMR analysis (too many atoms with no H attached); and partly it was due to the presence of impurities. To move ahead, it was necessary to determine the elemental formula of the compound.

The accurate mass of the protonated molecule was measured, to yield 1290.25 Da with ca 0.02 Da accuracy using a high-resolution sector instrument. At the time, it was considered an excellent result (using FAB, with no conventional internal mass standard available). This accuracy still allowed hundreds of possible elemental formulae—not a great leap ahead! Help came from elemental analysis, which showed the crucial information that there was no chlorine, but there were several (five to seven) sulphur atoms in the molecule. It also showed that there were many N atoms in the molecule, but the accuracy of the ratio of C, H and N atoms was not accurate enough to be of significant help. It was possible to use the ^{13}C NMR spectrum to count the number of carbon atoms quite accurately (55–58), even though the spectrum was too complex for structure determination. This information (55–58 carbon, five to seven sulphur, over 10 N atoms) combined with accurate mass measurement reduced possible elemental compositions to three possibilities. Relatively simple checks using proton and ^{13}C NMR eliminated two alternatives, so the results evaluated together yielded the elemental formula of the novel antibiotic: $C_{56}H_{55}N_{15}O_{10}S_6$.

The elemental formula, UV, IR and NMR studies evaluated together indicated that the compound was a heavily modified cyclic peptide. This information was still not sufficient to determine the structure. Following isolation of an even larger amount of substance (in the order of 100 mg), acidic hydrolysis was used to degrade the molecule. Structures of hydrolysis products were determined (using GC, GC-MS, UV, IR, MS and NMR). The resulting information gave sufficient help to NMR spectroscopy to determine the structure unequivocally; using elegant 2D techniques. The resulting structure is shown in Figure 2, which also indicates fragmentation processes yielding the fragments shown in Figure 1. These fragmentation processes support structural assignments and could be very useful studying structural analogues or metabolites. Nevertheless, it was impossible to use them for structure elucidation of a novel antibiotic.

The research described above took ca six to ten months to perform (starting from the isolation of a small amount of crude antibiotic). This may seem a long time; but in the 1980s it was considered particularly fast. There are two main messages from this story. First, very often information from different sources needs to be combined to resolve complex analytical and/or structural problems. The second is that mass spectrometry is often crucial in the exploratory stage and to support decisions on the direction of research. This is well known in the pharmaceutical industry, explaining its widespread use of mass spectrometry. On the other hand, MS is often of secondary importance for definitive structure assignments—which is sadly reflected in many papers, where MS is relegated to the experimental section only.

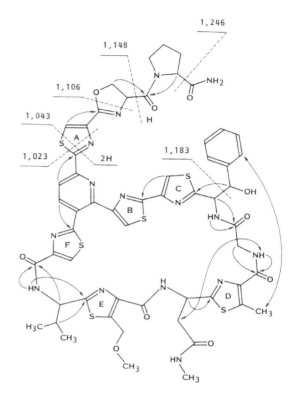

Figure 2. Structure and main fragmentation processes of antibiotic GE 2270. Reproduced from Kettenring *et al.*, *J. Antibiotics* **44**, 702–715 (1991).

BIOMEDICAL AND CLINICAL APPLICATIONS

These two fields are very similar; in both cases biological samples (for example, blood or tissue) are studied. "Biomedical" usually implies fundamental studies and analytical developments for example, to define biomarkers for potential use in the medical field; this often involves identification and characterisation of particular biochemical pathways. Clinical applications, as the name implies, relate directly to healthcare issues. Biomedical analysis involves both human and animal samples; clinical applications always require human samples. Research in these fields has been well summarised in two European reviews of E. Gelpí and K. Vekey *et al*.

The first biomedical applications of mass spectrometry relate to the use of stable isotopes. The significance for using isotope tracers in biochemistry goes back to the work of Hevesy in the 1920s. While the use of radioactive labels is quite restrictive (especially in healthcare), mass spectrometry is ideally suited to separate (identify, quantify) labelled and unlabelled compounds. This is most often done using D, ^{13}C or ^{15}N or ^{18}O isotopes. Based on the molecular mass, a compound labelled with a heavy isotope can easily be identified; and the respective peak areas provide an easy way for quantitation. Isotopically-labelled compounds may be synthesised, introduced into the organism and their metabolic fate studied using

Károly Vékey

mass spectrometry detection. An alternative is to use isotope-labelled derivatising agents. The latter has found ample use in proteomics, pioneered by M. Mann (Germany) and R. Aebersold (Switzerlamd) in particular.

The importance of clinical applications of mass spectrometry was realised very early, in the 1950s. At that time, analysis of biological fluids was not feasible, but gas analysis was already well advanced. This clearly pointed towards analysis of respiration, which was pioneered by Muysers and Smidt, often using specialised instrumentation developed by C. Brunnée. Gas analysis was straightforward, allowing quantitative and qualitative analysis of small volatile molecules. Probably an even more important advantage of respiration analysis is the absence of the "biological matrix" (usually the worst factor hindering clinical applications). These studies yielded valuable information not only on the physiology of respiration and circulation, but were also used to study pathophysiology.

While in the 1950s and 1960s gas analysis was the only way to overcome the problem caused by the biological matrix, it is still a significant advantage today. Respiration analysis, and in general analysis of volatile organic compounds in gas samples (for example, air, or head-space), is still growing. Gas samples can be analysed either directly or using GC-MS. Development of the so-called "proton-transfer-reaction mass spectrometry" (PTR-MS) in the 1990s by W. Lindinger (Austria) provided new impetus, as this provides increased sensitivity. Present day technologies are capable of analysing hundreds of trace components in breath which are mainly used to find clinically applicable biomarkers, in particular for lung cancer and other lung diseases. The advantage over biological fluids is still the same it was 50 years ago: the absence of a biological matrix makes analysis far more sensitive and technologically easier.

Most biological matrices are so complex that their analysis requires interfacing of a separation technique to the mass spectrometer. There are three common options; GC-MS, HPLC-MS and MS/MS. The latter is not a "separation method" in the conventional sense, but the first analyser is used as a mass filter, allowing efficient mixture analysis to be performed. In chronological order, the advent of GC-MS in the 1960s made it possible to study compounds (and minor components) in complex matrices, such as body fluids such as blood or urine. This allowed advances in metabolism, pharmacology, pharmacokinetics and toxicology to be made with spectacular results. This established the GC-MS method among the medical profession to such an extent that they began to talk about and consider GC-MS, even when current HPLC-MS methods might be more suitable for a given problem. The main limitation of GC-MS is the frequent need for derivatisation of polar or thermally-labile compounds, which complicates analysis. Advent of solid phase micro-extraction (SPME) in the 1990s allowed very sensitive head-space analysis with GC-MS; giving new impetus to the use of GC-MS in the biomedical field.

When HPLC-MS became feasible in the 1970s and 1980s, there was great enthusiasm in the biomedical community. Most biologically active and interesting compounds are highly polar, so are difficult or impossible to study by GC(-MS). HPLC-MS thus provided new impetus. Technical difficulties surrounding HPLC-MS, however, prevented its widespread use. Developments in the 1990s resulted in simple and robust HPLC-MS instrumentation, which was followed by a plethora of bioanalytical and clinical applications. Development of MALDI and surface-enhanced laser desorption/ionisation (SELDI) methods gave further impetus, as these methods allow the study of complex materials (even tissues) with high sample throughput. One such person pioneering research in these areas is P. Traldi and his studies on non-enzymatic glycation is an interesting example. It is relevant for various illnesses, including diabetes. Initial research was carried out in 1985; the extensive use of MALDI allowed the development of new analytical procedures which describe in detail the glycation level of circulating proteins. It can be related to the "glycemic stress" experienced by the patients and to the possible changes in protein functionality. As an example, the high specificity of the method enabled proof that the HbA1c value (usually considered the glycation level of β-globin and widely employed in metabolic control of diabetic patients) is really due to the total amount of α- and β-globins glycated and glyco-oxidised. The MALDI method was also employed to characterise possible changes in circulating protein profiles due to the development of specific disease. This approach, now currently employed, was firstly proposed in the Padova MS lab as a diagnostic tool for melanoma development in 2000. Other prominent European scientists in this field are E. Gelpí in the study of liver diseases, serotonin and nitric oxide metabolism, G. Allmaier in the characterisation of allergens and various bacteria, P. Somerharju (Finland) in the characterisation of lipidomes and A. Raffaelli (Italy) in psychoactive drug analysis.

Tandem MS made a spectacular entry into clinical studies, especially with respect to metabolic disorders. These form an important class of diseases which have to be detected early (a few days after birth) to avoid serious and permanent damage to the new-born child. The developed method relies on the analysis of dried blood spots involving a straightforward sample preparation, and a simple MS/MS scan to detect a whole class of metabolic disorders. While it was originally developed to detect various acidemias, now, after various developments, this approach is capable of unequivocally diagnosing over 100 diseases. It is now performed in nearly all European countries on a routine basis, screening all newborns—and is by far the most widely used mass spectrometric analysis in the clinical field. Its success depends on a number of desirable features: dried blood spots are easy to transport, so one or a few centres are sufficient in most countries. Analysis is easily automated and an analysis requires only *ca* one minute of instrument time so is very cost-efficient. The most important contributors pioneering and developing this field in Europe are O. Bodamer (Austria), G. La Marca (Italy), B. Casetta (Italy), A. Roscher (Germany) and J. Cocho (Spain).

DEVELOPMENTS OF SMALL MOLECULE STUDIES IN CENTRAL AND EASTERN EUROPE

Part of this section related to the Soviet Union was kindly provided by Professor A.T. Lebedev and Dr M.V. Kosevich

Developments in this part of Europe had distinct characteristics in contrast to those in Western Europe during the communist period (up to 1990) and influenced developments for at least another decade. This was due partly to the relative isolation of science and scientists which slowly eased in the 1970s and 1980s, and partly to a scarcity of resources (for example, instrumentation or spare parts). Results, even excellent ones, were often published in journals which were not widely read in the West and had little impact on the mainstream development of science. Isolation worked both ways; for example, the sale of scientific instruments to Eastern Europe was often embargoed, which did not seem to concern the regimes, but did cause problems for scientists.

Isolation and scarcity of resources had various consequences. Main trends in mass spectrometry and commercial instrumentation arrived in Eastern Europe with a delay of *ca* a decade. Mass spectrometers of modest specifications were produced locally. Mass spectrometer modifications and developments were often home-built—for example, in my own lab we built a pyrolysis-MS and a FAB ion source, a GC-MS coupling and a data acquisition system. In this example pyrolysis was performed *in vacuo*. To do so we have modified the standard AEI-902 electron impact ion source (the project was led by K. Ujszaszy), attaching a small pyrolyser unit to it (shown in Figure 3). Partly due to the scarcity of resources, fundamental and physico–chemical studies and method developments were (at least in relative terms) more advanced than analytical applications, both in research institutions and in educational establishments. This is reflected partly in some excellent results and partly in the education of a generation of outstanding young scientists who made spectacular careers abroad. Some of the leading mass spectrometrists working in Central Europe are V. Hanus (Czech Republic) on organic applications, M. Ryska (Czech Republic) on pharmaceutical applications, Z. Herman (Czech Republic) on fundamental MS, M. v. Ardenne (East Germany) on instrumentation and pioneering negative ion mass spectrometry, W. Danikiewitz (Poland) on organic applications, J. Silberring (Poland) on medical applications and proteomics, M. Kowalczyk (Poland) on polymer MS, I. Cornides (Hungary) on inorganic MS, J. Tamas (Hungary) on alkaloids and pharmaceutical applications, O. Kaposi (Hungary) on high temperature MS and K. Vekey (Hungary) on the role of energetics and biomedical applications.

The Soviet Union was possibly even more closed than Central Europe. The early history of the development of mass spectrometry at the territory of the Former Soviet Union (USSR) was somewhat hidden from the English-speaking community, since the majority of publications in the area at that time were either in Russian or classified. In this connection, many discoveries in the field were made independently and simultaneously in the two communities.

The first mass spectrometric instruments designed in the USSR were, as anywhere else, for physical, chemical and military research. The first commercial instruments, which for many decades were supplied to the whole USSR, Eastern Europe and China, were produced at the "Electron Works" (Sumy, Ukraine). Major design and developments of mass spectrometric equipment were carried out at the Institute for Analytical Instrumentation (Leningrad–St Petersburg). During the final decades of the 20th century, the general trend of advancement of biological and biomedical research had stimulated related developments in mass spectrometry in the USSR.

Figure 3. Picture of a pyrolyser-MS ion source home-built in Budapest by K. Ujszaszy in 1978.

G.D. Tantzyrev (Institute for Chemical Physics, Moscow) had proposed the application of neutral argon atoms, actually fast atom bombardment, for analysis of organic polymers as early as 1973. He had also pioneered applications of low temperature secondary ion mass spectrometry (SIMS) to studies of frozen water (1971).

Many laboratories were involved in the search for methods for the introduction of biomolecules into a mass spectrometer from liquid solutions. A technique named "field evaporation of ions from solutions" was introduced by V.E. Skurat and co-workers (Institute of Chemical Physics) in 1986 for studies of biomolecules. The most dramatic events are connected with the development of the electrospray technique. Two papers on electrospray were published in 1984, one by the future Nobel prize winner J. Fenn and a second by a team from the Institute for Analytical Instrumentation (Leningrad) with L.N. Gall as the main inventor. In the latter paper, mentioned in the Press Release of the Nobel Committee (2002), application of the electrospray method, named in Russian as "extraction of ions from solutions at atmospheric pressure", to biomolecules and protein analysis was described.

After "perestroika" in the former Soviet Union (FSU) in the 1990s of the last century, the break of the real Berlin wall and the virtual "Iron Curtain" between Eastern and Western Europe, the achievements of the older generation of FSU scientists became acknowledged worldwide. At the same time, many bright young scientists had the possibility of migrating to other countries where they have contributed significantly to the advancement of modern mass spectrometry. Considering international awards as a criterion of recognition of scientific contribution, the following examples can be cited.

The long-term head of the USSR mass spectrometric association, academician V.L. Talroze (Institute of Energy Problems of Chemical Physics, Moscow) was the first FSU scientist to receive the Thomson Medal (2003) in recognition of his renowned discovery of CH_5^+ ions (1952) which formed the basis of chemical ionisation. The invention of the mass-reflectron (1972), which is presently used in the majority of TOF instruments, by B.A. Mamyrin (Ioffe Physical Technical Institute RAS, Saint-Petersburg) was acknowledged by the Distinguished Contribution in Mass Spectrometry Award of the American Society for Mass Spectrometry (2000). The principles of orthogonal extraction of ions for TOF instruments were elaborated by A.F. Dodonov (Institute for Chemical Physics, Chernogolovka). The development of electron capture dissociation by R.A. Zubarev (present affiliation Karolinska Institute, Sweden), who started his career in Russia and the Ukraine, was marked by the Curt Brunnée Medal (2006) and by the Klaus Biemann Medal of the American Society for Mass Spectrometry (2007). J. Laskin (EMSL, USA) was awarded the Biemann Medal of the American Society for Mass Spectrometry (2008) for developments in the thermodynamics of biomolecular mass spectrometry. The most picturesque example is the real success story of A.A. Makarov, the inventor of the "Orbitrap" mass analyser (2000). Receiving his education at the Moscow Engineering Physics Institute, he continued his engineering work in Europe and succeeded in the commercialisation of his invention at the Thermo Fisher Scientific company (Bremen, Germany). His achievement is marked by being awarded the ASMS Distinguished Contribution in Mass Spectrometry Award (2008) and Curt Brunnée Award

Boris Mamyrin

Roman Zubarev

(2009). Makarov recalls that he was inspired to try to design "an ideal mass analyser" when, during his student days, he attended a lecture given by Curt Brunnée in Moscow.

It is of interest to note that A.A. Makarov's Russian supervisor, Professor A.A. Sysoev (Moscow Engineering Physics Institute) has been well-known for over 40 years as an experienced designer of mass spectrometric instruments, while his son, A.A. Sysoev (Jr), is at present continuing the development of new pilot versions of instrumentation for biomedical and pharmacological research, combining mass spectrometry and ion mobility.

In 2003, the Russian Society for Mass Spectrometry activities began, due to efforts of its first chairmen, A.T. Lebedev (Moscow State University), who has demonstrated the ability of mass spectrometry to predict the directions and yields of various monomolecular reactions in solutions and V.G. Zaikin (Institute of Petrochemical Synthesis, Moscow) working in the field of mass spectrometry of oil products. The present generation of Russian mass spectrometrists would be happy to acknowledge their indebtedness to their professors who have made significant contributions and created new fields of mass spectrometry in the former Soviet Union, as well as having educated and trained their scientific schools of current active researchers and have been awarded honourable membership and medals of the Russian Society for Mass Spectrometry:

- O.S. Chizhov: organic mass spectrometry; long-term member of the Managing Board of *European Journal of Mass Spectrometry*
- R.A. Khmelnitsky: environmental mass spectrometry
- V.I. Khvostenko: negative ion mass spectrometry
- A.A. Polyakova: organic and petrol mass spectrometry
- P.B. Terentiev: organic mass spectrometry
- B.V. Rozynov: one of the first mass spectrometrists in the world dealing with mass spectrometry of peptides
- E.N. Nikolaev: significant contribution to integration of Russian mass spectrometry to international community and creation of ICR cells
- I.A. Revelskii: created the method of atmospheric pressure photoionisation in the mid-80s.

Distinguished mass spectrometry schools were developed in other states of the FSU. In the Ukraine in the 1970s and 1980s of the last century, pioneering work in the applications of field ionisation and field desorption to studies of organic and biological molecules were made by E.N. Korol and V.A. Pokrovskiy (Institute for Physical Chemistry and Institute for Surface Chemistry, Kiev). The use of secondary ion mass spectrometry for analysis of metals, dielectrics and organic compounds was developed by V.T. Cherepin (Institute of Metal Physics, Kiev). The enthalpy of interaction of nitrogen bases of recently discovered nucleic acids were determined for the first time by temperature-dependent field ionisation techniques developed by B.I. Verkin, I.K. Yanson and L.F. Sukhodub (Institute for Low Temperature Physics and Engineering, Kharkov). Low temperature secondary emission mass spectrometry was applied to cryobiophysical problems by M.V. Kosevich at the same institute.

ACKNOWLEDGEMENTS

The author wishes to thank H. Budzikiewitz, B. Casetta, E. Gelpí, N. Haskins, M.V. Kosevich, A.T. Lebedev and M. Ryska for their help identifying key developments and scientists mentioned in this chapter; and G. Spiteller for a personal account of early historical aspects.

FURTHER READING

M.L. Aleksandrov, L.N. Gall, V.N. Krasnov, V.I. Nikolaev, V.A. Pavlenko and V.A. Shkurov, *Doklady Akademii Nauk USSR* **277,** 379–338 (1984). (Extraction of ions from solutions at atmospheric pressure, in Russian.)

M. v. Ardenne, K. Steinfelder and R. Tümmler, *Elektronenanlagerungs-massenspektrographie organischer Substanzen*. Springer, Berlin, Germany (1971).

C. Brunnée and L. Delgmann, *Z. Anal. Chem.* **197,** 51 (1963).

H. Budzikiewitz, C. Djerassi and D.H. Williams, *Structure Elucidation of Natural Products by Mass Spectrometry*. Holden-Day, San Francisco, CA, USA (1964).

E. Gelpi, "Biomedical and biochemical applications of liquid-chromatography mass-spectrometry", *J. Chromatogr. A* **703,** 59–80 (1995).

G. Hevesy, *Biochem. J.* **17,** 439 (1923).

J. Kettenring, L. Colombo, P. Ferrari, P. Tavecchia, M. Nebuloni, K. Vekey, G. Gallo and E. Selva, "Antibiotic GE2270-A—A Novel Inhibitor of Bacterial Protein-Synthesis 2. Structure Elucidation", *J. Antibiot.* **44,** 702–715 (1991).

W. Lindinger, A. Hansel and A. Jordan, "On-line monitoring of volatile organic compounds at pptv levels by means of proton-transfer-reaction mass spectrometry (PTR-MS)—medical applications, food control and environmental research", *Int. J. Mass Spectrom.* **173,** 191–241 (1998).

K. Muysers and U. Smidt, *Respirations Massenspektrometrie*. Schattauer (1969).

G. Vas and K. Vekey, "Solid-phase microextraction: a powerful sample preparation tool prior to mass spectrometric analysis", *J. Mass. Spectrom.* **39,** 233–254 (2004).

K. Vekey, A. Telekes and A. Vertes, *Medical applications of mass spectrometry*. Elsevier, Amsterdam, The Netherlands (2008).

K. Heyns and H.-F. Grützmacher, "Massenspektrometrische Untersuchungen, 4. Massenspektren von N-Acetylpeptiden einfacher Monoaminocarbonsäuren", *Liebigs Ann. Chem.* **669,** 189 (1963).

Industrial and environmental applications

Jim Scrivens

University of Warwick, Coventry, UK

SCOPE

This chapter attempts to document the contribution to mass spectrometry development made by scientists whilst working in an industrial environment. It does not seek to undervalue the contributions made by scientists who carried out their work in academia, research institutions or whilst working for mass spectrometry manufacturing companies but rather to highlight the changing industrial environment of the last 50 years and the effect of these changes on mass spectrometry development.

INTRODUCTION

Industrial mass spectrometry

The impact of industrial research scientists on the field of mass spectrometry can be seen to follow a number of clearly defined stages. In the early years (1950–1970s) instrument development and innovation stemmed from the need of the industrial scientist to invent new ways of understanding the often complex products that were being produced. This period, which led to the foundation of mass spectrometry as we know it today, was characterised by a small number of influential scientists employed by large global companies working with colleagues in the embryonic mass spectrometry manufacturing industry.

A second phase of interaction (1970s–1990s) between industrial scientists and manufacturers focussed on developments that were, for the most part, carried out by the manufacturers themselves and were based around the more complex requirements of industry. Industry was a major market for the developing mass spectrometry business and its needs naturally drove technical developments. Industrial mass spectrometry was still focussed on a small number of laboratories based within large companies but the use of the technique was growing and many companies had more than one centre for mass spectrometry. With the development of the Speciality Chemical and Pharmaceutical industries, mass spectrometry was no longer to be found only within specialist laboratories. The impact of the technique was such that many non-specialised users were making use of its power. This led to the development (1990s–2000s) of easier to use, more specialised, instruments that could be incorporated within general research projects. Mass spectrometry experts were still to be found within industrial companies but often they either had an advisory role or became more involved with management issues.

As industry, particularly the pharmaceutical industry, increasingly outsourced a significant component of its measurement science needs from around 2000, contract laboratories grew up which, by virtue of specialisation and volume of work, were able to offer cost effective solutions to the requirements of industry. These specialised companies were once again able to employ specialised experts in mass spectrometry leading to active collaboration with academia and instrument manufacturers.

Opposite: ZAB
instrument at ICI Wilton.

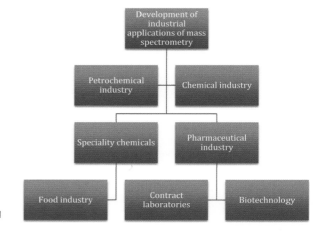

Figure 1

Industrial development

The role of the specialist mass spectrometry expert within industry has changed as the industrial landscape has evolved. Figure 1 shows a simplified schematic of the major changes in industrial focus for those businesses for which mass spectrometry formed an important research component.

DEVELOPMENT OF INDUSTRIAL MASS SPECTROMETRY

After an initial focus on hydrocarbon analysis for the petrochemical industry, mass spectrometry became an essential component of research and development within the rapidly growing chemical industry. This period saw rapid development of mass spectrometry instrumentation and the growth of the mass spectrometry manufacturing industry. The chemical industry evolved from a focus on commodity manufacturing to an increasing interest in low volume, high value materials and this led to the development of the speciality chemical and pharmaceutical businesses for which mass spectrometry was an essential requirement. Recent changes have seen the development of specialised contract research and measurement companies and the rapid growth of small, highly technically-focussed biotechnology enterprises requiring techniques and instrumentation that were often highly sophisticated.

MASS SPECTROMETRY TECHNIQUES

Because of the changing needs for specialised mass spectrometry expertise within industry resulting from the changes in the industrial landscape, new mass spectrometry methods have been developed in order to meet these needs.

APPLICATIONS OF INDUSTRIAL MASS SPECTROMETRY

Figure 2 shows the development of mass spectrometry applications from the early identification and quantitation of hydrocarbon mixtures through to its becoming an extremely

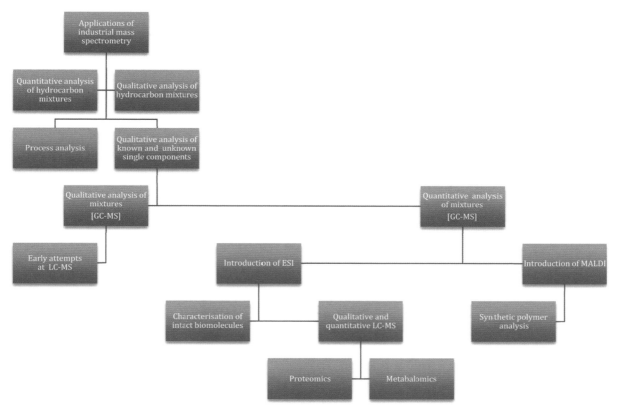

Figure 2

powerful analytical tool with the development of chromatographic introduction. These technical developments, based on the innovative research of a number of both academic and industrial scientists, were all rapidly adopted and exploited by the industrial community, a process that continues to this day.

Early application areas

The earliest applications of mass spectrometry were naturally associated with studies of the fundamental properties of matter, an activity that is still of considerable importance. This remained the case for over 30 years after the first instrument was built. Thereafter, the first application areas began to be identified, leading to the rapid development and acceptance of mass spectrometry as a major instrumental analytical technique in a wide range of disciplines.

The first major application area that captured the interest and investment of industry was the analysis of liquid hydrocarbons. This met an important commercial need and aimed to quantify the amounts of known compounds, for which standards were available, present in mixtures which were often complex. This method of analysis became more established with the advent of the first commercial mass spectrometer, the MS-2, introduced by Metropolitan-Vickers, Manchester, UK in 1948. Early challenges gave rise to efforts to extend the molecular weight range that could be studied, to devise improved methods for the preparation of appropriate standards and to the development of relatively robust, stable instrumental platforms. Oil companies, who were among the first to adopt the technique, had by necessity to have their own specialist personnel to maintain and often improve the instruments. Mass spectrometry was used to quantitate components in complex hydrocarbon streams. Standard spectra were used to establish fragmentation patterns (cracking patterns) and the spectra of the hydrocarbon mixture obtained were deconvoluted using simple matrix calculations. This placed a premium on reproducibility of ionisation and mass analysis which at the time was difficult to achieve. This application area benefits greatly from improvements in instrumental performance and drove much of the commercial development of the technique at the time. This is just as true in the 21st Century when ultra-high performance mass spectrometers based on high magnetic field Fourier transform ion cyclotron resonance (FT-ICR) technology are used to characterise complex commercial oil samples.

EARLY MEETINGS

Conferences with a focus on mass spectrometry were held in England in 1950 and 1953 organised by the Institute of Petroleum. In London in 1958, reflecting the increasing focus on the characterisation of hydrocarbon mixtures, a joint meeting was held with the influential American Society for Testing and Materials (ASTM E-14) Committee on Mass Spectrometry. This committee had been formed in 1952 in Pittsburgh and had held its first meeting (also in Pittsburgh) in 1953. It held annual meetings at various centres in the USA from 1953 to 1969 when, with support from the main ASTM Committee, the American Society for Mass Spectrometry (ASMS) was formed and subsequent meetings were of ASMS in cooperation with ASTM. At the first meeting organised by the Institute of Petroleum in London in 1950, there were 20 or so users or potential users but as a result of the rapid development of the technique, the attendance had risen to over 200 from 10 different countries at the meeting held in 1958. Influential figures at these early meetings included John D. Waldron, the managing director of Metropolitan-Vickers (who had introduced the first commercial mass spectrometer in 1948) and Alan Quayle who was the Head of Mass Spectrometry Research at Shell Thornton Research Centre and a major proponent of the use of mass spectrometry in hydrocarbon analysis. John Waldron edited the proceedings of the meeting (published as *Advances in Mass Spectrometry*, Pergamon Press, 1959) and personally reviewed many of the papers. Alan Quayle, in addition to running an active research group in Shell, became the first UK editor of the *International Journal of Mass Spectrometry and Ion Physics*, a position he held from 1968 to 1982, where he had a well-deserved reputation for encouraging young research workers.

JOHN BEYNON

Much of the early development of mass spectrometry instrumentation was driven by the needs of the petrochemical and chemical industry. There has always been a symbiotic relationship between academic research groups, the instrument manufacturers and the oil and chemical industry. This relationship is exemplified in the scientific career of John Beynon who was a major global influence in the development of modern mass spectrometry instrumentation and capability.

Beynon obtained a degree in Physics from University College, Swansea, in 1943 and, after a period of four years working for the government in the Ministry of Supply, he obtained employment with ICI (a global chemical company) in their Dyestuffs Division in 1947. At this time ICI had a research department of 750 people with over 250 PhD scientists. Until this point, he had no experience in the embryonic field of mass spectrometry but his career path was changed dramatically by the decision of his new manager (A.J. Hailwood) to ask the young physicist to design and build a mass spectrometer. In retrospect it would be difficult to imagine that Mr Hailwood ever made a better decision! Beynon based his design on an instrument that had been built in Canada by Graham, Harkness and Thode. This was a 90° magnetic sector design with a six-inch radius and incorporated the source design developed by Nier. The instrument was built entirely in his laboratory and took two years to complete. It had originally been commissioned in order to characterise metabolites in pharmaceutical formulations without having to label them isotopically. When Beynon demonstrated the power of the approach in the identification of unknown compounds, the focus was rapidly switched since this had much more commercial relevance. It is interesting to note that, with the passage of time, mass spectrometry became the dominant technique for the characterisation of drug metabolites. In ICI, mass spectrometry rapidly became the method of choice for the identification of unknown samples and this had a major impact on the characterisation of products of both ICI and competitors, proving to be of considerable importance in commercial and patent fields.

Building on the success of this work, Beynon then looked into the possibility of building an improved instrument which incorporated double focussing. He recognised that he needed to work with an instrument manufacturer in order to bring this idea to fruition and he approached Metropolitan-Vickers with his ideas. John Waldron (who was the managing director at the time) agreed that they would accept the commission to build a double focussing instrument but without providing a guarantee of the performance of the completed instrument. This instrument was based on a 90° electric sector and a 90° magnetic sector, a modification of the Nier–Johnson geometry that had recently been developed. As part of the development team, Beynon spent a significant period (six months) working full time, whilst funded by ICI, at the Metropolitan-Vickers factory. While there, he worked closely with Robert Craig who later became a senior figure in the mass spectrometry manufacturing industry. This prototype (referred to as the MS8) was extremely successful providing a resolving power (not previously demonstrated) of 13,500. As is often the case, however, the prototype was immediately cast aside and not produced commercially as it was decided to manufacture an instrument of improved design. This was twice the size of the MS8, with an electric sector of radius 15 inches and a magnetic sector of radius 12 inches and was referred to as the MS9, the first of which was shipped to Shell research laboratories, Amsterdam, in 1962.

John Beynon

Beynon's main responsibility was to provide support to the organic chemists working in the Dyestuffs division of ICI at Blakeley. Shortly after receiving his new double focussing instrument, his group were able to demonstrate the advantages of having a high-resolution instrument even when working with samples of relatively low molecular weights. Earlier instruments had been able only to produce peaks given by ions of the same nominal mass so that, for example the peak at m/z 44 could arise from the presence of ions such as CO_2^+, $C_3H_8^+$, CH_3CHO^+ or N_2O^+. Working with a mass resolution of several thousand, it was possible to separate the peaks given by these ions and if all four were present, a multiplet of four peaks could be observed. The major advantage of this was that this made it possible to measure the masses of the particular ions precisely thereby giving the elemental composition of the ion. This was done by using the relationship that for a magnetic field of constant strength, the product of the mass m of a singly charged ion and the accelerating voltage V required to bring it to focus, mV, was a constant. Hence for two ions of masses m_1 and m_2 for which accelerating voltages V_1 and V_2 were required to collect the ions, $m_1/m_2 = V_2/V_1$ so that if the mass of one of the ions was known accurately, an accurate measurement of V_2/V_1 gave the mass of the other ion. This procedure was of little value at low resolution since if either of the peaks was a multiplet, the measured mass would be a weighted average of the ions contributing to the peak. When used to determine the mass of a molecular ion, this technique was the equivalent of carrying out an elemental analysis of the compound; when used to determine the elemental composition of a fragment ion, this aided the interpretation of the spectrum and helped in the identification of the compound.

A second and equally important aspect of mass spectrometry was the very high sensitivity of the technique and hence the ease with which one could identify trace impurities, which were often very revealing. On one occasion, Beynon recalled how they had crushed the crystals of a competitor's product, thereby releasing traces of the solvent from which the product had been recrystallised. Not only could the solvent be identified but the trace impurities in the solvent indicated from which supplier the solvent had been obtained. Similarly, different synthetic routes to a particular product invariably gave rise to traces of impurities, which were characteristic of the particular synthetic route employed. A particular use of this technique was in the investigation of illicit drugs. If several samples of a drug were found to have identical impurities, they were almost certainly from a common source but different impurities indicated different sources.

A particular challenge at this time was the acquisition of data in a form that could be stored and manipulated. Beynon, together with David Shields (who was a member of his research team) pioneered the use of computer acquisition of data from the MS9 instrument. This work was presented at the Fourth International Mass Spectrometry meeting in Berlin in 1967.

Although much of his day-to-day work was concerned with the analysis of dyestuffs and their intermediates, Beynon also found time to follow up a number of unusual observations of a more fundamental nature, most notably his work on metastable ions. In double focussing instruments such as the MS8 and MS9, fragmentations of ions of mass m_1 to give a product ion of mass m_2 in the field free region between the electric and magnetic sectors gave rise to diffuse peaks of apparent mass m_2^2/m_1 the shape of which varied with the translational energy released during the fragmentation. Beynon's group was the first to demonstrate this relationship in an analysis of the peak shapes given by the loss of NO by molecular ions of the isomeric nitrophenols. This interest in metastable transitions later led to his seminal work on MIKES, mass-analysed ion kinetic energy spectroscopy, following his retirement from ICI.

Beynon worked full time for ICI until 1969 and during this period he became increasingly influential in the scientific management of the company, ending as a Senior Research Associate (a job title introduced especially for him). Mass spectrometry became a very influential component of the research of ICI and his expertise was in constant demand across the increasingly expanding company. After a period in which he attempted to combine an academic career (in the University of Purdue) and his senior ICI post he decided to retire, in 1974, from the chemical industry, leave Purdue, and take up an offer from the Royal Society of a Royal Society Research Professorship. He had been elected as a Fellow of the Royal Society in 1971. This appointment could be taken up at any University and he chose to return to his undergraduate home at the University of Swansea.

Beynon's contribution to the instrument development field had not finished, however, and after initial studies on linked scanning techniques, carried out with Bob Boyd, he again convinced a major instrument manufacturer (VG based in Manchester) to develop an instrument of novel design. He, together with Dudley Williams from the University of Cambridge, obtained major government funding to purchase an instrument with reversed, horizontal frame, geometry. This development, carried out by a team at VG in Manchester led by Brian Green (himself a major figure in the development of mass spectrometry instrumentation) led to a variety of new applications and kept Beynon's laboratory at the forefront of mass spectrometry research until his retirement in 1986 at the age of 63. His career is unique in that he was outstandingly successful in a number of fields that are rarely, if ever, combined. He was a major research figure in what was, at the time, the world's largest chemical company. In an environment where financial success is the most important metric, he delivered considerable commercial advantage through scientific innovation. He was recognised academically at the highest level with his election to the Royal Society and then established a major research group from scratch, which consolidated his reputation as an outstanding academic. He was also comfortable in the commercial world of mass spectrometry manufacturing, influencing and directing the introduction of novel technology. His contribution to the industrial adoption and utilisation of mass spectrometry is immense.

PROCESS ANALYSIS

Since the early adoption of mass spectrometry by industrial companies, there has been an on-going focus on the requirement to measure the composition of process streams. This was largely in order to study the variation of concentration of the desired product as various changes to the process were made. In the early stages this involved taking samples from the process and taking them back to the central research facility where they would be analysed and the results communicated to the plant. This was unsatisfactory in many cases since the turnaround time was too long and the sample changed during collection, transport and analysis; furthermore, changes in plant operating conditions had to be carried out over extended periods. During the 1950s, mass spectrometry instrumentation was increasingly used as a direct measure of process composition and appeared to have become established as the method of choice. The development of techniques based on gas chromatography, which had lower cost requirements and higher reliability, provided effective compositional analysis and resulted in a decline of the use of mass spectrometry. In the 1970s, the advent of more stable electronics, more reliable vacuum systems and inexpensive computing led to a re-evaluation of methods making use of mass spectrometry. These systems, based largely on quadrupole and magnetic sector analysers, became established as both technically superior and more reliable than systems based on gas chromatography. The nuclear industry, iron and steel manufacture and a number of processes in the chemical industry, including ethylene oxide, acrylonitrile and vinyl chloride manufacture and fermentation processes, benefited from the introduction of the new technology. Significant process savings were claimed, resulting in more efficient and lower cost production. Commercial instrumentation became available and expanded the market for this application. A number of modern plants now have purpose-built mass spectrometry instrumentation, sited in analyser houses and with control feedback loops as part of the design. The commercial nature of this application has meant that there are few publications which describe the science behind the measurements. The industrial scientists who carried out the work, whilst making a significant contribution to the financial performance of their companies, will, as is often the case, remain unknown to the wider community.

QUALITATIVE ANALYSIS

As the brief account of the career of John Beynon indicates, the ability of mass spectrometry to identify unknown components rapidly extended the utility of the technique in an industrial context. It became a financial imperative for an industrial company to have access to the new technology in order to remain competitive. This resulted in the chemical industry being a major market for the rapidly developing mass spectrometry industry and the need for effective communication between the two groups. The need to study complex mixtures meant that the introduction of gas chromatography greatly extended the range of application of methods based on mass spectrometry. James and Martin developed gas chromatography in 1952 when they were working at the Medical Research Institute, Mill Hill, London. Griffin and George (London, UK) introduced the first commercial instruments in 1954. The technique was of great importance to the hydrocarbon and chemical industries and, in the early days, they manufactured their own instruments. The need for the technique often led to one chemical company manufacturing instruments for another and, in one such arrangement H.N. Wilson, ICI Billingham, UK, made a number of instruments for the Dow Chemical Company. The first GC-MS was assembled by Roland Gohlke and Fred McLafferty at Dow Chemical Research Laboratory in Midland, MI, using a Model 12–101 Time-of-Flight mass spectrometer manufactured by the Bendix Corporation. Sampling was accomplished by direct coupling of the GC effluent using a needle valve. Ragnar Ryhage later (1964) developed a rather more effective enrichment device while working at the Karolinska Institute in Stockholm, Sweden.

ICI AFTER JOHN BEYNON

Although Beynon left ICI in 1974 his influence, and the importance of mass spectrometry, continued to be felt within the company. Like many other global chemical companies, such as Dupont, Dow and BASF, ICI invested heavily in mass spectrometry instrumentation and personnel. A.E. (Bert) Williams, who had been Beynon's right-hand man for many years (and who was co-author of many of his papers and books) continued to work for ICI Dyestuffs Division (later ICI Organics). John J. Monaghan who, together with Eddie Clayton, maintained the ICI profile in mass spectrometry, joined him in 1975 and during the period (1976–2000), Monaghan and Clayton were secretary and chair, respectively, of the ICI Mass Spectrometry Panel. This panel, which had representatives from each major ICI research site, met twice a year (often with more than 20 attendees) and visited mass spectrometry manufacturers and academic laboratories in addition to rotating around the various ICI sites. Clayton had obtained his PhD with Rowland Reed in the University of Glasgow, joining the group in 1961. At that time Reed's group was one of a very small number carrying out research in organic mass spectrometry and Beynon was a regular visitor to his laboratory, encouraging Reed to study materials of interest to ICI. During the period Clayton was at Glasgow, the group took delivery of the first MS9 to be delivered to an academic laboratory. He later joined Shell to work at their Carrington laboratories but, when that site was closed he joined ICI, initially at Runcorn and then later at the Pharmaceutical research centre at Alderley. Hilson Hill, another PhD student working with Reed, also joined ICI to work at their Billingham laboratories where, among other notable accomplishments, he designed and built a high temperature probe (based on an 8 kV transformer) which enabled the study of less volatile samples such as copper phthalocyanine dyes for the first

ICI Mass Spectrometry Team (Runcorn) with ZAB-Q instrument. Left to right: John Myatt, John Monaghan, Martin Wagner, Bill Morden, Eileen Charles, Gary Rawlinson.

time. He wrote an excellent introductory textbook for mass spectrometry, (*Introduction to Mass Spectrometry*, Heyden & Son, 1972), but his early death prevented him from reaching his full potential. In keeping with the requirements of industry to keep up with important developments, Monaghan and Clayton were involved in providing funding and encouragement to Mickey Barber and his group at Manchester during the development of Fast Atom Bombardment (FAB). Monaghan left the Organics Division of ICI to join the ICI Corporate Laboratories at Runcorn where he managed the ICI corporate tandem mass spectrometry facility based on the first commercially available ZAB-Q hybrid instrument. This instrument was of particular interest for the low level quantitation of compounds in complex mixtures where the additional selectivity provided by the tandem mass spectrometry separation enabled low levels of detection to be obtained. An interesting example of the use of this approach involved the improved detection of the carcinogenic compound bis(chloromethyl) ether (BCME) in atmospheric samples. After Barber's early death in 1979, Monaghan joined the group at Manchester (on secondment from ICI) to provide continuity. He later retired from ICI and became a Professorial Fellow at the University of Edinburgh. Monaghan was awarded the honour of Member of the Order of the British Empire (MBE) for services to chemistry and has occupied a number of positions on the committee of the British Mass Spectrometry Society including those of Chairman and President. He was influential in the setting up of the International Mass Spectrometry Society and has served on many international mass spectrometry committees. He is also Editor in Chief of *Rapid Communications in Mass Spectrometry* (*RCMS*). Clayton continued to manage an active research group at Alderley making a number of important contributions to ICI's business. He was, for the major part of his career, widely regarded as a leading expert in the interpretation of mass spectra and was often consulted by other scientists, both inside and outside the company, for help with particularly difficult spectra. He maintained an interest in new instrumental approaches and was closely involved in the introduction of the first commercial orthogonal time-of-flight instrument developed by VG at Manchester.

Jim Scrivens, who joined ICI initially to carry out nuclear magnetic resonance (NMR) spectroscopy experiments, later replaced Hilson Hill at ICI's laboratories in the North-East. He carried on the tradition of working closely with instrument companies, encouraging them to develop novel technologies, which could be exploited in an industrial context. He, together with his long-term academic research collaborator, Keith Jennings from the University of Warwick (who was responsible for the development of collisional induced dissociation (CID) which greatly enhanced the information content of mass spectrometry), commissioned a number of instruments, initially from VG in Manchester and then later, as they evolved, from Micromass and Waters. These included a four-sector magnetic instrument, based on the ZAB design and incorporating an array detector (ZAB-T) and the first commercial ion mobility mass spectrometer (based on the successful Q-TOF geometry), the Synapt. The ZAB-T was the first industrial instrument of this type and was used for the study of synthetic polymer microstructure and to obtain field desorption (FD) MS and MS/MS spectra. Field desorption, initially developed by Beckey in Bonn in 1969, was a difficult experiment but was of particular relevance to the characterisation of non-volatile high molecular weight oligomeric systems. The Scrivens group had made significant use of this approach to characterise a number of systems that were difficult to study using other

ZAB instrument at ICI
Wilton; Richard Jennings at
the controls.

existing techniques. The (FD-MS/MS) experiment, which was only possible thanks to the
array detector, was of particular value in the characterisation of blockages encountered
when using ester-based refrigeration lubricants, where the ability of field desorption to
ionise non-polar materials was crucial. Following in the steps of his predecessors, Scrivens
retired from ICI and became an academic (at the University of Warwick) where he continued to work on ion mobility mass spectrometry.

GEOGRAPHICAL CONSIDERATIONS

The coming together of industrial scientists with problems that could be solved by mass
spectrometry and instrument companies that developed the technology to meet these
needs was helped by the geographical proximity of many of the major players. The North-
West of England was the focus of much of the developing chemical industry driven by the
location of large chemical plants designed to meet the increasing requirement for commodity products. Integration with the petroleum industry was an essential component
of the rapidly growing manufacturing capability. It is perhaps not surprising therefore that
the North-West (and Manchester in particular) became the focus for the mass spectrometry industry. The requirements of industry became the driving commercial focus of the
early instruments and the industrial scientists closely involved in the specification, design
and development of the technology. Academic research was established to expand the
application base of the new technology and to develop an understanding of the fundamentals underpinning the measurements and these research groups later contributed to the
blossoming of the technique. A number of these scientists came out of either the chemical
industry (e.g. John Beynon) or the mass spectrometry manufacturers (Micky Barber) but the
melting pot that was the Manchester region certainly contributed to the exchange of ideas
essential in the early stages of exploitation of the technique.

MASS SPECTROMETRY AT SHELL AMSTERDAM AND OTHER INDUSTRIAL LABORATORIES IN THE NETHERLANDS

The research laboratories of Shell, based in Amsterdam, have significant importance in the development of industrial mass spectrometry. They adopted the technology very early, having taken delivery of the first MS9 double focussing mass spectrometer delivered to an industrial site, and maintained a high profile with a number of individuals contributing to both instrumental and application developments. Early workers who made significant contributions include J. van Katwiik, C. de Lau and N.C. Rol. Lau was interested in the performance of the electron detectors used in the instrumentation and studied the mass discrimination effects that could be produced. Rao was one of the first scientists to introduce the concept (in 1967) of delta-hydrogen migration followed by gamma cleavage (the McLaffery + 1 fragmentation). Later the laboratory focussed on process development studies (particularly associated with Fisher–Tropsch chemistry) and Biloen and Sachtler carried out excellent, and important, work utilising isotope labelling approaches. This led to the first observation of surface carbides in Fisher–Tropsch catalysis. A significant legacy of these fundamental studies is evident today with Shell about to commission the world's largest Fisher–Tropsch based chemical plant in Qatar. The interface of various chromatographic techniques with mass spectrometry has always been an important industrial focus and Wim Genuit carried out fundamental studies to enable mass spectrometry to be effectively interfaced with size exclusion chromatography (SEC). SEC is a particularly important separation science technique in the chemical industry since it covers a wide mass range. Genuit's work was based on a dual beam thermospray approach and initially focussed on the separation and characterisation of polystyrene oligomers. This work was presented at the 1992 Montreux symposium and the technique became widely used in industrial laboratories.

Mass spectrometry was a significant feature of the research of a number of other industrial companies based in the Netherlands. These included DSM in Heerlen, AKU (later AKZO Nobel) in Arnhem, Phillips in Eindhoven and Unilever in Vlaardingen. The scientists working in these laboratories focussed, for the most part, on the solution of industrial problems but, nevertheless, contributed to the development of the technique.

In recent years the application of mass spectrometry to the characterisation of synthetic polymers has become more widespread and the work of Michel Nielen at AKZO Nobel on the use of MALDI, combined with SEC, has had a significant impact.

SPECIALITY CHEMICALS

As the chemical industry developed there was a movement away from the petroleum based, commodity products and large tonnage materials towards a more specialised, targeted product range, which met the requirements of a wide variety of industries. These were often low volume products that were particularly well suited to be studied and characterised using mass spectrometry.

Willi Richter was a major influence in the use of mass spectrometry in this industry. He was educated at the University of Vienna and, after postdoctoral experience in the laboratories of both Al Burlingame and Klaus Biemann, became leader of the mass spectrometry group at the then recently founded company Ciba–Geigy in Switzerland. During his long and very successful career at Ciba–Geigy, he published more than 130 papers, a very significant number for an industrially based scientist! He was an early user of chemical ionisation and capillary GC and his work on the separation of sugar isomers was very influential. In later years, as the pharmaceutical interests of Ciba–Geigy developed, he was involved with the identification of post-translational modifications in proteins and made effective use of the recently developed tandem mass spectrometry techniques. A feature of his whole career was his love and great knowledge of fragmentation mechanisms, discussions of which were a feature of many of his publications and presentations. He became a Professor at the University of Stuttgart and was, for many years, the European Editor of the *Journal of Mass Spectrometry*.

Willi Richter

The rapid development and deployment of GC-MS techniques that expanded the use of mass spectrometry in the wider chemical industry gave rise to an increased need for storage and manipulation of the hitherto unheard of quantity of data produced. In the days before computer acquisition and data processing became widely available, ingenious methods were often needed. Bill Kelly, who worked for Unilever, developed a system based on audio tape and took great pleasure in listening to the various, distinct audio signals produced by individual compounds as they eluted from the GC column and were analysed by the mass spectrometer. The more abundant the ion, the louder the signal so that when playing back the mass spectrum of toluene on his portable tape recorder, the tropylium ion at *m/z* 91 could be heard loud and clear!

THE DEVELOPMENT OF THE PHARMACEUTICAL INDUSTRY

The initial industrial applications of mass spectrometry were focussed on quantitative hydrocarbon analysis. Then came an extended period during which the focus was on the identification of unknown compounds, either as pure materials or in complex mixtures. The development of gas chromatography-mass spectrometry as the first hyphenated technique greatly supported this work and mass spectrometry instruments, for the first time, became automated and relatively easy to use, allowing non-specialists access to the technology. As late as the 1969 ASMS meeting in Dallas (which by now included 206 oral presentations) there were no presentations with a biological focus.

The pharmaceutical industry as we know it today started in the 1950s as prescription and non-prescription drugs became differentiated. Increased knowledge of human biology, coupled with improved manufacturing methods, led to a number of new drugs being intro-duced. These became much more important in the 1960s as mass production and increased usage increased the financial impact. Among the drugs introduced at this time were those associated with oral contraception, treatment of high blood pressure, heart medication and tranquilisers such as diazepam.

Increased regulatory pressures led to the industry being required to spend more resources in providing detailed characterisation of their products and the increased use of mass spectrometric methods helped them to achieve these goals. The development of drugs which were used to treat various forms of cancer became more important in the 1970s together with the start of the outsourcing of manufacture to countries such as India. The industry remained relatively small scale until the 1970s after which rapid expansion took place. Legislation was introduced by many countries to protect the intellectual property of the manufacturing companies in order for them to justify further research spending. During the 1980s significant consolidation occurred in the industry with the establishment of a small number of very large companies which controlled the market. Pharmaceutical manufacturing became concentrated, with a few large companies holding a dominant position throughout the world and with a few companies producing medicines within each country. The 1980s saw increased regulatory pressures and the development of further drugs to treat heart disease and the challenge of AIDS. Further changes in business focus were seen in the 1990s with a dramatic increase in the use of specialised contract research companies covering the whole range of pharmaceutical business activities including clinical trials, basic R&D and measurement science activities.

The use of mass spectrometry in the industry followed these business trends. Initially only found in large companies and staffed by experts, mass spectrometry began to be found increasingly in the smaller contract organisations. This led to an increasing requirement for instruments that coupled high performance with ease of use and that could be operated by non-experts with confidence. The pharmaceutical industry has had a major influence on the development of mass spectrometry instrumentation in a different manner from that seen in the early days in the oil and chemical industries. Industry was such a large part of the market that its requirements tended to drive the design of new instrumentation. Industry itself did not focus on the design and building of new instruments but rather set the standards of performance required of these instruments and provided a rich and ready market for the products produced.

The need for industry to quantitate drugs in biological fluids drove many of the early applications of mass spectrometry. Before LC-MS, which with the advent of electrospray ionisation, became a commodity technique, much effort was expended in developing and evaluating a number of different approaches to LC-MS which were often very challenging technically. Industry worked in partnership with a number of academic groups, of which that of Dai Games was prominent. Games' research group was initially in the University of Cardiff and then later at the University of Swansea, where he replaced John Beynon as Professor of Mass Spectrometry. His work with Neville (Nev) Haskins (who worked for a number of pharmaceutical companies) pioneered the use of LC-MS for the assays of drugs in biofluids and advocated the use of stable isotope techniques for quantitation. Another product of the Games group who obtained a senior position within the pharmaceutical industry was Christine Eckers who carried out important development work in LC-MS and became the Manager of Analytical Sciences at GlaxoSmithKline. Other scientists who made major contributions to the pharmaceutical industry before moving into the academic environment (following the example of John Beynon) were Frank Pullen and Jan van der Greef. Pullen's

Frank Pullen

career spans almost the whole history of the pharmaceutical industry covering 37 years. He pioneered the use of mass spectrometry not only to characterise the bioactive components of the drug formulations but also to follow the metabolomics products of the active ingredient within the patient. After a number of years as mass spectrometry team leader within Pfizer Global R&D, during which time he was associated with the development of Diflucan, Viagra and a number of treatments for HIV/AIDS, Pullen became a Senior Director at Pfizer R&D responsible for the Research Analytical Chemistry Section. He later accepted an appointment as Professor of Pharmaceutical Analysis at the University of Greenwich where he continues to carry out research focussed on the needs of the pharmaceutical industry. He is a strong advocate for the use of mass spectrometry and has been a spokesman for the British Mass Spectrometry Society (BMSS) as part of their Sponsored Lecturer Scheme. It is interesting to note that over 50% of the holders of the BMSS Life Membership award (of whom Frank Pullen is one) come from an industrial background, emphasising the importance of this aspect of mass spectrometry to the British mass spectrometry community.

Jan van der Greef

Jan van der Greef is another major figure in the modern development of mass spectrometry in the pharmaceutical industry. He obtained his PhD from Amsterdam in 1980. An early pioneer of LC-MS approaches he has had a major impact in the development of metabolomics, single cell profiling and systems biology. He has published over 300 papers and has presented over 250 plenary and keynote lectures at major international conferences. He has received numerous awards for his work. Like a number of other industrial mass spectrometry research workers, van der Greef also showed a talent for management and became Managing Director of TNO Pharmaceuticals. He accepted an appointment as Professor of Analytical Biosciences at the University of Leiden and couples this with his position as Scientific Director of the TNO Systems Biology and Personal Health Care Research organisation.

The need for higher throughput instrumental approaches and improved ease of use requirements drove on-going collaborations with mass spectrometry manufacturers. V. de Biasi and A. Organ at SmithKline Beecham in Harlow, UK, using a multiplexed electrospray sampling system, significantly improved the productivity of LC-MS experiments. This was rapidly taken up by a number of other groups. Selection of up to eight sprays allowed the use of eight HPLC columns in parallel. A further development (using only two sprays) was pioneered by Christine Eckers (also at SmithKline Beecham) to provide a continuous mass reference during LC-MS data acquisition. This simplified and greatly improved the generation of accurate mass data.

The career of Lester Taylor, another graduate of the Manchester cradle of mass spectrometry, can be used as an example of the contribution mass spectrometry expertise has made to this large, rapidly moving, industry. Taylor's career shows the increasing flexibility required for a scientist in industry.

Taylor obtained his PhD studying the ion optics of mass spectrometers at the University of Manchester Institute of Science and Technology (UMIST) in England where Barber developed Fast Atom Bombardment. He then joined an instrument manufacturer (Kratos

Analytical, Manchester) where he worked on the development of ion sources, hybrid mass spectrometers and inhomogeneous magnetic sector instruments. He then became an academic working at Indiana University in Bloomington, IN, and later joined Burroughs Wellcome Co. in Research Triangle Park, NC, where he held positions of increasing responsibility in Drug Discovery and became Assistant Director in the Organic Chemistry Division. During this time he was responsible for applying mass spectrometry methodologies to a wide range of analytical challenges in pharmaceutical drug discovery and development. In 1996 he left Glaxo Wellcome and moved to MDS Panlabs Inc., in Seattle, WA, to set up the Bioanalytical Services Department which provided contract LC-MS services for drug discovery to pharmaceutical and biotech companies. Following this, he joined Thermo Fisher in 2002 as the Marketing Director for Life Sciences Mass Spectrometry. In 2009, he joined Agilent Technologies, Santa Clara, CA, as the LC/MS Product and Platforms Manager.

His career therefore spanned fundamental research, mass spectrometry development in an instrument company, research within a large pharmaceutical company, provision of contract research services and a number of senior management roles in the measurement science industry. This flexibility and ability to move between academia, industry and instrument companies is an increasing feature of the rapidly evolving industrial utilisation of mass spectrometry instrumentation.

ENVIRONMENTAL APPLICATIONS

The use of methods based on mass spectrometry for the identification and quantification of environmental species did not really develop until after the coupling of gas chromatography with mass spectrometric detection (GC-MS). Early industrial applications focussed on the analysis of process effluent and studying the effectiveness of clean-up processes. Later work was directed by the requirement for industrial companies to establish that they were not exceeding agreed limits for discharge, either in a solid (soil), liquid (river) or gaseous (atmosphere) form. Later still the regulatory levels set by the authorities increasingly became based on the detection levels that could be achieved using methods based on mass spectrometry. The ability of GC-MS experiments to identify and quantify trace components in complex mixtures greatly improved the levels at which selected components could be measured.

The large majority of major industrial chemical companies carried out significant environmental studies although, due to confidential and commercial considerations, very few of these studies found their way into the open literature.

A major driving force in the development of environmental mass spectrometry was the discovery that 2,3,7,8-Tetrachlorodibenzo-p-dioxin (TCDD) was an extraordinarily toxic compound found originally as a by-product of the synthesis of the herbicide 2,4,5-trichlorophenoxyacetic acid (Agent Orange). The chemical stability and lipophilic nature of the compound meant that there was a significant danger that it could accumulate in the food chain. Baughman and Meselson (working at Harvard) identified mass spectrometry, coupled with gas chromatography, as a promising approach. An analytical detection level of 1ppt (part per trillion) was required and, initially this performance level could not be met by existing instrumentation which gave adequate sensitivity but insufficient selectivity to cope with the complex matrices involved. Very significant development effort was focussed on this problem. Extraction and purification methods and chromatographic separation were optimised. The combination of two benzene rings, two oxygen atoms and between four and eight chlorine atoms (found commonly in the extracts) led to the possibility of 75 separate molecules. The toxicity of these compounds was found to be isomer specific with the 2,3,7,8-tetrachlorodibenzo-*p*-dioxin very significantly more toxic than the other molecules. By the 1980s, isomer specific gas chromatography-high resolution mass spectrometry (HRGC-HRMS) became the gold standard for this analysis. This led to the development of double focussing magnetic sector mass spectrometers specifically sold for this purpose. The instruments, which achieved a dynamic resolution performance of greater than 10,000 (10% valley definition, more than 20,000 using the FWHH convention now commonly used) had electron impact sources specially optimised for this particular analysis and were required for regulatory compliance in many world markets. These instruments were very expensive and the extraction and concentration stages long, time-consuming and technically challenging. This resulted in few industrial companies investing in the technology themselves but rather they outsourced the activity to a number of contract laboratories which grew up to meet the demand. European interest in this problem was greatly stimulated following the industrial explosion in Seveso, Italy, in 1976, and this incident, coupled with greater communication regarding the medical implications of exposure to the chemical, meant that European regulation was developed in order to provide consumer confidence in many chlorinated industrial products such as those used in paper manufacture. J. Freudenthal and others were instrumental in developing appropriate methods for this analysis in Europe.

These requirements led to a significant worldwide market for these specialised instruments and VG, Kratos and Finnigan-MAT all developed products, based on double focussing magnetic sector instruments, which competed to meet the global need. Research gradually expanded to include all dioxins and furans with four or more chlorine atoms, and by 1978 it was clear that there were two major sources of these compounds. They were present as by products in chlorinated aromatic compounds formed in industrial processes and they were also emitted from the combustion of municipal and chemical wastes and therefore of much wider impact than thought previously. This meant that the detection and quantitation was no longer just an industrial problem but impacted on a much wider population.

As techniques based on LC-MS became established, the ability of mass spectrometry to be used for the detection and quantification of lower volatile environmental contaminants developed. As in the previous era, industry tended to respond to regulatory pressures rather than develop and publish their own in-house methods and new approaches were often initially developed by academically based research groups such as that led by Emilio Gelpí (Instituto de Investigaciones Biomedicas de Barcelona CSIC-IDIBAPS, Spain) whose group made very significant contributions to this field.

Selectivity, always a key requirement for environmental analysis, has been improved with the introduction of targeted assays based on the use of tandem mass spectrometry (MS/MS) where ions are selected, subject to activation using collisionally induced

Sergio Facchetti

dissociation (CID) and characteristic product ions measured. Sergio Facchetti (Euratom, Ispra, Italy), the first President of the Italian Mass Spectrometry Group, has also made important contributions in applying mass spectrometry to environmental problems and in recent years, he and others have used membranes (often based on silicones) in atmospheric and water analysis as a way of enriching the target compound.

FORGOTTEN HEROES

Any discussion on the impact on the development of mass spectrometry by scientists based in industrial companies is certain to underestimate their contribution. The nature of scientific history is that it relies on the publications of the people involved and a feature of industrial research is that external publication in peer-reviewed literature was not encouraged in many companies. Indeed in many cases, due to commercial or intellectual property considerations, it was forbidden. This has had the consequence, that in many cases, excellent work, which would have been suitable for publication (and in many cases would have had a significant impact) was lost to the wider scientific community and many very able scientists were unable to receive wider recognition for their efforts. In addition, the considerable impact on the development of instrumentation, which stemmed from the interaction between industry and instrument manufacturers was not often recorded. The market for mass spectrometry instrumentation has been influenced significantly by, initially, the petroleum industry, which required instruments to quantify components in complex hydrocarbon streams, then the chemical industry which required sensitive methods for identifying unknown components and then the pharmaceutical industry for which mass spectrometry was an essential component for all research and production activity. Improved resolution, sensitivity, selectivity, ease of use, reliability, footprint and cost reduction have all been achieved as the mass spectrometry industry has met the needs of the customers.

It is unfortunate that many very able industrial scientists have not had the recognition they deserve and I apologise in advance for any significant contributions by people, either alive or dead, that have been omitted in this short discussion.

RECOMMENDED READING

Advances in Mass Spectrometry
> This is a series of books based on contributions to the triennial International Mass Spectrometry Conference (IMSC). It is the oldest continuous series of publications in mass spectrometry includes many contributions by industrial scientists and can be recognised as the best source material.

Chemical Heritage Foundation, Oral histories, John H. Beynon. Interviewed by Michael A Grayson (2008).

Chemical Heritage Foundation, Oral histories, Keith R. Jennings, Interviewed by Michael A Grayson (2008).

S. Meyerson, "Reminiscences of the early days of mass spectrometry in the petroleum industry", *Org. Mass Spectrom.* **21(4),** 197–280 (1986).

A. Quayle, "Recollections of mass spectrometry of the fifties in a UK petroleum laboratory", *Org. Mass Spectrom.* **22(9),** 569–585 (1987).

A. Alford, "Environmental applications of mass spectrometry", *Biol. Mass Spectrom.* **4(1),** 1–22 (1977).

S. Facchetti, D. Pitea and S. Facchetti (Eds), *Chemistry and Environment: Legislation, Methodologies and Applications.* Springer (1995).

Environmental mass spectrometry and other topics
  The *Analytical Chemistry* reviews of mass spectrometry (various authors) can be recommended as good source material.

Scientific societies and meetings in Europe

Alison E. Ashcroft
University of Leeds, Leeds, UK

INTRODUCTION

The term "Society" can encompass a range of organisations or associations with varying degrees of formality from a regulated constitution to a much more informal group. In
its broadest sense, the word can be defined to describe a group of people with similar
interests who meet from time to time to deliberate about their common activity. The
European mass spectrometry community has many societies, each unique in its own way,
but each with a commitment to the advancement of mass spectrometry for the benefit of
its members. These societies will be described in this chapter. The conferences and scientific
meetings organised by the national societies, and also by others working in the same disci-
pline but not necessarily within one society, will also be highlighted. Much of this information
is now freely available from the internet, but for details of pre-internet events then I am
most grateful to all those who have contributed to the contents of this Chapter; their rapid
and helpful responses are characteristic of the true nature of the societies and meetings
herein described. In the Acknowledgements section towards the end of this Chapter there
is a long list of people who need to be thanked not only for their enthusiasm to revisit past
events and find old photographs, but also for their willingness and commitment to ensuring
the continuity of these organisations and events over the years. This is truly the spirit of the
mass spectrometry community! If any society or conference has been omitted or if any of
these data are incorrect, then the fault is entirely my own and I apologise sincerely to those
who may, totally unintentionally, feel neglected or misrepresented.

EUROPEAN SOCIETIES AND THEIR SCIENTIFIC MEETINGS (IN ALPHABETICAL ORDER)

Which came first, the societies or the meetings? The European Societies for which information is readily available are listed here in alphabetical order of their countries. The major
conferences held in each country are also tabled.

Gesellschaft für Analytische Chemie (ASAC), Austria, http://www.asac.at/agm.htm

The Austrian mass spectrometry community is served by the Gesellschaft für Analytische
Chemie (or ASAC, Austrian Society of Analytical Chemistry) which was established in the
late 1970s. In the early days this Group was headed by Erich Schmid (Institute of Analytical
Chemistry, University of Vienna) and since 2005 by Günter Allmaier (Institute of Chemical
Technologies and Analytics, Vienna University of Technology).

From 1989 an annual meeting, the "Massenspektrometrische Diskussionsveranstaltung",
has been organised as a forum to maintain contact within the scientific community. The
main organisers have been Allmaier and Schmid, who have recently been joined in this task
by Andreas Rizzi (University of Vienna). The latest meeting, the 21st Mass Spectrometry
Discussion Meeting, was held in 2010 at the University of Vienna.

Opposite: An early
AEI Users' Meeting
in Manchester in the
mid-1960s. Courtesy of
Robert Bateman.

Belgian Society for Mass Spectrometry (BSMS), Belgium, http://www.bsms.be

The Belgian Society for Mass Spectrometry (BSMS) was founded in 1996. The objectives of the Society are to "provide a forum for open discussion on all aspects of mass spectrometry between practitioners and individuals or companies interested in the field", and to "represent its members in the European and International Mass Spectrometry Societies". The main annual activity of the BSMS is the organisation of a scientific meeting. The BSMS is a registered charity whose statutes were published in Het Belgisch Staatsblad/Le Moniteur Belge on 4th July 1996.

Figure 1. Men in suits! An early AEI Users' Meeting in Manchester in the mid-1960s. Courtesy of Robert Bateman.

British Mass Spectrometry Society (BMSS), UK, http://www.bmss.org.uk/

The British Mass Spectrometry Society (BMSS) can trace its origins back to the 1950s. In the early days the foremost application of mass spectrometry was in the petrochemical industry, and the major UK manufacturer of mass spectrometers, the Metropolitan Vickers Company

Figure 2. An AEI MS9
Users' Meeting in
Manchester *ca* 1970.
Courtesy of Robert
Bateman.

Ltd (Metrovick or M-V)[1] (which later became the Associated Electrical Industries, AEI)[2] held regular users' meetings which reflected this situation (Figures 1 and 2). At the same time, the Institute of Petroleum's Hydrocarbon Research Group operated a Mass Spectrometry Panel, (initially chaired by Alan Quayle of Shell's Thornton Research Centre, UK), which promoted new techniques that could be beneficial to all petroleum companies.

Recognising that applications in other fields such as organic and physical chemistry, geology etc. fostered instrumental development to the benefit of all, the Institute of Petroleum's Panel organised a series of conferences, the first of which was held at M-V in 1950. The second meeting in London in 1953 included papers from other countries and the international involvement increased further at the international conference in London in 1958. This latter meeting was organised jointly by the Panel and the E-14 Committee of ASTM (American Society for Testing Materials) and covered all aspects of mass spectrometry. The published proceedings were edited by John Waldron, who led the mass spectrometry development group at M-V, and similar conferences were organised every three years from then on, with increasing international involvement (see "International Mass Spectrometry Foundation" below).

Figure 3. Four well-respected characters associated with the British Mass Spectrometry Society (BMSS): (a) John Beynon and (b) Allan Maccoll, who were influential in setting up the BMSS; (c) Michael Barber, who pioneered the application of Fast Atom Bombardment to the mass spectrometric analysis of biomolecules, after whom the annual BMSS prize for the best student lecture is named; (d) Francis Aston, the 1922 Nobel Prize Winner in Chemistry for his discovery of isotopes using a mass spectrograph, after whom the BMSS Aston Medal is named. Courtesy of (a) "John Herbert Beynon" by Robert Boyd in *Rapid Commun. Mass Spectrom.* **18,** 1–6 (2004); Wiley Interscience, doi: 10.1002/rcm.1300. Reproduced with permission from Wiley Interscience; (b) Archives, Chemistry Department, University College London; (c) the Michael Barber Centre for Mass Spectrometry, University of Manchester, UK; and (d) Library of Congress / Science Photo Library.

In the early 1960s the Institute of Petroleum's Panel continued its work and newer specialised applications of mass spectrometry in organic chemistry and quantitative inorganic analysis were largely covered by manufacturers' users' meetings. However, physical chemistry applications, and consequent instrumental modifications, did not have an equivalent forum, and the Mass Spectrometry Discussion Group (MSDG) was established. Informal MSDG meetings were held around the country two or three times per year. Early participants were Peter Knewstubb and Dudley Williams (University of Cambridge), Roy Lehrle and John Majer (University of Birmingham), Martin Elliott (M-V) and John Cuthbert (University of Oxford).

During this era, the Mass Spectroscopy Group (MSG), the precursor to the BMSS, was also established to reflect the need of the growing mass spectrometry community for a body to cover all aspects of mass spectrometry including general interests such as the fragmentation of organic compounds. An initial meeting of interested parties took place in 1964, followed by the first formal conference of the group the following year which was held at University College, London, in 1965 (Table 1). The main inaugurators of the MSG were John Beynon (then ICI, later University of Swansea)[3,4] [Figure 3(a)], John Waldron, by this time Head of Mass Spectrometry at M-V, Allan Maccoll (University College London (UCL)) [Figure 3(b)][5] and Martin Elliott (M-V), the Group's first Secretary. At their 3rd Annual Meeting at UCL in 1968, a constitution was proposed by Beynon which involved expansion of the Committee to include one representative each from the Institute of Petroleum (Alan Quayle), indicating the still high importance of petrochemical applications of mass spectrometry in those days, and the MSDG (Roy Lehrle). The constitution was duly adopted and the MSG took on a more formal role. In 1974, the name British Mass Spectroscopy Group (BMSG) was adopted and the Constitution was revised in 1976 to omit the specific representation of the Institute of Petroleum and the MSDG. Membership subscriptions were first introduced at the AGM in 1977. A further restructuring took place in 1981, when the BMSG merged with the Biomedical Mass Spectrometry Group, an interest group established in 1973 by Brian Millard (School of Pharmacy, London), Dai Games (University of Cardiff) and Neville Haskins (G.D. Searle Ltd) to promote discussion on the new techniques of the time, namely capillary GC-MS and LC-MS. The name "British Mass Spectrometry Society" was launched at this time and the Society was later registered with the UK Charity Commission, in 1980. The elected Committee currently includes the Chairman, Secretary, Treasurer, Secretaries for Meetings, Education, Publicity, and Papers, a Special Interest Group Co-ordinator, and the Web-Master. John Monaghan (University of Edinburgh), BMSS Chairman from 1999 to 2001, went on to become the 3rd President of the International Mass Spectrometry Foundation from 2003 to 2006. BMSS conferences have been held regularly every two years out of three, in concert with the International MS Foundation's triennial conference (Table 1) and the current membership is >700.

Over the years, the BMSS has fully funded seven PhD studentships in UK universities and has provided travel grants and annual prizes for its post-graduate student members, and summer studentships for undergraduates. The two post-graduate prizes are named in recognition of two eminent British scientists who contributed greatly to mass spectrometry during their lifetimes, the Bordoli[6] (after Bob Bordoli, VG Instruments and Micromass UK Ltd) and Barber[7] (after Michael Barber, AEI followed by UMIST) [Figure 3(c)] prizes for excellence in poster and oral presentations, respectively, which are presented at the annual conference. The BMSS started to recognise key individuals in mass spectrometry in 1989 when the Aston Medal [after Francis Aston, the 1922 Nobel Prize Winner in Chemistry for his discovery of isotopes using a mass spectrograph [Figure 3(d)] was established "to honour individuals deserving special recognition by reason of their outstanding contributions to knowledge in the biological, chemical, engineering, mathematical, medical, or physical sciences relating directly to outstanding exploitation, application or development of mass spectrometry" (Table 2). In 2002, the position of BMSS President was established and the BMSS Medal, an occasional award "to recognise sustained contributions by individual members of the British Mass Spectrometry Society to the development of mass spectrometry, primarily within the UK" first introduced (Table 2).

Not surprisingly, Allan Maccoll and John Beynon were the recipients of the first two Aston Medals, in 1989 and 1990, respectively. For Beynon, whose *Nature* paper of 1954 described the first determination of the elemental composition of an organic substance from an accurate mass measurement,[4] the Aston Medal was just one of ~17 awards in recognition of his pre-eminence as a researcher in mass spectrometry over four decades; additionally he was the originator of the journal *Rapid Communications in Mass Spectrometry*.[3]

Allan Maccoll's influence on mass spectrometry was also very considerable: he played a prominent role in founding the BMSS and hosted the first meeting of the MSG in 1965 at

UCL. In 1968, he became the founding Editor of the journal *Organic Mass Spectrometry* that was for over 20 years one of the major journals in the field and the immediate predecessor of the *Journal of Mass Spectrometry*. In 1994, Maccoll became the founding Editor of the journal *European Mass Spectrometry*. The BMSS marked his retirement by naming the plenary lecture at its Annual Meeting, which has been traditionally devoted to fundamental aspects of mass spectrometry, the "Maccoll Lecture".

Training courses have been a prominent feature of the mass spectrometry community in the UK. For example, the Royal Institute of Chemistry ran courses in 1968, 1970, 1972, 1976 and 1979 which involved a number of mass spectrometrists from various European countries, presenting lectures and problem classes based on the operation of magnetic sector instruments and the interpretation of electron ionisation spectra of simple organic molecules. Course tutors included Dudley Williams, Alan Maccoll and Keith Jennings from the UK, as well as Herbert Budzikiewicz and Gerhard Spiteller from Germany and Austria, respectively. Keith Jennings remembers that at the first school in 1968, topics such as the origin of metastable transitions and energy release during fragmentation, accurate mass measurement, use of isotope peaks and the fragmentation of the more common classes of organic compound, were discussed. These courses proved quite popular (*ca* 40 participants on each course) at a time when interpretation of mass spectra did not feature in most undergraduate courses, probably because few members of staff were in a position to teach the subject.

More recently, following the introduction of electrospray ionisation, 1993 saw the first BMSS LC-MS Course and Conference at Robinson College, University of Cambridge, organised by Janet Oxford and Christine Eckers (both of GSK). This format is still used for the popular bi-annual LC-MS meeting. Later organisers have included Soraya Monte (GSK), Pat Wright (Pfizer), Steve Pleasance (Quotient) and Mark Harrison (Thermo Finnigan). The BMSS has a range of Special Interest Groups which also hold focussed meetings on specific applications or technical developments.

Independent local area groups have also been formed as the inclination has dictated. An early example was the (now disbanded) "East Kent Mass Spectrometry Group" which involved local scientists from the University of Kent, Shell Research Ltd., Pfizer and Proprietary Perfumes. A current example is the London Biological Mass Spectrometry Discussion Group, a local group which started in 2006 for London-based mass spectrometrists to meet on a quarterly basis. This group, which is now affiliated to BMSS, has already held 16 meetings each with an attendance record of ~100 scientists.

Table 1. Annual Meetings and Chairmen of the British Mass Spectrometry Society and its predecessor the MSG, 1965–2011. (N.B. every third year the annual conference has been waived to avoid conflict with the International Mass Spectrometry Conference.)

MEETING	YEAR	VENUE	CHAIR	YEAR(S)
1st	1965	UC London	John Beynon	1964–1965
2nd	1966	Univ. Birmingham	John Waldron	1965–1966
	1967	IMSC4 Berlin	Alan Quayle	1966–1967
3rd	1968	UC London	Allan Maccoll	1967–1968
4th	1969	Univ. Sheffield	Allan Maccoll	1968–1969
	1970	IMSC5 Brussels	Keith Jennings	1969–1970
5th	1971	Bristol Univ.	Keith Jennings	1970–1971
6th	1972	Swansea Univ.	Dudley Williams	1971–1972
	1973	IMSC6 Edinburgh	Dudley Williams	1972–1973
7th	1974	Univ. Warwick	John Hasted	1973–1974
8th	1975	Keele Univ.	Norman Daly	1974–1975
	1976	IMSC7 Florence	Alan Carrick	1975–1976
9th	1977	Univ. Swansea	Alan Carrick	1976–1977
10th	1978	Durham Univ.	Henry Wilson	1977–1978
	1979	IMSC8 Oslo	Henry Wilson	1978–1979
11th	1980	Univ. Kent	Peter Knewstubb	1979–1980
12th	1981	Univ. Cambridge	John Todd	1980–1981
	1982	IMSC9 Vienna	John Todd	1981–1982
13th	1983	Univ. Warwick	Dai Games	1982–1983
14th	1984	Heriot-Watt Univ.	Allan Maccoll	1983–1984
	1985	IMSC10 Swansea	Patrick Powers	1984–1985
15th	1986	Univ. Sussex	Patrick Powers	1985–1986
16th	1987	Univ. York	Keith Jennings	1986–1987
	1988	IMSC11 Bordeaux	Keith Jennings	1987–1988
17th	1989	Univ. Nottingham	Stan Evans	1988–1989
18th	1990	UC London	Stan Evans	1989–1990
	1991	IMSC12 Amsterdam	Frank Cottee	1990–1991
19th	1992	St Andrews Univ.	Frank Cottee	1991–1992
20th	1993	Univ. Kent	Chris Johnson	1992–1993
	1994	IMSC13 Budapest	Chris Johnson	1993–1994
21st	1995	UMIST, Manchester	Tony Mallet	1994–1995
22nd	1996	Univ. Swansea	Tony Mallet	1995–1996
	1997	IMSC14 Tampere	Alison Ashcroft	1996–1997
23rd	1998	Univ. Warwick	Alison Ashcroft	1997–1998
24th	1999	Univ. Reading	John Monaghan	1998–1999
	2000	IMSC15 Barcelona	John Monaghan	1999–2000
25th	2001	Southampton Univ.	Frank Pullen	2000–2001

MEETING	YEAR	VENUE	CHAIR	YEAR(S)
26th	2002	Loughborough Univ.	Frank Pullen	2001–2002
	2003	IMSC16 Edinburgh	Gareth Brenton	2002–2003
27th	2004	Derby Univ.	Gareth Brenton	2003–2004
28th	2005	Univ. York	Mira Doig	2004–2005
	2006	IMSC17 Prague	Mira Doig	2005–2006
29th	2007	Heriot-Watt Univ.	Don Daley	2006–2007
30th	2008	York Univ.	Don Daley	2007–2008
	2009	IMSC18 Bremen	John Langley	2008–2009
31st	2010	Cardiff	John Langley	2009–2010
32nd	2011	Cardiff	Susan Crosland	2010–2011

Table 2. Recipients of the Aston Medal and the BMSS Medal.

NAME AND AFFILIATION	DATE OF AWARD
Aston Medal	
Allan Maccoll, University College London	1989
John H. Beynon, University of Swansea	1990
Brian N. Green, OBE, Micromass UK Ltd	1996
Keith R. Jennings, University of Warwick	1998
David E. Games, University College Swansea	2000
Colin T. Pillinger, Open University	2003
Tom Preston, University of Glasgow	2005
John F. J. Todd, University of Kent	2006
Robert H. Bateman, MBE, Micromass UK Ltd	2008
Richard Evershed, University of Bristol	2010
BMSS Medal	
Edward Houghton, Horse Racing Forensic Laboratory	2004
Anthony I. Mallet, University of Greenwich	2007

Czech Society for Mass Spectrometry (CSHS), Czech Republic, http://www.czechms.org/cz/

In the Czech Republic there has been an active mass spectrometry group since 1967 working within the framework of the national Ioannes Marcus Marci Spectroscopic Society (Table 3). The official registration process for the Czech Society for Mass Spectrometry (CSHS) was initiated in 2010 and the Society was formally established on 13 August 2010 at the University of Olomouc.

Table 3. Chairmen of the Czech Mass Spectrometry Group, 1967–2010.

DATE	CHAIR
1967–1970	Vladimír Čermák
1970–1977	Zdeněk Herman
1977–1993	Miroslav Ryska
1993–1995	Petr Verner
1995–2005	Vladimír Havlíček
2005–2010	Michal Holčapek
2010–	Jana Roithová

Dansk Selskab for Massespektrometri (Danish Society for Mass Spectrometry; DSMS), Denmark, http://www.dsms.dk/

The Danish Society for Mass Spectrometry (DSMS) started in the late 1960s as an informal discussion group. Three Danish mass spectrometrists, Joergen Moeller (Copenhagen University), Elfinn Larsen (Risoe Nuclear Research Center) and Peter Roepstorff (Danish Institute of Protein Chemistry), initiated a coffee club to discuss mass spectrometry issues and instrumentation. The Group met fortnightly over coffee and Danish pastries and called themselves the Royal Danish Society for Active Mass Spectrometrists. Soon they realised that they needed permission from the Queen of Denmark to use the title "royal" and then when a scientist who did not possess a mass spectrometer joined the group they removed the term "active", leaving the name as the Danish Society for Mass Spectrometry, which still exists. Originally this was an entirely informal group of people, with neither a statute nor membership fees. The early Secretaries who maintained the membership lists were Elfin Larsen and then later Tore Vulpius and Steen Pontoppidan. The Society arranges annual meetings every year in October at the University of Southern Denmark in Odense and is actively involved in collaboration with the other Nordic Mass Spectrometry Societies in arranging the Nordic Mass Spectrometry Meetings.

The DSMS remains very active and is an excellent network for interaction and exchange between the many mass spectrometry activities in Denmark. The Society has grown steadily in size in step with the increase of mass spectrometric equipment in Denmark—currently the Society has >100 members—and now has a formal constitution although there is still no membership fee. The purpose of the DSMS is to provide a "forum where users and people with an interest in mass spectrometry can meet and exchange information about their work", to "arrange meetings and conferences within mass spectrometry" and to strengthen the academic environment between mass spectrometry manufacturers and people with an interest in mass spectrometry.

European Society for Mass Spectrometry (ESMS)

The European Society for Mass Spectrometry (ESMS) was established in 1994 to promote and disseminate knowledge of mass spectrometry and related subjects throughout Europe. The Society operated as a federation of national mass spectrometry societies or groups from European countries. The role of the ESMS was not to organise Europe-wide meetings, but rather to improve communication and collaboration throughout the mass spectrometry community in Europe, to support those national societies wishing to run major European meetings, and to ensure that any overlap of dates between national meetings was kept to a minimum. The Committee included a President, Chairman, Secretary and three other representatives from national societies and held informal Committee meetings at the triennial International Mass Spectrometry Conference. The European Society for Mass Spectrometry ceased to be operational when the Articles of the International Mass Spectrometry Foundation were formalised in 2003.

Suomen Massaspektrometrian Seura (Finnish Mass Spectrometry Society; FMSS) Finland, http://www.fmss.fi/

The Finnish Mass Spectrometry Society (FMSS) was formally registered at the end of 2007, as a continuation of the Finnish Chemical Society's Massaspektrometriajaoston activity established in December 1980 (Table 4). The Founding members were Herman Adlercreutz, (University of Helsinki, President), Antti Hesso (University of Helsinki), Jorma Jalonen (University of Oulu), Jorma Korvola (University of Jyväskylä), Kirsi-Marja Marnela (University of Tampere) and Lalli Nykänen (Finnish State Alcohol Company). The Society operates a nationwide link within the mass spectrometry community and aims to promote interaction between its members and enhance the understanding of mass spectrometry. The FMSS organises training courses, visits to companies and equipment demonstrations as well as national and international conferences and currently has >500 individual members and six company members.

Table 4. Annual and International Meetings held in Finland, and Presidents of the Finnish Mass Spectrometry Society, 1982–2010.

MEETINGS	DATE	PRESIDENT	DATE OF OFFICE
1st Finnish MS	1982	Herman Adlercreutz	1981–1982
5th Nordic MS Conference	1983	Herman Adlercreutz	1983–1984
2nd Finnish MS	1984	Herman Adlercreutz	1983–1984
3rd Finnish MS	1986	Jyrki Taskinen	1985–1986
4th Finnish MS	1988	Jorma Jalonen	1987–1988
5th Finnish MS	1990	Jorma Jalonen	1989–1990
6th Finnish MS	1992	Antti Hesso	1991–1992
7th Finnish MS	1994	Antti Hesso	1993–1994
9th Nordic MS Conference	1995	Antti Leinonen	1995–1996
8th Finnish MS	1996	Antti Leinonen	1995–1996
14th IMSC	1997	Antti Leinonen	1997–1998
9th Finnish MS	1998	Antti Leinonen	1997–1998
10th Finnish MS	2000	Pentti Oksman	1999–2000
11th Finnish MS	2002	Tapio Kotiaho	2001–2002
12th Finnish MS	2004	Tapio Kotiaho	2003–2004
		Janne Jänis	2005–2006
13th Nordic MS Conference	2007	Janne Jänis	2007–2008
13th Finnish MS	2010	Olli Laine	2009–2010

La Société Française de Spectrométrie de Masse (SFSM), France, http://www.sfsm.info/

La Société Française de Spectrométrie de Masse was formalised in 1985 and is registered in France as an Association according to the law of 1901 (Table 5). Its objectives are to promote mass spectrometry and related techniques, provide a forum for scientists interested in these disciplines, and exchange information between the SFSM and other international societies. However, since 1980, an annual conference, the Journées Françaises de Spectrométrie de Masse (JFSM), has been organised in France and since 1989 there has been an annual prize for a young researcher (Table 6).

Table 5. Société Française de Spectrométrie de Masse Board Members, 1985–2011.

YEAR	PRESIDENT	SECRETARY	TREASURER
1985	J-L. Aubagnac	G. Bouchoux	G. Devant
1986	G. Bouchoux	Y. Le Beyec	G. Devant
1987	G. Devant	Y. Le Beyec	C. Julien-Larose
1988	Y. Le Beyec	F. De Maack	C. Julien-Larose
1989	F. De Maack	R. Botter	C. Julien-Larose
1990–1991	René Botter	Y. Hoppilliard	G. Devant
1991–1992	René Botter	J-P. Morizur	G. Devant
1992–1993	J-P. Morizur	J. Fraisse	C. Rolando
1993–1994	J-P. Morizur	J. Fraisse	C. Rolando
1994–1995	C. Rolando	J. Fraisse	J-C. Promé
1995–1996	J-C. Promé	C. Lange	J-C. Blais
1996–1997	J-C. Promé	C. Lange	J-C. Blais
1997–1998	C. Lange	Y. Hoppilliard	J-C. Blais
1998–1999	Y. Hoppilliard	E. Forest	J. Tortajada
1999–2000	Y. Hoppilliard	E. Forest	J. Tortajada
2000–2001	J. Tortajada	O. Laprévote	G. Bolbach
2001–2002	O. Laprévote	G. Bouchoux	G. Bolbach
2002–2003	O. Laprévote	G. Bouchoux	G. Bolbach
2003–2004	G. Bouchoux	N. Potier	A. Brunelle
2004–2005	A. Brunelle	L. Debrauwer	J-Y. Salpin
2005–2006	A. Brunelle	L. Debrauwer	J-Y. Salpin
2006–2007	L. Debrauwer	J. Chamot-R.	I. Fournier
2007–2008	J. Chamot-R.	E. Forest	I. Fournier
2008–2009	J. Chamot-R.	E. Forest	P. Dugourd
2009–2010	E. Forest	M.Salzet	P. Dugourd
2010–2011	M.Salzet	C. Afonso	S. Sagan

Table 6. Journées Françaises de Spectrométrie de Masse (JFSM) Conferences and Prize Winners, 1980–2011. From 2007, a combined conference with the Société Française d'Electrophorèse et d'Analyse Protéomique, named Spectrométrie de Masse et Analyse Protéomique (SMAP,) has been held every alternate year.

JFSM	DATE	CITY	ORGANISER	PRIZE WINNER
1ères JFSM	1980	Dijon	B. Maume	
2èmes JFSM	1981	Toulouse	J-C. Promé	
3èmes JFSM	1983	Palaiseau	Y. Hoppilliard	
4èmes JFSM	1984	Montpellier	J-L. Aubagnac	
5èmes JFSM	1986	Grenoble	A-M. Andreani	
6èmes JFSM	1987	Strasbourg	G. Teller	
7èmes JFSM	1989	Rennes	P. Guénot	F. Couderc
8èmes JFSM	1990	Nice	J-F. Gal	A. Brunelle
12th IMSC	1991	Amsterdam, Netherlands		R. Galera
9èmes JFSM	1992	Metz	J-F. Muller	M. Sablier
10èmes JFSM	1993	Paris	J-P. Morizur	M. Jacquinod
11èmes JFSM	1994	Rouen	C. Lange	C. Mauriac
12èmes JFSM	1995	Bordeaux	G. Bourgeois	E. Leize
13èmes JFSM	1996	Orléans	R.L. Inglebert	P. Liere
14èmes JFSM	1997	Lille	G. Briand	P. Chaurand
15èmes JFSM	1998	Lyon	M. Becchi	F. Halgand J.-Y. Salpin
16èmes JFSM	1999	Nancy	E. Lichtfouse	S. Gevrey
17èmes JFSM	2000	Villeneuve d'Ascq	C. Rolando	G. Van der Rest, J. Vinh, P.-J. Calba
18èmes JFSM	2001	La Rochelle	A. Brunelle	D. Lemaire
19èmes JFSM	2002	Chaville	O. Laprévote	W.V. Bienvenut
20èmes JFSM	2003	Toulouse	B. Monsarrat	A. Simon, D. Ruch
21èmes JFSM	2004	Strasbourg	A. Van Dorsselaer	S. Le Caer
22èmes JFSM	2005	Montpellier	J-L. Aubagnac	S. Le Gac
23èmes JFSM	2006	Nantes	F. André	N. Budimir
24èmes JFSM SMAP2007	2007	Pau	R. Lobinski	D. Touboul L. Quinton
25èmes JFSM	2008	Grenoble	E. Forest	T. Tabarin
26èmes JFSM SMAP2009	2009	Dijon	P. Ducoroy	A. Bagag
27èmes JFSM	2010	Clermont-Ferrand	B. Bouchon	J. Franck
28èmes JFSM SMAP2011	2011	Avignon	J. Armengaud	

Deutsche Gesellschaft für Massenspektrometrie (DGMS), Germany, http://www.dgms-online.de/

The German Society for Mass Spectrometry was established in 1997 as the successor to the earlier West German Arbeitsgemeinschaft für Massenspektrometrie (AGMS, founded in 1960) and the former East German Arbeitsgemeinschäft für Massenspektrometrie der DDR (AGMS-DDR, founded in 1957), with the continued aim to support mass spectrometry as a high precision tool of molecular investigation and as an arena for members to communicate.

The AGMS was founded on 20 October 1960 by a number of mass spectrometrists (many from a nuclear physics background!) from the Deutsche Physikalische Gesellschaft. The individual "founding fathers" came from the Max Planck Institute of Chemistry in Mainz (radiochemistry division), and the Universities of Frankfurt, Munich and Heidelberg, as well as from industries including the Philips Laboratory, Consolidated Electrodynamics Corporation (CEC), Balzers, and Atlas Werke. The first co-ordinator was Heinrich Hintenberger from the Max Planck Institute and shortly after the first meeting Hans Beckey (Bonn University) was invited to join the group as a physical chemist whose role was to serve as a bridge to the chemistry community. One original AGMS member remembers the meetings being "dominated by physicists in the early years and the heated controversies at the annual meetings between them and the organic newcomers who proposed fragmentation mechanisms". In 1967, the AGMS introduced sub-divisions (physics, organic and inorganic mass spectrometry) and Hans-Friedrich Grützmacher (Universität Bielefeld) became the Chairman of the Organic Mass Spectrometry subdivision. The AGMS held an annual conference from 1968 to 1998 [Table 7(a)], during which time, while the importance of physics within the AGMS was diminishing over the years, chemistry certainly flourished.

In the former East Germany (German Democratic Republic, GDR), mass spectrometry conferences were organised on a regular basis between 1975 and 1989 by the Association of Mass Spectrometry from within the Chemical Society of the GDR.

In the 1990s it was decided to formalise the loose coalition of mass spectrometry which existed between the AGMS, the Bunsen Society for Physical Chemistry and the German Physical Chemical Society. The chairman of the day, Jochen Franzen of Bremen, achieved this amalgamation and, with six colleagues, founded the Deutsche Gesellschaft für Massenspektrometrie (DGMS) in 1997 in Bremen. At the first general meeting of the DGMS in 1998 in Cottbus, two additional members were elected to the new board, Michael Przybylski and Jürgen Grotemeyer.

Table 7(a). Arbeitsgemeinschaft Massenspektrometrie (AGMS) Conferences, 1968–1998.

YEAR	AGMS	LOCATION	ORGANISER(S)	CHAIRMAN
1968	1st	Hamburg	H.Fr. Grützmacher	H.D. Beckey
1969	2nd	Freiburg	Achenbach	H.D. Beckey
1970	3rd	Mülheim	D. Henneberg	H.D. Beckey
1971	4th	Malente	D. Henneberg	

YEAR	AGMS	LOCATION	ORGANISER(S)	CHAIRMAN
1972	5th	Amorbach	D. Henneberg	
1973	6th	München MPI Martinsied	Dr Schäfer	
1974	7th	Marburg	G. Schaden	J. Franzen
1975	8th	Schloss Reisensburg Günzburg / Donau	H.-W. Fehlhaber	J. Franzen
1976	9th	Willingen	H.-W. Fehlhaber	J. Franzen
1977	10th	Bad Kissingen	M. Hesse	K. Heumann
1978	11th	Regensburg	K. Heumann	K. Heumann
1979	12th	Darmstadt	M. Veith	K. Heumann
1980	13th	Köln	H. Budzikiewicz	J. Müller
1981	14th	Heidelberg	D. Krauss	J. Müller
1982	15th	Bielefeld	H.Fr. Grützmacher	J. Müller
1983	16th	Berlin	H. Schwarz	H. Budzikiewicz
1984	17th	Göttingen	H. Ludwig-Köhn D. Hunnemann	H. Budzikiewicz
1985	18th	Ettal	J. Müller	H. Budzikiewicz
1986	19th	Mainz	M. Przybylski	D. Henneberg
1987	20th	Oldenburg	J.O. Metzger	D. Henneberg

Figure 4. Jasna Peter-Katalinic presented the Life Science Award of the Deutsche Gesellschaft für Massenspektrometris (DGMS) to Michael Przybylski (University of Konstanz) for making a significant contribution to the development and application of mass spectrometry in life sciences in 2004. The award was presented at a ceremony held at the UFZ Centre for Environmental Research, Leipzig-Halle GmbH at the Helmholtz Association, Germany. Left to right: Jürgen Grotemeyer (DGMS President), Jasna Peter-Katalinic (Chairman of the award jury), Michael Przybylski and Holm Sommer. Courtesy of Michael Przybylski, University of Konstanz and the DGMS.

YEAR	AGMS	LOCATION	ORGANISER(S)	CHAIRMAN
1988	21st	Würzburg	G. Lange	D. Henneberg
1989	22nd	Jülich	J. Rullkötter	C. Brunnée
1990	23rd	Konstanz	M. Przybylski	C. Brunnée
1991	24th	Dortmund	M. Linscheid	C. Brunnée
1992	25th	Braunschweig	M. Schiebel	M. Linscheid
1993	26th	Düsseldorf	Dr Keck	M. Linscheid
1994	27th	Halle/Saale	J. Schmidt	M. Linscheid
1995	28th	Tübingen	Dr Beyer	J. Franzen
1996	29th	Bremen	Dr. Wanczek	J. Franzen
1997	30th	Konstanz	M. Przybylski	J. Franzen
1998	31st	Cottbus	J. Grotemeyer	M. Przybylski

Table 7(b). Deutsche Gesellschaft für Massenspektrometrie (DGMS) Conferences, 1999–2009.

YEAR	AGMS/DGMS	LOCATION	ORGANISER(S)	CHAIRMAN
1999	32nd / 1st	Oldenburg	J.O. Metzger	M. Przybylski
2000	33rd / 2nd	Berlin	M. Linscheid	M. Przybylski
2001	34th / 3rd	München	Dr U. Boesl	J. Grotemeyer
2002	35th / 4th	Heidelberg	Lehmann	J. Grotemeyer
2003	36th / 5th	Münster	J. Katalinic-Peter	J. Grotemeyer
2004	37th / 6th	Leipzig	Wennrich	J. Grotemeyer
2005	38th / 7th	Rostock	M. Glocker	J. Grotemeyer
2006	39th / 8th	Mainz	K. Heumann	J. Grotemeyer
2007	40th / 9th	Bremen	K.P. Wanczek	J. Grotemeyer
2008	41st / 10th	Glessen	B. Spengler	J. Grotemeyer
2009	42nd / 11th	Konstanz	M. Przybylski	J. Grotemeyer
2010	43rd / 12th	Halle	J. Schmidt A. Sinz	J. Grotemeyer
2011	44th / 13th	Dortmund	A. Sickmann	J. Grotemeyer

Figure 5. Since 1997, the Deutsche Gesellschaft für Massenspektrometrie has initiated its annual meeting with the Wolfgang-Paul Lecture. A prestigious group of scientists have been invited to present this lecture, including Franz Hillenkamp (University of Münster) in 2001 (upper) and Herbert Budzikiewicz (Universität zu Köln) in 2004 (lower). Courtesy of the Deutsche Gesellschaft für Massenspektrometrie (http://www.dgms-online.de).

The DGMS has currently >700 members from academia, industry, research institutions and government laboratories with interests in developing techniques and applying them to fundamental analytical problems in chemistry, the life sciences, medicine, geology, forensics and physics. Continuing the format of the AGMS, the DGMS organises an annual conference, the first of which was held in 1999 in Oldenburg as the 32nd meeting of the AGMS [Table 7(b)]. There are also regular workshops and specialised meetings. With the support of various sponsors, the DGMS presents the Mattauch–Herzog Award (Mattauch–Herzog Förderpreis für Massenspektrometrie, established in 1988) for outstanding junior scientists working in the field, the Wolfgang-Paul Award (Wolfgang-Paul Studienpreis, established in 1998) for the best graduate and doctoral work in mass spectrometry, and the Life Science Prize in Mass Spectrometry in recognition of outstanding mass spectrometric work in the life sciences (Figure 4). Since 1997, the DGMS has initiated its annual meeting with the Wolfgang-Paul Lecture. A prestigious group of scientists has been invited to present this lecture, including two national scientific heroes, Franz Hillenkamp and Herbert Budzikiewicz (Figure 5).

Hellenic Mass Spectrometry Society (HMSS), Greece, http://www.hmss.gr

The principle objectives of the Hellenic Mass Spectrometry Society (HMSS) are to enhance and support the utilisation of mass spectrometry for basic and applied research. Although a steady number of mass spectrometers had been installed in Greece from the late 1960s onwards, it was a small group of Greek scientists who were active in the field in the USA who initiated the HMSS. The leading figures were Paul Vouros (Baylor College of Medicine/ Northeastern University) along with Chrys Wesdemiotis (Cornell University and then the University of Akron), Anthony Tsarbopoulos (Mayo Clinic) and Ioannis Papayannopoulos (MIT). This small group met during the annual American Society for Mass Spectrometry (ASMS) conference to discuss how to organise the slowly increasing number of Greek-origin mass spectrometry graduate students in the USA. Notable meetings of the group took place during the 36th and 41st ASMS Conferences in San Francisco, California, in 1988 and 1993, respectively. However, it was not until the 50th ASMS Conference in Orlando, Florida in 2002 that the first large gathering of Greek-origin mass spectrometrists working in USA, Canada, UK and Sweden took place and the discussion focussed on the establishment of the HMSS. Since then, annual group dinners during ASMS Conferences have been the place for sharing ideas and developing the HMSS.

The formal establishment of the HMSS was held on 17 April 2008 during a two-day international workshop on Metabolomics held at the GAIA Research Center in Athens. A five-member board with two-year tenure was elected, with the first HMSS President being Anthony Tsarbopoulos (University of Patras, Greece). Since then, the HMSS has sponsored a two-day International Workshop on Systems Biology held in Thessaloniki, Greece (2008), and a workshop on Drug Metabolism and Proteomics (2009).

Hungary

The Hungarian Chemical Society was founded by some 50 chemists under the guidance of Rudolf Fabinyi in 1907. The Mass Spectrometry Group is a division of the Hungarian Chemical Society, two of the principal Executive Committee members being Károly Vékey (Hungarian Academy of Sciences, Budapest) and Miklós Riedel (Eötvös University, Budapest).

International Mass Spectrometry Foundation (IMSF), http://www.imss.nl/

The origins of the International Mass Spectrometry Conference (IMSC) can be traced back to 1950, in which year the Institute of Petroleum in the UK held a meeting to discuss current developments in mass spectrometry.[1] This was followed in 1953 by a second conference entitled "Applied Mass Spectrometry" held at the Institute of Electrical Engineers in London, and then a further meeting in London in 1958 which was a joint affair between the Institute of Petroleum's Mass Spectrometry Panel & Hydrocarbon Research Group and the American Society for Testing and Materials (ASTM). Thereafter, the meeting was held triennially, with the next gathering in Oxford, UK, in 1961 followed by subsequent meetings in other European countries[i] (Table 8).

The venue for a subsequent IMSC was decided at a meeting of representatives from all of the national Mass Spectrometry societies which was held at the beginning of each conference, and this group of national societies comprised the International Mass Spectrometry Society. The Society was formalised in 1998 as the International Mass Spectrometry Foundation (IMSF) with the establishment of a legal framework in the Netherlands.[8] Since then, the Articles of the IMSF, the Bylaws of the IMSF and the Conference Committee Rules and Regulations have been added to the constitution. The Foundation was first constituted in Tampere, Finland, at the 14th IMSC in 1997, its first Executive Committee comprising: President: Graham Cooks (USA), Vice-President for the Conference: Emilio Gelpí (Spain), Treasurer: Nico Nibbering (Netherlands), Secretary: John MacLeod (Australia), and regional representatives: Alison Ashcroft (UK), Marcos Eberlin (Brazil), Yuzo Nakagawa (Japan). Since 2000, additional Committee members have been added: a Past-President and a Vice-President of the Society. As a Foundation, the Executive Committee is legally the IMSF Board and the Governing Committee the IMSF Affiliates, rather than the 36 member (i.e. national) societies. However, the Affiliates can advise the IMSF and make suggestions and proposals in a Meeting of Affiliates and the IMSF Board makes decisions on the basis of that input.

Figure 6. The Plenary and Keynote Speakers of the 10th International Mass Spectrometry Conference held in Swansea, UK in 1985. Courtesy of (a) "John Herbert Beynon" by Robert Boyd in *Rapid Commun. Mass Spectrom.* **18,** 1–6 (2004); Wiley Interscience, doi: 10.1002/rcm.1300. Reproduced with permission from Wiley Interscience.

The IMSF has four aims:

1) organising international conferences and workshops in mass spectrometry,
2) improving mass spectrometry education,
3) standardising terminology in the field,
4) aiding in the dissemination of mass spectrometry through publications.

The IMSC has been held on a triennial basis from 1958 to 2012 (Table 8; Figures 6 and 7). However, from 2012 the conference is going to a new format in which meetings will be held every other year. Although the name "international" correctly describes the wide coverage of the Foundation, it has been included in this Chapter because the first 18 conferences, which spanned from 1958 to 2009, were held in Europe. The following European national mass spectrometry societies are all current Affiliates of the IMSF: Austria, Belgium, Croatia, Czech Republic, Denmark, Finland, France, Germany, Hungary, Ireland, Italy, the Netherlands, Norway, Poland, Portugal, Romania, Slovakia, Slovenia, Spain, Sweden, Switzerland, and the United Kingdom.

Table 8. International Mass Spectrometry Conferences, Conference Chairs and IMSF Presidents, 1958–2014.

CONFERENCE	DATE	LOCATION AND CONFERENCE CHAIR	PRESIDENT IMSF
1st	1958	London, UK (R.R. Gordon)	
2nd	1961	Oxford, UK (R.R. Gordon)	
3rd	1964	Paris, France (R.R. Gordon, E. Roth, V.H. Dibeler, P. Laurent)	
4th	1967	Berlin, Germany (H.D. Beckey, A. Quayle, N.M. Rosenstock, E. Roth)	
5th	1970	Brussels, Belgium (P. Goldfinger, J. Kistemaker)	
6th	1973	Edinburgh, UK (A. Quayle)	
7th	1976	Florence, Italy (S. Facchetti)	
8th	1979	Oslo, Norway (O.H.J. Christie)	
9th	1982	Vienna, Austria (J.F.K. Huber)	
10th	1985	Swansea, UK (J.H. Beynon) (Figure 6)	
11th	1988	Bordeaux, France (Y. Hoppilliard)	

CONFERENCE	DATE	LOCATION AND CONFERENCE CHAIR	PRESIDENT IMSF
12th	1991	Amsterdam, The Netherlands (N.M.M. Nibbering) (Figure 7)	
13th	1994	Budapest, Hungary (I. Cornides)	
14th	1997	Tampere, Finland (H. Aldercreutz, A. Hesso)	R. Graham Cooks (USA)
15th	2000	Barcelona, Spain (E. Gelpi) (Figure 8)	Nico Nibbering (The Netherlands)
16th	2003	Edinburgh, UK (J.J. Monaghan)	John Monaghan (UK)
17th	2006	Prague, Czech Republic (Z. Herman)	John Traeger (Australia)
18th	2009	Bremen, Germany (J. Grotemeyer)	Marcos Eberlin (Brazil)
19th	2012	Kyoto, Japan (Y. Wada)	
20th	2014	Geneva, Switzerland (R. Zenobi) (N.B. joint bid by the Swiss, French and Italian MS Societies).	

Figure 7. The Organising Committee of the 12th International Mass Spectrometry Conference held in Amsterdam, The Netherlands in 1991. Courtesy of Nico Nibbering.

Figure 8. A scene from one of the busy daily poster sessions at the 15th International Mass Spectrometry Conference organised by Emilio Gelpi in Barcelona, Spain in 2000. Courtesy of Emilio Gelpi.

In practice, all IMSC conferences are organised by the national mass spectrometry society of the country in which they are located. The IMSF sponsors two distinguished and highly valued awards which are presented at the IMSC symposia (Figure 9). The Thomson Medal, named after Sir Joseph J. Thomson who was responsible for the first mass spectrograph more than 100 years ago,[9] is awarded to individuals for their "outstanding achievements in, and distinguished service to, international mass spectrometry". This medal was first presented at the 10th IMSC in Swansea, UK in 1985 (Table 9). The Curt Brunnée[10] Award, which is sponsored by Thermo Fisher Scientific, carries a research prize of US $5000. Since 1994, it has been presented to an individual "for outstanding contributions to the development of instrumentation for mass spectrometry by a person under the age of 45 at the time of the award" at each IMSC symposium from 1994 onwards (Table 10).

Table 9. Thomson Gold Medal Awardees for their "outstanding achievements in, and distinguished service to, international mass spectrometry". The Thomson Medal is awarded to one or more recipients at each IMSC symposium.

IMSC	THOMSON GOLD MEDAL AWARDEES
1985 (10th)	John H. Beynon (University of Swansea, UK) R. Graham Cooks (University of Purdue, USA) Keith R. Jennings (University of Warwick, UK) Fred W. McLafferty (Cornell University, USA) Alfred O.C. Nier (University of Minnesota, USA)
1991 (12th)	Klaus Biemann (Massachussetts Institute of Technology, USA) H. Matsuda (Osaka University, Japan) Nico M.M. Nibbering (University of Amsterdam, The Netherlands)
1994 (13th)	Curt Brunnée (Finnigan MAT, Germany) Carl Djerassi (Stanford University, USA) Helmut Schwarz (Technical University Berlin, Germany)
1997 (14th)	Michael T. Bowers (University of California Santa Barbara, USA) David E. Games (University of Swansea, UK) John F.J. Todd (University of Kent, UK)
2000 (15th)	John B. Fenn (Virginia Commonwealth University, USA) Donald F. Hunt (University of Virginia, USA) Alan G. Marshall (Florida State University, USA)
2003 (16th)	Richard B. Caprioli (Vanderbilt University, USA) Franz Hillenkamp (University of Münster, Germany) Victor L. Talrose (Russian Academy of Science, Russia)
2006 (17th)	John H. Bowie (University of Adelaide, Australia) Michael L. Gross (Washington Uni, St Louis, USA) Michael Karas (University of Münster, Germany)
2009 (18th)	Catherine E. Costello (Boston University School of Medicine, USA) Catherine C. Fenselau (University of Maryland, USA) Peter Roepstorff (University of Southern Denmark, Denmark)

Figure 9. Curt Brunnee (Atlas, Krupp, Varian, Finnigan, Thermo, Bremen). Both Curt Brunnee and Sir J.J. Thomson (see page 4) have IMSF awards named in their honour. Photo courtesy of M.C. ten Noever de Brauw, "A short story about the life of Curt Brunnée", *Rapid Commun. Mass Spectrom.* **11**, 708–713 (1997), doi: 10.1002/(SICI)1097–0231. Reproduced with permission from Wiley Interscience.

Table 10. The Curt Brunnée Award Winners. The award, which is sponsored by Thermo Fisher Scientific, carries a research prize of US $5000. It has been made "for outstanding contributions to the development of instrumentation for mass spectrometry by a person under the age of 45 at the time of the award" at each IMSC symposium from 1994 onwards.

IMSC	CURT BRUNÉE AWARD WINNER
1994 (13th)	Gareth Brenton, University of Swansea, UK
1997 (14th)	Michael Guilhaus, University of New South Wales, Australia
2000 (15th)	Scott McLuckey, Purdue University, USA
2003 (16th)	Michisato Toyoda (Osaka University, Japan)
2006 (17th)	Roman Zubarev (Uppsala University, Sweden)
2009 (18th)	Alexander Markarov (Thermo Scientific, Germany)

Irish Mass Spectrometry Society (IMSS), Ireland, http://www.imss.ie

The first Irish mass spectrometrists' meeting was held in 1987 at University College, Dublin. Following this, in September 1993, an MS Users group was established and an inaugural meeting held in May 1994, during which the Irish Mass Spectrometry Society (IMSS) was formed and a Committee established. The IMSS is a voluntary society with the aim of providing a forum for practitioners of mass spectrometry in Ireland. The Society is run by a committee elected every two years and aims to hold one full-day scientific meeting and another half-day event each year. The Society was reactivated in 2007 following a dormant period from 2003 to 2007.

Divisione di Spettrometria di Massa (DSM), La Società Chimica Italiana (SCI), Italy, http://www.soc.chim.it/divisioni/spettrometria_di_massa

The first Italian Mass Spectrometrists' Congress was organised in April 1968 at Euratom's Joint Research Centre in Ispra (Varese) by Dr Sergio Facchetti. More than 50 scientists attended and the main topics included ionisation phenomena, gas chromatography-mass spectrometry coupling and inorganic solids. Mass spectrometry had been introduced in Italy some years prior to this and the first mass spectrometer built there in 1949 by Giorgio

Careri.[11] In September 1971, the second Mass Spectrometry Congress took place in the same location, when a group of pioneers from industry and academia founded the Group of Mass Spectrometry within the Italian Chemical Society specifically for the dissemination of theoretical, instrumental and applications knowledge. Those pioneers included: P. Capella, S. Facchetti, A. Frigerio, G. Galli, S. Pignataro, A. Selva and L. Zerilli.

The third Mass Spectrometry Congress moved to central Italy in April 1974 at the Italian National Institute of Health (Istituto Superiore di Sanità) in Rome, and in 1976, Sergio Facchetti, the first President of the Group of Mass Spectrometry, hosted the 7th IMSC in Florence. In 1985 the "Group of Mass Spectrometry" became the "Division of Mass Spectrometry" (DSM) of the Italian Chemical Society, under the Presidency of Antonio Malorni. The "Mass Spectrometry Congresses" continued with triannual meetings until 1987. From 1991, the series of "Congresses of Mass Spectrometry" became known as "MASSA" and since then have been held on an annual basis. The new series was opened by "MASSA 91" organised in L'Aquila (Table 11). MASSA 2008 was held jointly with the Société Française de Spectrométrie de Masse, the Société Française de Chimie and the Universities of Siena and Pierre et Marie Curie, Paris, as the 1st French–Italian Conference on Mass Spectrometry, thus constituting an example of co-operation among MS societies of different countries.

Table 11. Presidents (1975–2010) and Conferences (1968–2010) of the Group/Division of Mass Spectrometry (DSM) of the Italian Chemical Society.

PRESIDENT	DATES	CONFERENCE	LOCATION
		1st (1968)	Ispra
		2nd (1971)	Ispra
		3rd (1974)	Rome
Sergio Facchetti	1975–1977	4th (1977)	Catania
Antonio Selva	1978–1980	5th (1980)	Rende
Nicola Uccella	1980–1982	6th (1983)	Sorrento
Antonio Malorni	1984–1986	7th (1986)	Torino
Gian Angelo Vaglio	1987–1989		
Sergio Daolio	1990–1992	MASSA 91 MASSA 92	L'Aquila Milan
Giovanni Galli	1993–1995	MASSA 93 MASSA 95	Ischia Palermo
Giovanni Sindona	1996–1998	MASSA 96 MASSA 97 MASSA 98	Siena Urbino Arcavacata di Rende
Francesco De Angelis	1999–2001	MASSA 99 MASSA 2001	Siena Elba Island
Lorenza Operti	2002–2004	MASSA 2002 MASSA 2004	Cetraro Bari
Leopoldo Ceraulo	2005–2007	MASSA 2005 MASSA 2007	Rome Lucca
Gianluca Giorgi	2008–2010	MASSA 2008 MASSA 2010	Siena Milan

In 1983 a series of "Meetings of the Mass Spectrometry Group, Area North/East Italy" was initiated in Padova by Pietro Traldi (CNR). From the sixth of these annual meetings, the conferences became known as the "Informal Meeting on Mass Spectrometry" and their organisation was extended to the Hungarian Academy of Sciences. From then, the meetings were held alternatively in Italy and in Hungary, until 1997, when other Eastern European countries became involved. These meetings, held in a friendly environment often without a prefixed agenda, have been an important contribution to the spread and diffusion of mass spectrometry in Italy.

Owing to the wide interest in mass spectrometry in the pharmaceutical arena, the "1st MS-Pharmaday" congress was organised by Gianluca Giorgi (Università di Siena) in 1993 in Siena. This was followed by two further meetings in the same location which were combined with the MASSA conferences of 1996 and 1999. Other "MS-Pharmaday" meetings have been organised by pharmaceutical companies [Parma, 2006 (Chiesi Farmaceutici) and Verona 2008 (GSK)] whilst the sixth such meeting was combined with MASSA 2010 in Milan.

An "MS-FoodDay" series of meetings, devoted to the application of mass spectrometry to food chemistry, was established in Parma in 2009, and the second event will be held in Trieste in 2011. The "1st MS-EnviDay", focussing on mass spectrometry and the environment, was organised by the DSM and the "Regional Agency of Prevention and Environment" (ARPA) in Bologna in 2011.

The DSM has organised MS schools and courses from 1987 to 2006, including the "School of interpretation of mass spectra" ("Scuola di interpretazione degli spettri di massa") in addition to an advanced course in GC-MS from 1989 until 2004, and a series of LC-MS courses initiated in Pisa in 1994 by Andrea Raffaelli (CNR-Istituto di Chimica dei Composti Organo Metallici-Sezione di Pisa, Pisa) which is still running. The "Corso di Spettrometria di Massa per Dottorandi di Ricerca" ("Mass spectrometry course for PhD Students") was initiated by Francesco De Angelis (Ingegneria Chimica e Materiali, Universita' dell'Aquila) in 1997. This residential course is held at the Certosa di Pontignano in Siena every year and is attended by 70–100 delegates from universities, public and private institutions and companies. The course comprises a general introduction to mass spectrometry, covering all aspects, and the 15th such course will be held in March 2011.

Over the years, the DSM has instituted several awards and medals, including the DSM-SCI "Award for Research" for outstanding results in the international community of mass spectrometry. Recipients have included Giula de Petris (Sapienza University, Rome, 2002) Giorgio Montaudo (University of Catania, 2003). There is also the DSM-SCI "Award for Activity" for scientists who have contributed significantly to the development and promotion of mass spectrometry and the awardees to date have been Gloriano Moneti and Giuseppe Pieraccini (CISM Università di Firenze, 2002), Silvio Garattini (Instituto di Ricerche Farmacologiche Mario Negri, 2003), Pietro

Traldi (CNR Padova, 2004), Giorgio Giacomo Mellerio (Università di Pavia, 2005), Gianluca Giorgio (Università di Siena, 2006), Sergio Pucci and Andrea Raffaelli (Lab. Spettr. Massa CNR, Pisa, 2007) and Francesco De Angelis (Universita La Sapienza, Rome, 2008).

Since 2002 the DSM has instituted the "Fabrizio Bruner" medal in memory of Professor Fabrizio Bruner,[12] who is renowned for his successes in interfacing chromatography to mass spectrometry. The medal is awarded to Italian scientists as recognition of their contribution to the development of mass spectrometry in Italy. The winners have included Antonio Selva (2002), Luigi Zerilli (2003), Salvatore Pignataro (2004), Alessandro Ballio, Gennaro Marino and Antonio Malorni (2005), and Gian Angelo Vaglio (2006). The DSM also recognises achievements by young researchers in the field of mass spectrometry: in 2000 the "DSM-SCI awards for young researchers in mass spectrometry" was established and since 2007 mobility fellowships for young researchers have been awarded to enable them to carry out research in other Italian or overseas mass spectrometry groups.

De Nederlandse Vereniging voor Massaspectrometrie (NVMS), The Netherlands, http://www.denvms.nl/

The Nederlandse Vereniging voor Massaspectrometrie (NVMS), or the Dutch Society of Mass Spectrometry, was founded as a Mass Spectrometry Discussion Group (MSDG) on 26 February 1964 by Piet van der Haak and Henk Hofman from the Laboratory of Organic Chemistry, University of Amsterdam, out of the Chemical Society Infrared Discussion Group (Table 12). In 1964, the MSDG had 38 members from the universities of Amsterdam, Utrecht, Leiden and Eindhoven, R&D institutes such as FOM-AMOLF and TNO, and industrial R&D laboratories including Shell, DSM, Philips, Polak Frutel and the uranium enrichment factory, UCN. In 1992, the MSDG was renamed as the NVMS and became a sub-section of both the Royal Dutch Chemical Society and the Dutch Physics Society. However, in legal terms the NVMS is an independent association having its own board, voting members, annual business meetings and financial reports. The NVMS board consists of a President, a Secretary, a Treasurer and two programme committee members (currently, 2011) Michel Nielen, Sander Koster, Rob Vreeken, Henk Dekker and Maurien Olsthoorn, respectively). Nico Nibbering,[13] the NVMS President from 1974 to 1976, went on to become the second President of the International Mass Spectrometry Foundation (2000–2003). The NVMS now has >600 registered members and sponsors a fund to enable scientists to attend conferences.

Table 12. Presidents of the Dutch Society of Mass Spectrometry, 1964–2010.

DATE ELECTED	PRESIDENT
1964	Piet van der Haak, University of Amsterdam
1971	Peter Korver, Duphar
1972	Bert Schram, Unilever
1974	Nico Nibbering, University of Amsterdam
1976	Henk van't Klooster, University of Utrecht
1977	Johannes de Ridder, Organon
1979	Rowald Neeter, NIZO
1981	Piet Leclercq, TU Eindhoven
1983	Mike ten Noever de Brauw, TNO Nutrition Zeist
1997	Andries Bruins, State University of Groningen
2001	Ron Heeren, FOM Institute AMOLF, Amsterdam
2006	Eric van Beelen, Waters, Eindhoven
2006–current	Michel Nielen, Wageningen University

Every fifth year the NVMS organises a two-day international conference on mass spectrometry. The most recent meeting was in 2009 to celebrate the 45th anniversary of the Society when the conference was co-organised with the Belgian Society for Mass Spectrometry. Several of these events have been organised at the Rolduc venue, a former monastery in the southern part of the country. Thanks to the remote and serene location, and the informal atmosphere for discussing mass spectrometry, these "Rolduc-meetings" have become very popular.

Norsk Selskap for Massespektrometri—NSMS (Norwegian Society for Mass Spectrometry) Norway, http://www.nsms.no/

The Norsk Selskap for Massespektrometri (NSMS) (Norwegian Society for Mass Spectrometry) was founded on 6 April 1973 in Oslo. The initiative was taken by Olav Christie, Georg Hvistendahl, Egil Jellum, Einar Solheim and Jon Pettersen, the latter becoming the first President. The NSMS now has >350 members and its goal is to provide a forum for all who are interested in mass spectrometry which it achieves by organising an annual Winter Meeting as well as a MS Users' Meeting (Table 13). The NSMS also co-organises the Nordic Mass Spectrometry meetings.

Table 13. Presidents and Conferences of the Norwegian Society for Mass Spectrometry, 1973–2011.

PRESIDENT	DATE OF OFFICE	WINTER MEETING IN MS	MS USERS' MEETING
Jon Pettersen	1973–1975		
Georg Hvistendahl	1975–1977		
Georg Hvistendahl	1977–1979		
Georg Hvistendahl	1979–1981		
Arne Stabel	1981–1983	1st meeting 1982	

PRESIDENT	DATE OF OFFICE	WINTER MEETING IN MS	MS USERS' MEETING
Arne Stabel	1983–1985	2nd meeting 1984	
Arne Stabel	1985–1987	3rd meeting 1986	
Arne Stabel	1987–1989	4th meeting 1987	
Einar Uggerud	1989–1991	5th meeting 1991	
Einar Uggerud	1991–1993		
Einar Uggerud	1993–1995	6th meeting 1993	
Einar Solheim	1995–1997	7th meeting 1995	1st meeting 1995
Einar Solheim	1997–1999	8th meeting 1997	2nd meeting 1998
Einar Solheim	1999–2001	9th meeting 1999	3rd meeting 1999 4th meeting 2000
Einar Solheim	2001–2003		5th meeting 2001 6th meeting 2002
Dag Ekeberg	2003–2005	10th meeting 2003	7th meeting 2003 8th meeting 2004
Dag Ekeberg	2005–2007	11th meeting 2005	9th meeting 2006
Dag Ekeberg	2007–2009	12th meeting 2007	
Dag Ekeberg	2009–2011	13th meeting 2009	10th meeting 2010
		14th meeting 2011	

Rede Nacional de Espectrometria de Massa Portugal (RNEM) (Portuguese Mass Spectrometry Society), Portugal, http://rnem.fc.ul.pt/

Mass spectrometry has recently been consolidated in Portugal through equipment programmes and more recently with the establishment of the Portuguese Mass Spectrometry Network, Rede Nacional de Espectrometria de Massa Portugal (RNEM). After a period of dormancy (the 3rd Portuguese MS meeting was held in 1997) the 4th Portuguese MS meeting was held in Lisbon at the end of 2010 with the mission of bringing together all researchers working on this field in Portugal, to encourage the presentation of cutting edge research and to stimulate scientific discussion and co-operation opportunities. The first RNEM course on "Protein Identification by Mass Spectrometry" was held at the beginning of 2010.

Conferences organised by the MS group of the Portuguese Chemical Society took place in the 1990s: the first meeting was held in 1993 at the University of Aveiro followed by a second meeting at the University of Lisbon in 1995 and a third in 1997 organised by the Faculty of Science and Technology of the New University of Lisbon at the Water Museum in Lisbon.

Sociedad Española de Espectrometría de Masas (Spanish Society of Mass Spectrometry) (SEEM), Spain, http://www.e-seem.org/

The Sociedad Española de Espectrometría de Masas (SEEM) is a society constituted to facilitate communication between scientists involved in all aspects of organic, inorganic and biological mass spectrometry. The roots of SEEM can be traced back to the local Group of Mass Spectrometry in Barcelona which was created in 1992 during the annual meeting of the Group of Chromatography & Related Technologies, a division of the Real Spanish Society of Chemistry in Granada. This local Group celebrated its first meeting in 1993 in Barcelona, which was organised by Damiá Barceló (Chemical and Environmental Research Institute of Barcelona) and Emilio Gelpí (Instituto de Investigaciones Biomédicas de Barcelona) under the sponsorship of the Generalitat de Catalunya, Fisons Instruments, Varian and the Group of Chromatography & Related Technologies (Table 14).

Barcelona was also the venue for the three International Symposia on Applied Mass Spectrometry in the Health Sciences, organised by Emilio Gelpi in 1987, 1990 and 1995 (Table 14; Figure 10) and also for the 15th IMSC meeting in 2000, which was also organised by Gelpi (Figure 8).

The constitution of the SEEM was proposed in 1997 by Emilio Gelpí and formalised at a meeting the following year organised by Gelpí and Teresa Galcerán (University of Barcelona). An Executive Committee with a President, Secretary, Treasurer and a minimum of five other Committee members was approved. The first President was Emilio Gelpí (1998–2006) and the second and current President is Damià Barceló (2006-). The current membership of SEEM is ~200.

SEEM held its first conference, the Reunión Nacional de Espectrometría de Masas, in Madrid in 2002, the second in Barcelona in 2004, the third in Oviedo in 2006 and the fourth in Castellon in 2009[14] (Table 14). In addition to this, four out of six highly successful annual workshops on LC-Tandem mass spectrometry for Environmental Applications and Food Safety have been held in Spain (Barcelona 2005 and 2006; Guelph 2007; Barcelona

Figure 10. A panel of experts at the 3rd International Symposium on Applied Mass Spectrometry in the Health Sciences in Barcelona, Spain in 1995. Left to right: Simon Gaskell (UK), Emilio Gelpi (Conference Organiser, Spain) and Peter Derrick (UK). Courtesy of Emilio Gelpi.

2008; Toronto 2009; Barcelona 2010).[15] A summary of the varied and numerous conferences organised in Spain is shown in Table 14.

Table 14. MS Conferences held in Spain, 1987–2010.

DATE	SYMPOSIUM	LOCATION
1987	1st International Symposium on Applied MS in the Health Sciences	Barcelona
1990	2nd International Symposium on Applied MS in the Health Sciences	Barcelona
1993	1st Meeting Local MS Group of Barcelona	Barcelona
1994	2nd Meeting Local MS Group of Barcelona	Barcelona
1995	3rd International Symposium on Applied MS in the Health Sciences	Barcelona
1995	3rd Meeting Local MS Group of Barcelona	Barcelona
1997	4th Meeting Local MS Group of Barcelona	Barcelona
1998	5th Meeting Local MS Group of Barcelona	Barcelona
2000	6th Meeting Local MS Group of Barcelona	Barcelona
2000	15th IMSC, Barcelona	Barcelona
2002	1st Reunión Nacional de Espectrometría de Masas	Madrid
2002	7th Meeting Local MS Group of Barcelona	Barcelona
2004	2nd Reunión Nacional de Espectrometría de Masas	Barcelona
2005	1st International Workshop on LC-MS/MS for Screening and Trace Levels Quantitation in Environmental and Food Samples	Barcelona
2006	2nd International Workshop on LC-MS/MS for Screening and Trace Levels Quantitation in Environmental and Food Samples	Barcelona
2006	3rd Reunión Nacional de Espectrometría de Masas	Orviedo
2007	1st Workshop de la Sociedad Española de Espectrometría de Masas	Granada
2008	4th International Workshop on LC-MS/MS for Screening and Trace Levels Quantitation in Environmental and Food Samples	Barcelona
2009	4th Reunión Nacional de Espectrometría de Masas	Castellon
2010	6th International Workshop on LC-MS/MS for Screening and Trace Levels Quantitation in Environmental and Food Samples	Barcelona

Svenska Masspektrometrisallskapet (Swedish Mass Spectrometry Society, SMSS) Sweden, http://www.smss.se/

Prior to the formation of the Svenska Masspektrometrisallskapet (SMSS), or the Swedish Mass Spectrometry Society, mass spectrometry research was presented at meetings held by other societies in Sweden. For example, mass spectrometry featured at the Swedish Biochemical Society's meetings in Uppsala in 1958 and 1964, at the Biochemistry of Lipids meeting in Stockholm in 1963 and at an EMBO workshop in Applied Mass Spectrometry at the Karolinska Institutet in Stockholm in 1969. The Swedish involvement in mass spectrometry goes back much further than this, however; for example, the Karolinska Institute has hosted one of the earliest mass spectrometry laboratories in Europe since 1944.[16]

At the 5th Nordic Mass Spectrometry Conference in Finland in 1983, it was decided that the following Nordic Conference should be held in Sweden in 1986 which prompted the need to establish an organising committee. Upon the initiative of Birgitta Sjöquist and Jan Sjövall (both from the Karolinska Institutet), a Swedish Mass Spectrometry Club was established in 1984 under the auspices of the Analytical Section of the Swedish Chemical Society, with a steering committee consisting of Gunnar Bergström (Goteborg University), Ingemar Björkhem (representing the Board of the Analytical Section of the Swedish Chemical Society), Curt Enzell (Swedish Tobacco Company), Bengt Karlsson (the Swedish Chemical Society), Birgitta Sjöqvist and Jan Sjövall.

The first meeting organised by the MS Club was a workshop in Stockholm in November 1985 entitled "Soft ionization methods and LC/MS". 150 participants attended and lectures were given by Marvin Vestal (thermospray LC/MS), Peter Roepstorff (a comparison of FAB and plasma desorption MS for peptide analysis) and Patrick Arpino (evaluation of LC-MS compared with GC-MS). After the 6th Nordic MS conference in 1986, the SMSS organised a mini-symposium at the "Analysdagarna" meeting (the Analytical Days of the Chemical Society) in Lund the following year. The first Annual Meeting was held at the Royal School of Technology in Stockholm in 1988, at which Bergström, Enzell, Sjövall, and Christoffer Rappe (University of Umeå) were elected as board members. Further annual meetings were held in 1989 and 1990. At the latter conference, which was held in Gothenburg, it was decided that the MS Club should form a separate section within the Swedish Chemical Society. This took place later that year. In 1991, a spring meeting entitled "Liquid chromatography/mass spectrometry-current status and future trends" was arranged by Claes Lindberg (Draco) in Lund, and a fall meeting of the Swedish MS Club was arranged by Bo Sundqvist (Uppsala University) in Uppsala. In 1992, the Annual Meeting was held at the offices of the Swedish Chemical Society.

1993 was also a busy year, with the Annual Meeting at Kabi Pharmacia in Stockholm and an autumn meeting on "Biomedical Applications of Mass Spectrometry" arranged in November. The board of the MS Club then consisted of Lindberg, Markides, Sjövall, Bengt Norén (Pharmacia) and Bo Samuelsson (Goteborg University). In 1994, the Annual Meeting was held at the Karolinska Institutet at which Leif Bertilsson (Karolinska Institutet) and Carl-Axel Nilsson (Chemical Unit in Umeå) were elected new members of the board succeeding Enzell and Markides. It was during this year that the MS Club introduced an annual membership fee of 30 SEK. In 1995, the Annual Meeting was held in Gothenburg in connection with the meeting "KEMI 95". In the same year, a Symposium entitled "Impact of Biomedical Mass Spectrometry" in the "Frontiers in Medicine" series at Nobel Forum was arranged by members from the Karolinska Institutet.

In 1996, the MS Club held both its Annual Meeting and a mini symposium in Lund and also co-organised a conference with the Swedish Academy of Pharmaceutical Sciences entitled "Mass spectrometry in pharmaceutical research and development". 1997 brought the Annual Meeting to Huddinge Hospital, Stockholm and the EUCHEM-Conference: "Mass Spectrometry in Biology" was held at Hindås, some 30 km east of Gothenburg surrounded by forest and close to the beautiful lake Västra Nedsjön.

The 1998 Annual Meeting was held in Gothenburg. The major activity that year, however, was the 10th Nordic Conference on Mass Spectrometry which took place in Umeå. In the following year the Annual Meeting was held at the Karolinska Institutet. This year saw the MS Club change its name to the Swedish Society for Mass Spectrometry (SMSS) and Markides succeeded Samuelsson as Chairman. In 2000, the Annual Meeting was held at Astra Zeneca in Lund, in 2001 at Uppsala and in 2002 at Stockholm University.

In 2003, the Annual Meeting was held in Gothenburg. Due to competition with other meetings in the field of chemistry, there was no Annual Meeting in 2004 but in 2005 the meeting was held at the Royal Academy of Sciences, Stockholm. Stockholm has been the location for subsequent Annual Meetings until 2009. In 2010, SMSS arranged both the 14th Nordic MS Conference and the Annual Meeting in Uppsala. At the latter, it was decided that the board should consist of seven members and subsequently the board comprised Gunnar Hansson (Goteberg University) as Chairman, Jonas Bergquist (Uppsala University), Leopold Ilag (Karolinska Institutet), Niclas Karlsson (Goteborg University), Elke Schweda (Karolinska Institutet), Roman Zubarev (Karolinska Institutet), Patrik Önnerfjord (Lund University) and Jan Sjövall (honorary member).

The SMSS has members from the fields of chemistry, medicine, pharmacy, pulp and paper, environment, biology, and physics, based within universities/colleges, companies, institutes, hospitals and governmental laboratories. In addition to national conferences, the SMSS has hosted the international Nordic Mass Spectrometry Conference regularly over the years (see Table 16) and also the Uppsala Conference (UPPCON). UPPCON was first organised in 2003 on a boat trip between Stockholm (Sweden) and Helsinki (Finland) by Roman Zubarev (Uppsala University), a co-founder of the electron capture dissociation method of structural elucidation. Since then this Conference, with its objective of providing a forum for scientists to exchange views and ideas on the scientific development of the electron capture and electron transfer dissociation mass spectrometry, has moved to Scotland, UK (2004), Seattle, USA (2005), Hong Kong (2006), Paris (2007), Madison, USA (2008), Nara, Japan (2009) and is next being organised in Villars-sur-Ollon, Switzerland (2011).

Schweizerische Gruppe für Massenspektrometrie, Groupe suisse de spectrométrie de masse, Gruppo svizzero di spettrometria di massa (Swiss Group for Mass Spectrometry, SGMS), Switzerland, http://www.sgms.ch/

The formation of the Swiss Group for Mass Spectrometry (SGMS) dates back to the early 1980s.[17] In November 1981, Hubert Milon, working at the Nestlé Research Center in Orbe, Switzerland, proposed to form "a group which would permit an exchange of experience and ideas when facing a technical problem, when confronted with the need to purchase a new instrument, or implement a new technique". Thus, the incentive to form the SGMS was the creation of an informal association with a very broad range of applications. The founding document was signed by Hans Brandenberger (University of Zurich), Armand Buchs (University of Geneva), Wilhelm Richter (Ciba-Geigy), Bruno Willhalm (Firmenich) and Hubert Milon (Nestec). The following year, in 1982, the first general assembly of this new society was held at Urs Schlunegger's laboratory in the Institute of Organic Chemistry at

Figure 11. Four past presidents from the Swiss Group for Mass Spectrometry, together at the 25th Anniversary meeting in Beatenberg, Switzerland in 2008. From left to right: Laurent Fay (Nestlé, Lausanne), Andreas Stämpfli (Syngenta, Basel) Marc Suter Federal Institute of Aquatic Science and Technology, Dübendorf) and Urs Schlunegger (University of Bern). Courtesy of the Swiss Group for Mass Spectrometry (http://www.sgms. ch/).

the University of Bern. The 35 participants consolidated the first statutes of the SGMS and elected the first committee, with Milon as President, Schlunegger as Vice-President, Richter as Treasurer, and Laurent Rivier (University of Lausanne) and P. Weibel as auditors. Further members of the Committee at this time were Brandenberger, Buchs and Willhalm.

As Switzerland recognises four official languages: German, French, Italian and Romantsch, English was chosen as the official language for the meetings of the SGMS. Accordingly, the first "SGMS Newsletter", which has appeared two to three times per year from 1983 onwards, was published in English. However, in 1983 the statutes of the SGMS appeared with French and German translations, and the name of the Society was fixed in four languages. In 1995, the SGMS became an associated member society of the New Swiss Chemical Society (NSCS), which in turn had been founded in 1992 from the Swiss Chemical Society and the Association of Swiss Chemists. At present, the SGMS has some 180 members.

From 1983 until 1999 the SGMS held the majority of its annual conferences on the Rigi Mountain, high above Lake Lucerne in the heart of Switzerland, and hence the meeting is often referred to as "The Rigi-meeting". However, for the 10-year jubilee in 1992, the conference was held at the Ecole Polytechnique Fédérale in Lausanne, hosted by the then president Daniel Stahl (Swiss Federal Institute of Technology). Since 2002 all meetings have been held in Beatenberg, above Lake Thun. The 10th (1992), 20th (2002) and 25th (2007) anniversary meetings were special occasions celebrated with additional speakers and special social programmes. The photograph of the 25th Anniversary meeting held in 2007 is shown in Figure 11.

International meetings held in Switzerland have included the 8th Uppsala Conference (UPPCON) on electron capture and transfer dissociation in Les Diablerets, Switzerland, in

2011, the 9th European FTMS Workshop in Lausanne in 2010, and numerous LC-MS symposia at Montreux.

OTHER MASS SPECTROMETRY MEETINGS HELD IN EUROPE

European Fourier Transform Mass Spectrometry Workshop

The European Fourier Transform Mass Spectrometry Workshop has been held every two to four years throughout Europe since 1991 (Table 15).

Table 15. The European Fourier Transform Mass Spectrometry Workshop (1991–2010).

DATE	ORGANISER	LOCATION
1991	Hans Friedrich Grützmacher	Bielefeld, Germany
1993	Luc van Vaeck	Antwerp, Belgium
1995	Karl Peter Wanczek	Bremen, Germany
1997	Jean-Francois Muller and Gilles Ohanessian	Pont à Mousson, France
1999	Peter Derrick	Coventry, UK
2001	Ron Heeren	Kerkrade, The Netherlands
2004	Michael Przybylski	Konstanz, Germany
2008	Eugene Nikolaev	Moscow, Russia
2010	Yury Tsybin and Renato Zenobi	Lausanne, Switzerland
2012	Peter O'Connor	Coventry, UK

Montreux LC-MS Meeting

The Montreux LC/MS Symposia, which take the form of workshops on LC-MS and Tandem MS, have Dutch roots as well as Swiss: this series of meetings, which was founded by the late Roland Frei (Free University of Amsterdam) in 1980 and are still organised biannually by Jan van der Greef (TNO and Leiden University), are held in Montreux, Switzerland.

The Montreux LC/MS symposium focusses on LC/MS and all related hyphenated technologies including important aspects of application challenges such as sample pre-treatment, separation technologies and novel software/bioinformatics approaches. Introductory courses are held to introduce newcomers to LC/MS. The conference also hosts a large exhibition.

The Nordic Mass Spectrometry Conference

This is an international meeting held every three years which has been organised and hosted in turn by the four Nordic mass spectrometry societies (Table 16), starting from the early 1970s.

Table 16. Dates and venues of the Nordic Mass Spectrometry Conference (1971–2013).

NUMBER	DATE	LOCATION
1	1975	Sandefjord, Norway
2	1976	Sandefjord, Norway
3	1977	?
4	1980	Vejle, Denmark
5	1983	Finland
6	1986	Borgholm, Sweden
7	1989	Geilo, Norway
8	1992	Helsingor, Denmark
9	1995	Turku, Finland
10	1998	Umeå, Sweden
11	2001	Leon, Norway
12	2004	Nyborg, Denmark
13	2007	Savonlinna, Finland
14	2010	Uppsala, Sweden
15	2013	Norway

Summer Course on Mass Spectrometry in Biotechnology and Medicine, Dubrovnik, Croatia, http://www.msbm.org/

This course, which has been held in 2001, 2007, 2009 and 2010 in Dubrovnik, Croatia focusses on "teaching and discussing modern knowledge in mass spectrometry to advanced graduate students, post docs and scientists in the area of biochemistry, biology, molecular biology, biotechnology and medicine" (http://www.msbm.org/). The meetings, which are held in the Centre for Advanced Academic Studies in Dubrovnik, are attended typically by over 120 scientists and topics are presented by distinguished lecturers from Europe, Asia and the USA. The conference organising committees over the years have included Jasna Peter-Katalinić (Munster University, Germany), Ljiljana Paša-Tolić, (Richland, WA, USA), David Goodlett (University of Washington, WA, USA), Laura Bindila (Munster University, Germany), Michael Mormann (Munster University, Germany), Mario Cindrić (Rudjer Bošković Institute, Zagreb) and Gary Corthals (Turku Centre for Biotechnology, Finland). The next conference is planned for summer 2011.

Informal Meeting on Mass Spectrometry (IMMS)

As mentioned under the Italian Society for Mass Spectrometry's history, a series of "Meetings of the Mass Spectrometry Group, Area North/East Italy" was initiated in Padova by Pietro Traldi (CNR Instituto di Scienze e Tecnologie Molecolari, Padova) in 1983. From the sixth meeting onwards, the conferences became known as the "Informal Meeting on Mass Spectrometry" and the further meetings were co-organised with the Hungarian Academy of Sciences. From 1997, other Eastern European countries have been involved (Table 17). The aims of the Informal Mass Spectrometry Meetings are to focus on research in mass spectrometry and provide an opportunity for young scientists to present their work. The number of delegates attending these conferences is usually ~120.

The 14th in this series of informal meetings was held in Padua in 1996 and was organised jointly by the mass spectrometry groups of the Consiglio Nazionale delle Ricerche, Area di Ricerca di Padova, Italy and the Central Research Institute of Chemistry of the Hungarian Academy of Sciences, Budapest. In 2009, the 27th Informal Meeting was held for the first time in Retz, Lower Austria, and was organised by Günther Allmaier, Martina Marchetti-Deschmann and Ernst Pittenauer from the Austrian Mass Spectrometry Society and brought together scientists from Central and Eastern Europe.

Table 17. Dates and venues of the Informal Meeting on Mass Spectrometry from **1983 to 2010**.

NUMBER	DATE	LOCATION
1st	1983	Italy
2nd	1984	Italy
3rd	1985	Italy
4th	1986	Italy
5th	1987	Italy
6th	1988	Budapest, Hungary
7th	1989	Padova, Italy
8th	1990	Padova, Italy
9th	1991	Budapest, Hungary
10th	1992	Padova, Italy
11th	1993	Budapest, Hungary
12th	1994	Pordenone, Italy
13th	1995	Budapest, Hungary
14th	1996	Padua, Italy
15th	1997	Smolenice, Slovakia
16th	1998	Budapest, Hungary
17th	1999	Fiera di Primiero, Italy
18th	2000	Prague, Czech Republic
19th	2001	Noszvaj, Hungary
20th	2002	Fiera di Primiero, Italy
21st	2003	Antwerp, Netherlands
22nd	2004	Tokaj, Hungary
23rd	2005	Fiera di Primiero, Italy
24th	2006	Ustroń, Poland
25th	2007	Nyíregyháza-Sóstó, Hungary
26th	2008	Fiera di Primiero, Italy
27th	2009	Retz, Austria
28th	2010	Koszeg, Hungary

NATO Schools on Mass Spectrometry

A number of NATO Schools on mass spectrometry and ion chemistry were held every four years at various European locations. The first was in 1974 at Biarritz, France, followed by one in 1978 at La Baule, France, then in 1982 at Vimeiro, Portugal, in 1986 at Les Arcs, France, in 1990 at Mont Ste Odile, France and finally, one year late, in 1995 at Garmisch-Partenkirchen, Germany. The organising committee comprised Pierre Ausloos and Sharon Lias (both of NBS, Washington), Rose Marx (Université de Paris-Sud, France), Hans-Friedrich Grützmacher (Universität Bielefeld, Germany), Nico Nibbering (University of Amsterdam, Netherlands), Maurizio Speranza (Università di Roma "La Sapienza", Italy) and Keith Jennings (University of Warwick, UK). The subject matter covered both analytical mass spectrometry and ion–molecule reactions including some aspects of radiation chemistry and the Schools had as their objective the instruction of students from any European country. Lecturers came from both North America and Europe and the number of students was limited to 90. The meetings allowed many young mass spectrometrists the opportunity to meet well-known academics. A book containing the lectures and a summary of workshop discussions was published after each School and all students received a copy.

THE HISTORY OF JOURNALS ORIGINATING IN EUROPE

One of the issues in the 1960s was that there was no obvious journal suitable for publication of specialised mass spectrometry papers. The feeling was that some journals were not interested in "technique" manuscripts and that gas-phase ion chemistry was not considered "proper" chemistry by others. It was against this background that Gunter Heyden of Heyden & Son was persuaded by Allan Maccoll to launch the journal *Organic Mass Spectrometry* (*OMS*). The first *OMS* Editor-in-Chief (1968–1989) was Allan Maccoll (UK) followed by Peter Derrick (UK) who took over from 1990 to 1993. However, although *OMS* aimed to publish any paper on mass spectrometry, physical chemists felt that this journal did not really cater for them and this led Elsevier to launch the *International Journal of Mass Spectrometry and Ion Physics* (*IJMSIP*) with Harry Svec as the North American editor and Alan Quayle the UK editor. Thus, *OMS* and *IJMSIP* started simultaneously in 1968.

Heyden started a second mass spectrometry-focussed journal, named *Biological Mass Spectrometry* (*BMS*), which was aimed at the rapidly emerging life science applications at the time. *BMS* spanned two decades, from 1974 to 1994, also being called *Biomedical and Environmental Mass Spectrometry* (*BEMS*); its first Editors were Brian Millard (UK) and Catherine Fenselau (USA) (1974–1980), who were followed by Catherine Fenselau and Dai Games (UK) (1981–1989), and finally Richard Caprioli (USA) (1990–1994) alone. *International Journal of Mass Spectrometry and Ion Physics* became *International Journal of Mass Spectrometry and Ion Processes* in 1983 and finally *International Journal of Mass Spectrometry* in 1998.

In 1982, the scientific journals and books of Heyden were bought by John Wiley & Sons Ltd and incorporated into the Wiley operation. In 1994, Wiley decided to subsume *OMS* and *BMS* into the *Journal of Mass Spectrometry* (1995–current), with Richard Caprioli (USA) as Editor (1995–current). *European Mass Spectrometry* (*EMS*), published by IM Publications, also arose from the ashes of those two popular, early journals, thanks to the determination of Allan Maccoll (UK). The first issue of EMS was published in 1995 with Peter Derrick (UK) as Editor-in-Chief (1995–current). EMS made a small change to its title in 2000, becoming the European Journal of Mass Spectrometry (EJMS).

Rapid Communications in Mass Spectrometry (RCM) was the brain-child of John Beynon (UK)[3] who pushed for the launch of a journal which could publish high quality research manuscripts quickly. The journal began publication in 1987, with Beynon as its founding Editor-in-Chief. Interestingly, this was published by Heyden, now freed from anti-compete restrictions following the earlier sale to Wiley. However, after a few years (in 1992) RCM was sold, along with a few other analytical journals, to Wiley. In 1997, Bob Boyd (Canada)[18] took over the role of Editor-in-Chief until 2005, when the current Editor-in-Chief, John Monaghan (UK), was established. In 2004, to mark the 80th birthday of John Beynon, John Wiley & Sons established an annual award named the "RCM Beynon Prize". This award (US $1000) is bestowed annually on the corresponding author(s) of a paper published during the two preceding two calendar years that describes an innovative advance in MS instrumentation or methodology that has had the greatest immediate impact in its particular sub-discipline.

Of course, many well-known text-books have been published from the European continent. There are far too many to write about in any detail, but a selection of key publications over the years must be mentioned. For example, the seminal works from John Beynon and co-workers in the UK on the applications of MS to organic chemistry,[19] and the tables of masses[20] and metastable transitions.[21]

Also deserving mention are the early books from Germany by Hans Beckey (Bonn University) describing the fundamentals behind Field Ionisation and Field Desorption[22,23] and also one by Karsten Levsen (also from the University of Bonn) on the "Fundamental aspects of organic mass spectrometry".[24]

A classic French text is that by Pierre Longevialle on the principles of the mass spectrometry of organic compounds[25] and the ever popular and useful texts of the British mass spectrometrists John Chapman (Kratos Analytical)[26–28] and Dudley Williams (University of Cambridge).[29]

OMS—ORGANIC MASS SPECTROMETRY

by Gunter Heyden

It all started when Tommy Cairns joined Heyden & Son shortly after having received his doctorate from Glasgow University now exactly 50 years ago. I had for many years been connected with spectroscopy as the European distributor for Sadtler Standard Spectra, an ever growing collection of identified IR spectra of organic compounds. That brought me into personal touch with universities and industrial laboratories throughout Europe and also spending time at Sadtler in Philadelphia. In 1966 I visited Professor Cornu, at the French Research Centre for Nuclear Studies in Grenoble, as he was a user of the IR spectra collection. He showed me a print out of a collection of mass spectral data he had compiled and did not ask me but told me, that I should take it away with me and publish it! He felt that Heyden & Son were ideally suited to the task as they were the most connected people in the world of spectroscopy and that the sales of a previous smaller collection of data he published with a French publisher hardly became known outside of France.

So Heyden & Son was now in IR and Mass Spectrometry. Next we published a small *Introduction to Mass Spectrometry* by H.C. Hill in 1966 which even went into a reprint and later into a second edition.

Through these activities and being young and enthusiastic we decided after some research, that the world of Mass Spectrometry should have its own international monthly journal bringing all the important work done under one umbrella publication. So the idea of *OMS* was born. We approached many eminent workers in the field to see if they agreed with our feelings.

Well—you can't start a journal without having an editor and when talking the project over with Professor Allan Maccoll at University College London, he finally agreed to take on the task—after getting permission from his wife he said! So we had an editor-in-chief but the task now was to find an American counterpart. We had high hopes of Professor Carl Djerassi (Stanford University) taking on the part. Meanwhile the news of our endeavours must have reached competitive ears and suddenly we saw an announcement from a "Dutch publishing company" who were turning out one new journal after another, that they were going to publish "The Journal of Mass Spectrometry". What a blow to us. We soon realised, however, that they had not even named an editor in that announcement. We had meanwhile learned that most of the papers involved concerned organic materials and therefore we should beat the "competition" by calling our journal *OMS—Organic Mass Spectrometry*.

At the international spectrometry conference in Berlin in 1967 we met with Professor Djerassi and tried to win him over to be our US editor. He gave it a lot of thought but declined. However, the next morning I received a call from him in my room at the hotel and he told me of a likely person to do the job. He said he had a brilliant student who was also at the conference Bob (Robert) Shapiro and recommended us to talk to him. We did and a huge friendship ensued which lasted until his untimely death. Bob eventually became Dean of the US Naval Academy!

So the *International Journal of Mass Spectrometry* was born but we were now to set up a versatile editorial board. We invited a selected group of the top movers and shakers in Mass Spectrometry to an extended lunch at one of the best restaurants Berlin had to offer where we could present our vision for the journal's future. It was a success and the likes of Fred Maclafferty, Klaus Biemann, Aime Cornu, Hans-Friedrich Grützmacher, Geoff Dijkstra, N.K. Kotchekov and a number of others—I can't remember them all—sat and listened to what we had to say. Eventually as time was pressing for some to return to the conference we heard repeatedly "I leave my proxy with you". That was a good sign! When I finally asked the remaining guests in a summing up "well—are you with us or against us" the

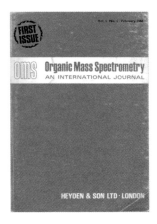

Figure 12: The cover of the first issue of *OMS*; it was printed in bright red as chosen by Carl Djerassi.

answer came from Fred MacLafferty, "if we were against it we wouldn't still be sitting here". That was the final seal of approval and things got organised.

What should the cover of the journal be like—we sent a mock-up of the cover to everybody who had now become a board member. When Carl Djerassi chose that red should be the colour we ignored all else. Red it was (Figure 12), as it was due to him that we got Bob Shapiro on board!

The journal started to publish papers in English, French and German but after a while we found that we should drop the other languages. If it were that important that an author should publish in his country's language we felt that in that case he ought to publish in a national chemistry journal. It took a lot of convincing but finally the board agreed. We also found that the "academic size" of the journal (about 17 × 24 cm) wasn't ideal for illustrations and that if we went to publish the journal in A4 format and double column text it would be far more readable and illustrations need not be turned sideways. Now we had devised a very elegant house style in typography which we carried over to all the other journals we were about to publish.

We went on to publish 16 journals in total before we were romanced by John Wiley & Sons, who had little experience publishing journals at the time, to sell out to them. As the then managing director said at a staff dinner "Gunter put us on the map as journal publishers".

Gunter Heyden looks back and says that his life as a science publisher was the finest part of his career because above all he met the nicest people ever. The many editorial board meetings usually held at international conferences all over the world were creative and contained a good measure of fun. Our "Flag Ship Journal" became *ISR—Interdisciplinary Science Reviews*, it had no less than seven Nobel Prize winners on the editorial board.

Later there was much jealousy and talk was around that Journals should only be published by Societies, and "commercial publishers" were looked down on, after all they only do it for the money! Not so—we were part of the scene and enjoyed our work and mixing with so many interesting people.

ACKNOWLEDGEMENTS

For their help and the invaluable information, dates, memories and photographs they have provided for this chapter, the following people are thanked most sincerely:

Esteban Abad Holgado, Günter Allmaier, Damià Barceló, Robert Bateman, Gareth Brenton, Herbert Budzikiewicz, Edward Clayton, Susan Crosland, Dag Ekeberg, Martin Elliott, Helena Florencio, Eric Forest, Emilio Gelpi, Gianluca Giorgi, Brian Green, Jürgen Grotemeyer, Gunnar Hansson, Neville Haskins, Vladimir Havlíček, Michal Holčepak, Keith Jennings, Dietmar Kuck, Olli Laine, John Langley, Thorleif Lavold, Giorgio Mellerio, Ian Michael, John Monaghan, Michel Nielen, Nico Nibbering, Steen Pontoppidan, Peter Roepstorff, Mathias Schäfer,

Jan Sjovall, Marc Suter, John Todd, Paul Trevorrow, Einar Uggerud, Anna Upton, Renato Zenobi.

REFERENCES

1. R.I. Reed, "International Mass Spectrometry Conferences: one man's recollections", *Org. Mass Spectrom.* **7**, 1013–1017 (1973).

2. J.R. Chapman and G.A. Errock, "Science and technology in Manchester: the nuture of mass spectrometry", *Rapid Commun. Mass Spectrom.* **11**, 1575–1586 (1997).

3. R. Boyd, "John Herbert Beynon", *Rapid Commun. Mass Spectrom.* **18**, 1–6 (2004).

4. J.H. Beynon, "Qualitative analysis of organic compounds by mass spectrometry", *Nature* **174**, 735–737 (1954).

5. K.R. Jennings, "Allan Maccoll (1914–1999)", *J. Mass Spectrom.* **34**, 904–905 (1999).

6. J.J. Monaghan, "Robert Bordoli", *Rapid Commun. Mass Spectrom.* **15**, 70–71 (2001).

7. B.N. Green, "Michael Barber, B. N. Green", *Org. Mass Spectrom.* **27**, 67 (1992).

8. R.G. Cooks, E. Gelpi and N.M.M. Nibbering, "International Mass Spectrometry Society", *J. Mass Spectrom.* **36**, 119–123 (2001).

9. J.J. Thomson, "Cathode rays", *Philos. Mag.* **44**, 293–316 (1897).

10. M.C. ten Noever de Brauw, "A short story about the life of Curt Brunnee", *Rapid Commun. Mass Spectrom.* **11**, 708–713 (1997).

11. G. Boato and G.C. Volpi, "Experiments on the dynamics of molecular processes: a chronical of 50 years", *Ann. Rev. Phys. Chem.* **50**, 23–50 (1999).

12. L.S. Ettre, "Professor Fabrizio Bruner sixty years old", *Chromatogaphia* **40**, 117–118 (1995).

13. N.M.M. Nibbering, "Four decades of joy in mass spectrometry", *Mass Spectrom. Rev.* **25**, 962–1017 (2006).

14. F. Hernandez, J.V. Sancho and D. Barcelo, "Mass spectrometry: 4th conference of the Spanish Society of Mass Spectrometry (SEEM)", *Anal. Bioanal. Chem.* **397**, 2761–2762 (2010).

15. D. Barcelo and M. Petrovic, "Tandem mass spectrometry for environmental and food analysis", *Anal. Bioanal. Chem.* **398**, 1143–1144 (2010).

16. R. Ryhage, "The Mass Spectrometry Laboratory at the Karolinska Institute 1944–1987", *Mass Spectrom. Rev.* **12**, 1–49 (1993).

17. Editorial, "Swiss group for mass spectrometry", *CHIMIA* **52**, 96–96 (1998).

18. D.A. Volmer, "Dedication to Dr. Robert Boyd", *Rapid Commun. Mass Spectrom.* **20**, 1492–1496 (2006).

19. J.H. Beynon, *Mass Spectrometry and Its Applications to Organic Chemistry.* Elsevier Publishing Company (1960).

20. J.H. Beynon and A.E. Williams, *Mass and Abundance Tables for Use in Mass Spectrometry.* Elsevier Publishing Company (1963).

21. J.H. Beynon, R.A. Saunders and A.E. Williams, *Table of Meta-Stable Transitions for Use in Mass Spectrometry.* Elsevier Publishing Company (1965).

22. H.D. Beckey, *Field Ionization Mass Spectrometry.* Pergamon Press, Oxford (1971). ISBN: 0080175570.

23. H.D. Beckey, *Principles of Field Ionization and Field Desorption Mass Spectrometry*. Pergamon Press, Oxford (1977). ISBN: 0080206123.

24. K. Levsen, *Fundamental Aspects of Organic Mass Spectrometry (Progress in Mass Spectrometry)*. Verlag Chemie (1978). ISBN: 9780895730091.

25. P. Longevialle, *Principes de la Spectrométrie de Masse des Substances Organiques*. Masson (1981). ISBN: 2-225-68255-0.

26. J.R. Chapman, *Computers in Mass Spectrometry*. Academic Press (1978). ISBN: 9780121687502.

27. J.R. Chapman, *Practical Organic Chemistry*. John Wiley & Sons (1985). ISBN: 0471906964.

28. J.R. Chapman, *Practical Organic Chemistry: A Guide for Chemical and Biochemical Analysis*. John Wiley & Sons (1995). ISBN: 047195831X.

29. D.H. Williams, *Mass Spectrometry: Principles and Applications*. McGraw Hill (1981). ISBN: 0070705690.

Index